RELUCTANT HEROINE:

The Life and Work of Hélène Duhem

By the same author

Les tendances nouvelles de l'ecclésiologie

The Relevance of Physics

Brain, Mind and Computers
(Lecomte du Nouy Prize, 1970)

The Paradox of Olbers' Paradox

The Milky Way: An Elusive Road for Science

*Science and Creation: From Eternal Cycles
to an Oscillating Universe*

*Planets and Planetarians: A History of Theories
of the Origin of Planetary Systems*

The Road of Science and the Ways to God
(Gifford Lectures: University of Edinburgh, 1975 and 1976)

The Origin of Science and the Science of its Origin
(Fremantle Lectures, Oxford, 1977)

*And on This Rock: The Witness of One Land
and Two Covenants*

Cosmos and Creator

Angels, Apes and Men

Uneasy Genius: The Life and Work of Pierre Duhem

Chesterton: A Seer of Science

The Keys of the Kingdom: A Tool's Witness to Truth

Lord Gifford and His Lectures: A Centenary Retrospect

Chance or Reality and Other Essays

(continued on p. [336])

RELUCTANT HEROINE

The Life and Work of Hélène Duhem

Stanley L. Jaki

SCOTTISH ACADEMIC PRESS

PUBLISHED BY
SCOTTISH ACADEMIC PRESS
56 HANOVER STREET
EDINBURGH EH2 2DX

First edition, 1992

Jaki, Stanley L. (1924 -)
Reluctant Heroine: The Life and Work of Hélène Duhem

1. Publication of the *Système du monde*. 2. Historiography of science

ISBN 0 7073 0724 4

Printed in the United States

Distributor in the United States:
Christendom Press
2101 Shenandoah Shores Rd
Front Royal, VA 22630

Contents

Foreword

This work draws heavily on thick dossiers which the late Norbert Dufourcq kindly let me photocopy in full in 1985 and 1986. I have also greatly benefited from conversations with his niece, Mlle Marie-Madeleine Gallet, who was equally generous in putting at my disposal very valuable manuscript material, including photographs. Without her collaboration, which helped me enormously in writing *The Physicist as Artist: The Landscapes of Pierre Duhem* (Edinburgh: Scottish Academic Press, 1988), this book could not have been written. The letters of Pierre Duhem to his daughter, Hélène, mostly used in Ch. 2, were deposited by Mlle Gallet in 1982 in the Archives of the Académie des Sciences in Paris, where they have been available for study since January 1991, the beginning of the hundreth year since Hélène's birth. I am now preparing a selection of those letters for publication under the title, *Lettres de Pierre Duhem à sa fille, Hélène*. Only the most essential documentation is given here. For further references the reader may conveniently turn to my book, *Uneasy Genius: The Life and Work of Pierre Duhem* (1984; 2d ed.: Dordrecht: Martinus Nijhoff, 1987), which may be used as a companion volume to this work.

Introduction

"And you talk of feminism . . . ," wrote Pierre Duhem, towards the end of 1910, to his daughter and only child, Hélène, who had then just turned nineteen. Duhem referred to the academic promotion given to an acquaintance of his daughter, another Hélène, Mme Baudeuf, a former doctoral student of his at the University of Bordeaux. To those who peruse this book, Hélène Duhem will hardly appear a feminist in the sense which that word has taken on for some time. Feminism did not, of course, appear on the contemporary scene with no warning of its coming. Insofar as feminism stands for that emancipation which is the revolt against values and standards independent of the fashions of the day, its origins go back to late-Victorian times. It was then that Western society thematically opted for a new philosophy of life that had no room for the love of wisdom and ultimately for a love that means more than sensuality.

In this radical change, a heavy role was played by the claim that only what is established by the sciences deserved consideration. The claim served a program that heavily relied on parroting catchy words, science in particular. Being used, or rather abused, in this way, science functioned as a shibboleth that needed only to be parroted without being understood. In those late-Victorian times even within the scientific community few were seriously interested in what science was really about. Among those few, Hélène's father, Pierre Duhem (1861-1916), had the gigantic stature of a true genius. Had he published only his analysis of the nature and purpose of physics, he would have done more than enough to perpetuate his name. Almost a hundred years after its publication, Duhem's *La théorie physique: son objet et sa structure* (1906), is still the most reliable and incisive guide about what physics, or exact science, truly is and what it is not. Being a quantitative study of things in motion (nothing more and nothing less), physics is not a philosophy and much less that conceptual monster which is quantitative or "scientific" philosophy. Physics, or exact science, cannot therefore serve as a guide in precisely those problems in life that lie far deeper than quantities.

Had Duhem showed nothing more, he would have done more than enough to make himself a chief target of those cultural gurus according to whom behavioral patterns alone count. Even when they heap praises on human values, they cannot help reducing them to mere patterns. Their thinking is caught in a mistaken respect for science whose chief business is to count data and cast them into a framework almost invariably statistical. There, however, any count, or quantitatively evaluable pattern, differs from another only in respect to its pragmatic usefulness, but not as something that embodies a value higher than any other pattern. Patterns are invariably relative and remain very different from principles that are absolute. It is in the studied oversight of this difference that lies the conceptual and cultural source of the conflict, "patterns versus principles," the fearsome alternative in terms of which the societal drama of our times is unfolding.

Among Duhem's achievements one particularly keeps irritating those who wage the "patterns alone count" campaign. Unlike his theoretical and conceptual analysis of what physics is about, this achievement of his concerns a great concrete fact of intellectual or scientific history. Therein lies the rub.

Whereas the touting of patterns has effectively desensitized most moderns to philosophical arguments, human nature has retained an incorrigible sensitivity for concrete facts, and especially for their unrepeatable kind that makes human history.

Within an outlook which takes science, as a chief deliverer of patterns, for the ultimate arbiter in life, no question can be so sensitive as the question about its origin. In fact, it has become a dogma with that "patterns alone count" ideology that a long-ingrained view about the origin of science cannot be questioned at all. In stating in 1906 that "science descended upon earth on the inclined plane of Galileo," Bergson merely gave a stylistically seductive garb to that view. Yet by then Duhem had provided ample evidence to the contrary and he himself was very much astonished by the evidence. He found, through a painstaking and pioneering study of many medieval manuscripts, that the origins of Newtonian science go well beyond Galileo and even Copernicus.

To make matters even more problematic for the coming century of "patternism," Duhem found that the first formulation of the law of inertial motion, the first and most fundamental of all three laws of Newton's, took place within a framework which is the very opposite of "patternism." For the framework was not only philosophical, but that highest form of the love of wisdom which is Christian theology.

Against his arguments and presentation of facts, silence proved itself the most effective shield. The story told in this book is about a heroic struggle against the systematic cultivation of silence with respect to Duhem's great achievements, especially the one about the pre-Galilean history of modern science. Had it not been for the heroic persistance against monumental odds of a frail woman, with not even a high-school certificate to her credit, one half (or five large volumes) of Duhem's *Système du monde*, arguably the greatest scholarly achievement by a single author in modern times, would still lie unpublished and perhaps be lost forever.

Feminism should appear in an unexpected light when one considers the opportunity of doing justice to such genuinely feminine heroes as Hélène Duhem. If and when it ever becomes the custom to confer honorary doctorates on the dead, Hélène Duhem should be among the very first to qualify for such an honor. All the more so, as her heroic achievement related not to patently non-academic pursuits for which honorary degrees are being busily handed out nowadays. Her achievement concerned that pure scholarship which should forever remain the chief pride of academic life.

In the absence of such an honor, she should at least be honored by making her memory alive within an academia all too ready to honor its members for achievements, however dubious and ephemeral at times. Her achievement will last as long as cultural and scientific history is seriously and sincerely studied. In these times when deconstructionism brings added fuel to a senseless cavorting in the study of patterns for patterns' sake, her example shows that it is possible, even for a frail and professionally untrained woman, to struggle effectively against the tide of the times, however oppressively glorified.

But this is always what has been done by truly great feminine figures and in particular by the one who wanted to be known forever as a mere "handmaid of the Lord." She was a chief source of courage for Hélène who did not hanker for a heroic role. She took that role upon herself reluctantly. However, once she recognized her historic calling, nothing could deter her from securing the crowning touch to a major breakthrough in man's knowledge of his own intellectual history and precisely there where it nowadays counts most, in science.

May 31, 1992   S. L. J.

1

Child Hélène

A baby and a heroic mother

The first written accounts about Hélène Duhem are two letters by her father in the early evening of Tuesday, September 29, 1891, when she was not yet six hours old. With a precision befitting a physicist, the happy father recorded that Hélène's birth took place five minutes after midday. The two-story house that witnessed her birth was Nr 78 in Rue Caumartin, a quiet residential street even now. The house was only five minutes' walk from the physics department of the University of Lille where her father, Pierre Duhem, had just begun his third year of teaching physics with an electrifying originality. Much of the affection in which Pierre Duhem was held by his students quickly devolved to little Hélène, who could confidently count on it more than forty years later.

Her father's joy was overflowing. "Mlle Hélène," Pierre Duhem wrote to his mother and sister, Marie, in the early evening of that radiant day, "is a splendid little girl. We have not weighed her yet, but the doctor, on holding her, estimated her to be seven pounds. She did not wait to be cut off from her mother in order to open her beautiful deep blue eyes. She has but little hair which is brown; she is large, has delightful

1

hands with exquisite little fingernails and lovely little feet. Her face is now very rested. She is wide awake, drinks very well, sucks my finger when I give it to her and is not deaf, because a little click of the tongue quiets her right away when she cries."

In the other letter, sent to the parents of the happy mother, little Hélène was described in almost exactly the same words. There she was not, however, referred to as Hélène but as "Mlle Lenon Jr." Hélène was the name of one of the four elder sisters of her mother, née Adèle Chayet, and was spoken about in the family as "Lenon," a shortened form of "Hélèn-on," a diminutive of Hélène. Before long "Lenon Jr." was known in the family as Toumy or Toumi. In that letter it was also stated that she was not yet 30 minutes old when her little lips gripped her father's finger and that by the time she was six hours old she was voraciously hanging on her mother's breasts.

There was nothing extraordinary in all that, not even the extraordinary joy of her parents. Nor was anything extraordinary about Pierre Duhem's asking a certain Abbé Mayet in Lille, an old acquaintance of his from Collège Stanislas in Paris, "to make of Hélène a little Christian." In the same letter Pierre Duhem also reported that "given the good weather and her vigor" the happy parents could not obtain permission to have her baptized at home right away. Her godparents were to be the maternal grandfather and paternal grandmother, both in Paris, to be represented by Ernest and Martha Balthus.

Ernest Balthus, professor of medicine at the Institut Catholique of Lille, was then just forty, in the prime of his life and proud of his having been a volunteer in the Franco-Prussian War as a nineteen-year-old lad. His wife, Martha, was none other than Adèle's oldest sister. It was through Dr. Balthus that the birth of little Hélène was expertly supervised by Dr. Delassus, who for two days and nights did not leave Mme Duhem's bedside. For the time being, the five days which Mme Duhem had spent in increasingly severe labor did not

bode ill. She felt rested and strong after giving birth in agoniz-
ing pains. In addition to Dr. Delassus, Mme Duhem was
assisted by a young nursing nun, Sister Stanislas, who earned no
less the Duhems' gratitude. Since there was no hemorrhage, the
prospect for the future looked excellent. In fact, the young
mother asked her husband to assure his mother that she "would
produce, as Volume II, the little Pierre so hoped for." The
reference to Volume II had to do with the first volume, just off
the press, of a vast treatise on electricity and magnetism[1] of
which Duhem remained particularly fond. In addition, he had
just published a two-volume work on hydrodynamics.

The appearance of several volumes at the very start of a
promising career could not have been better matched than by
the arrival of the first child. There was nothing to make the
soon-famous young physicist expect anything untoward either
professionally or family-wise. The conclusion of his letter to his
mother was both an overflowing anticipation of the future and
an enthrallment with the present: "As to our little Hélène, who
is without dowry, we shall regale her through affection with all
the happiness that money could not have assured her — PS. I
have just moved over to see her at her mother's breast. This
little doll, of just six hours minus five minutes, has set herself to
the task with a rapidity that astonished the Sister." The letter to
Adèle's parents came to a close on an even more effusive note:
"Maddy and I embrace you with all our hearts. We are so
radiant that this kiss could well give you sunstroke."

The next notice about Hélène was a letter which Pierre
Duhem wrote three days later to Joseph Récamier, a young
doctor. He was Pierre Duhem's best friend from their years at
Collège Stanislas and was to earn three years later national
renown as the doctor who cared for the dying Comte de Paris
without leaving his bedside for eight full days. The letter began
with a strophe from the dramatic poem "La Mer" of Jean
Richepin (1849-1926), a strophe echoing with the jargon of

sailors, obviously dear to amateur sailors as Duhem and
Récamier were. Then Duhem turned to the subject:

> Yes, here we are, I shall start to bring you up to date.
> Hélène (Marie, Alexandrine, Adèle) Duhem, born in Lille
> (Nord) at noon on Sept. 29, 1891, of poor but brave
> parents, is, I bet, a very comely little girl. But it is strange
> all the same: a few days ago she was but an organ, an
> appendix, and now she screams, squalls, pushes, shows the
> desire to sleep, to eat, to move, in short to exist. . . . I
> cannot leave her, I pass my time in watching this little doll
> in her little nest. What an idiot I must look, but this is
> nothing in comparison to when I walk with her in my
> arms. Look up a photo which Michet took of you in the
> same posture.
>
> Announce this good news to your entire family,
> parents, parents-in-law, brother, sisters, brothers-in-law,
> sister-in-law, uncles, aunts, and cousins. I want the whole
> universe to know that Pierre Duhem is a father — how far
> this puts us from the time when our principal affection was
> directed at those planks called Kitty!
>
> My wife suffered a great deal, but all has gone well
> and her health is as satisfactory as possible. She sends Mme
> Récamier her most affectionate greetings. As for me . . .
> one can very well embrace (can one not?) in such circum-
> stances. Well, I embrace you.

The letter was signed Ped or Pedant, the nickname by which
Récamier knew his friend, obviously because of his bent on
rigorous accuracy in more than one field.

Récamier's reply was written the next day. (Those were
the legendary days when a first class letter was duly delivered
within 24 hours practically anywhere in France, especially
between such big cities as Lille and Paris.) The letter contained
a poem which dealt as much with the superior qualities of little
Hélène as with the joy of her parents.[2] That joy lasted only ten
short months. Hélène was never consciously to know her

mother whose last letters to her family were carefully kept. The
better part of her letter written to her parents in the latter half
of May 1891 was still about Hélène:

> My Lenon is as good as gold. Yesterday Martha [Balthus]
> invited me so that I might dine more comfortably. Lenon
> was put on the table with three dolls that occupied her all
> the time. She did not ask for anything, she did not incon-
> venience anybody — apart from a few cries of joy, she was
> not heard at all . . . . I believe I have not said to you yet
> that for some time now my darling has been saying "papa"
> in a distinct way.

But the letter contains the admission that "this year I feel less
strong than last year. But rest assured, I beg you, about my
health. I feel infinitely better, only the appetite is not what it
should be."

In the next letter little Hélène is mentioned only to the
extent that "the walks in the park which I have resumed two
days ago are good for me and indispensable for my darling for
whom this is the only place where she finds a little air." The
letter is more about the expectant mother's health. She had a
relapse two days earlier but "thanks to Ernest's energetic
interventions," she feels "alleviated from bronchitis and
neuralgia." Adèle was furthermore worried about reports given
to her parents about her health. She rather blamed "the atro-
cious heat" that had just replaced the cool days. The letter gives
details about Pierre's plans to secure a house on the edge of the
Marmon forest, only two hours away by express train from
Lille.

Perhaps at that point Adèle thought of the trip which she
and Pierre made to Bruxelles, Anvers, and the little seashore
village Anserème les Dinants in mid-summer of the previous
year, just two months before Hélène's birth. Adèle's pregnancy
inconvenienced her in visiting the art gallery of Bruxelles where
she and Pierre ran into the geologist Abbé Bénard, Pierre's old

friend from the Collège Stanislas, who guided them to the best pictures. "There," she wrote to her sisters on August 1, 1891, "I recognized the paintings whose description we read together in a book lent to us by some friends."

In all likelihood the book was Fromentin's *Les Maîtres d'autrefois*, a favorite with Pierre.[3] Their satisfaction with the paintings in the Musée de Bruxelles was so great that they decided on the spur of the moment to include Anvers in their itinerary: "The port especially interested us because Pierre and I both love to travel and to depart in thought with the big ships we watched as they were loaded and unloaded." No mention was made in the letter, written from Anserème les Dinants, of Pierre making some fine sketches,[4] although she must have admired the rapidity with which he did a sketch to be completed in inkwash at home.

Now there could be no repetition of such a sightseeing trip although the second childbirth was more than two months away. Going to the Marmon forest, instead of meeting their families in Provence, was a necessary precaution:

> Although little Pierre does not inconvenience me at this moment, he will interfere with our vacation, because in the state I am in, I do not plan to travel. Last year each of my trips that lasted only two hours completely put me down. No wonder that I could not drag myself alone in the streets of Bruxelles and that I seriously feared an accident [miscarriage]. Therefore, my dear father and mother, Pierre, whom my indisposition has terribly frightened, is looking for a place in the Marmon forest.

Adèle's next letter was completed on June 3rd. About Hélène she wrote: "My little Lenon cut two teeth on June 1st without any problem and pain, after an admirable night." The other reference to Hélène evokes a dark cloud. She cannot be seen by her mother who is under strict medical order not to touch her! Nor is she allowed to do as much as sew or knit.

She has to keep to her room "in the most absolute rest. . . . There are moments when my little bit of courage is on the point of abandoning me." She was not informed, so the letter says, about the result of the consultation between Dr. Balthus and Dr. Desplats.

Yet she obviously rallied to the great surprise of both doctors, as she put it in a letter dated as "Sunday":

> With much care and for good reasons I will quickly recover, I hope, my full health. The Chayets are of strong stock and quickly get over even the gravest maladies. I hope that my little Pierre or my little Germaine will arrive in good health. This is my greatest concern and the motive which shall cure me, although I do not really feel sick. I have begun to work a bit and I read fairly well.

Further to cheer her was little Hélène's progress: "My Lenon continues to be resplendent. Her cheeks are hard like rock. She eats like a little tigress and laughs all day. She cut her teeth without noticing it and without any encumbrance. She wakes up only once during the night." Her concluding lines were about some poor families: "My heart breaks for the poor." Little did she guess that her own heart was soon to stop and some hearts would really break.

A month or so later all that cheerful progress came to a halt. The basis on which to reconstruct events are three letters, two written by Pierre's mother, the third by Pierre himself. In the first Mme Duhem notified a friend in Cabrespine on July 17th that because "Madame Pierre is still very sick, she would most likely not go to Cabrespine" and, because "her sickness would last for some time," her own plans of going there had to be cancelled. The second letter, addressed to Adèle's mother, begins with the question: "I do not know whether Dr. Balthus has informed either Pierre or you about Adèle's condition. He certainly did not speak to me about it." After a reference to the help which Martha Balthus, herself pregnant, was giving her sister, Mme Duhem mentioned that her own maid had been placed at Adèle's disposal and that it was difficult to care for Adèle: "I have many times heard my son lament of the impossibility of persuading Adèle to eat." This phrase may be an indication that Adèle had developed hypertension during her first childbirth and that it reappeared as eclampsia during her second pregnancy. This would explain her chronic lack of appetite as a symptom of inadequate salt and water metabolism in such cases.

At any rate, since the matter was not fully understood then and no real cure was yet available (some herb teas could at best be palliatives), it was natural for Pierre to think of a resort place as a means of building up his wife's appetite and strength for another difficult delivery. On July 15 though, Pierre informed his father-in-law that the plans for going to the countryside [Marmon forest] had to be cancelled.

> Ernest finds that Didi [Adèle] is not strong enough yet to travel. We do not therefore go to Bonsecours. Didi strongly wishes us to pass some time near you and her family when she gets stronger. I therefore ask you to take us on. This request is already very indiscreet. Nevertheless, I turn to you with another which may be no less so. If the place of your vacation has not yet been chosen, I would be most grateful if you were to come closer to Lille rather than farther away from it. In Didi's condition a somewhat long trip might provoke an accident [miscarriage].

Less than two weeks later, on July 28, she died while giving birth to a premature baby boy. The infant, baptized Joseph by his heartbroken father, was buried with his mother. After a requiem mass on July 30 at Saint-Michel, their parish church, the bodies of mother and son were taken by train to Paris. There, after another ceremony at Saint-Sulpice on August 2, they were laid to rest in the Chayet family vault in Montparnasse cemetery. Years later Marie Duhem stated in a letter to

Hélène that her mother had known that she might die in childbirth. By then Hélène must have gazed on more than one occasion on a piece of paper on which her mother wrote in trembling hand her very last words: "I have said that death will win out . . . I am afraid of being suffocated while asleep."

Substitute mothers

As a little girl who never really knew her mother, Hélène could but ask about her after visiting her playmates' homes and being given a caress or two by their mothers. Long before she was mature enough to sense what no words could properly convey, she could easily learn some facts and data. She was to meet uncles, aunts, and cousins — the Chayets, a large and well-to-do family. Grandpa Chayet, retired director of the big iron works in Fourchambault, had a vineyard in Mas Marin in Provence which Hélène as a young girl was to visit several times with her father. The Chayet's residence, 7 rue Michelet in Paris, was an imposing three-story house just south of the Jardin du Luxembourg, across from the Ecole de Pharmacie. It was there that Hélène's parents had their wedding reception on Saturday afternoon, October 27, 1890, after the ceremony in Saint-Sulpice. They religiously kept the text of the sermon preached.

Their marriage was preceded by only a few months' of engagement which in turn was the result of a courtship of again but a few months. Hélène's mother, the youngest of five sisters, was of Pierre's age, twenty-eight, when they first met in Lille, in the house of Eugène Monnet, a chemistry instructor at the Institut Catholique. Monnet, to whom Pierre had given permission, at no small risk to his own career, to follow his courses at the University of Lille, was therefore a colleague of Dr. Balthus. In fact, Monnet and his wife must have been friends of Dr. and Mrs. Balthus. Otherwise Monnet would not have thought that one of Mrs. Balthus' sisters might be a perfect match for Pierre, then in love only with physics and sailing. The Monnets had already extolled to him the qualities of a certain young woman who happened to be the youngest of the sisters. He was to meet them "accidentally" when the Balthuses took them for a visit with the Monnets sometime in the Spring of 1890. Pierre arrived early in the hope of departing well before the young woman in question showed up with two of her elder sisters, Marie and Hélène. (Another, Marguerite, was a nun, Soeur Marie du Bon Pasteur). All three were already there and the youngest conquered.

Pierre Duhem used to go each summer to Britanny for a few weeks' sailing and was also very familiar with the Morbihan area where he had spent several summer vacations as a teenager. He could therefore easily go to Pouliguen, a fashionable Breton seashore resort where the Chayets spent several weeks in the summer of 1890. The very good impression Pierre made in Pouliguen was mentioned in a letter by his future father-in-law as he was to have a "working lunch" with his prospective son-in-law. By mid-summer Pierre's mother and Adèle's mother were exchanging letters concerning the engagement of their children. Pierre himself was invited to Mas Marin, near Tarascon, though not offered a room by Mme Chayet as there were already too many guests there. Mr. Chayet, however, rightly guessed that this would matter little to Pierre: "I believe," Mr. Chayet wrote him, "that the miserable town of Tarascon and the ancestral house overcrowded by guests will nevertheless leave you with pleasant memories because you come there to look for your Adèle."

Three days later, August 24, 1890, Pierre accepted the invitation in a letter written from his mother's ancestral home in Cabrespine just north of Carcassonne, to his future mother-in-law:

> Madame and dear Mother,
>   Allow me to call you mother since you want me to consider myself henceforth as your son. . . . I am very

happy, Madame, dear Mother, that the few days to be spent with you near Tarascon will offer me the means of demonstrating to you all the filial respect I have for you. I believe you will not need much time to see the intensity, very difficult to dissimulate, of the love I have for our dear little Maddy (she asked me not to call her Adèle any longer except when we shall be at cross purposes: consequently the name Adèle may fall into oblivion). If I give her only the tenth of the happiness I want to give her, I can assure you that there will remain for her plenty to fill her dear little heart with joy.

A copy of the wedding invitation was kept by Hélène's father. More is revealed about the wedding by the marriage register of Saint-Sulpice. There were four witnesses: Louis Ollé-Laprune, professor of philosophy at the Ecole Normale and a cousin of the bride; Jean-Auguste Chayet, a finance inspector, also a cousin of the bride; Jules Tannery, vice-director of the Ecole Normale and professor of mathematics there, who had early recognized the bridegroom's extraordinary talents; and Félix Benoit, an industrialist from Reims. The latter, a friend of Pierre's late father in all likelihood, may have been the one who around 1881 held out for Pierre the prospect of a prosperous commercial career had he chosen a more profitable and practical field than theoretical physics. Pierre dashed these hopes, shared by his father, by choosing the Ecole Normale and not the Ecole Polytechnique.

Years later Hélène could read the text of the sermon preached by the Vicaire of Saint-Sulpice in the latter's careful handwriting. She could, however, only dream about the wedding gown her mother wore as she inherited only four photos of her mother. One small photo, made before the wedding, shows her face in profile; another shows her standing as a child of about ten, a third is part of a glass paperweight which contains the small portraits of her four elder sisters as well. The fourth shows her on her deathbed. That no photo of the wedding survived is perhaps symbolic of the pain which the young widower was to carry for twenty-five more years with manly reserve.

Hélène came eventually also in possession of the diary which her mother kept of her honeymoon trip to Bruges and its environs. It contained references to Pierre Duhem's sketching this or that scene, but no reference to a camera. Cameras were, in 1890, far from being the general commodity which Eastman Kodak made them shortly thereafter. Hélène was already a young adult when her father regaled her with a Kodak for which he himself showed as little fondness as he did for typewriters and bicycles.

That honeymoon diary did not contain a detail which Hélène later learned about her mother from her father's sister, Marie. One day on their honeymoon they met a young seminarian. As soon as Adèle learned that the seminarian had great financial difficulty in continuing his studies for the priesthood, she suggested to her husband that her dowry be used for his education. Hélène may have learned about that detail long before her Aunt Marie included it in a long letter about her brother's childhood and short married life. But that letter may have been the first information for Hélène about her mother's last wish. She wanted her husband to let their little daughter be raised by his mother and marry again on the ground that she knew how kind and affectionate he was. As Hélène grew up she could not help becoming increasingly aware of the fact that her father never did consider another marriage. Neither was he to leave his little daughter entirely in his mother's care.

Of course, he needed the help of his mother, who had become a widow four years earlier, to raise a little girl not yet one. But Hélène always remained the apple of her father's eye. She was his "Toumy" (Toumi, Toumelle), a name which he took from a novel of Dickens, a great favorite with Duhem, where the little maid refers to papas who are fond of speaking of their daughters as their "toumis."

Hélène was approaching her third birthday when she was referred to in the following words in a letter which her father wrote to her grandmother: "Really, in order to realize how much one loves Toumy, one has to be absent from her. You have no idea of the effect made on me when I see the few lines drawn in pencil by her little paw." The last line of that letter, "I devour my little one in my thoughts," also speaks for itself. Not that Hélène would be spared of being shown paternal firmness: "Toumy, est-elle sage?" was the last line of the next letter written two days later, on September 7, 1894, also from Bruxelles, where her father attended the Congress of Catholic Scientists.[5] Two more days later Duhem concluded his letter to his mother with the sigh: "How I suffer for not having received word from Toumy. Kiss her on my behalf."

In that letter there was a remark which she could not have yet understood even if she had been ten years older: "I had time," Duhem wrote his mother, "to revisit the Museum in Antwerp. These visits are sad for me because I keep thinking of the time when I was not visiting there alone." Only three years had gone by since Hélène's mother was at her father's side in that very museum. Meanwhile, Duhem must have received a letter from his mother in St. Briac where she, her daughter Marie, and granddaughter Hélène were vacationing. He in turn was already in Lille on his way back to rejoin them in St. Briac when he advised them about his arrival and added: "As to my Toumy's wisdom, I am very satisfied. Grandmother may tell her so." The last lines in the letter, in which Duhem gave an account of his visit to Louvain to see a friend, Forget, belonged to Toumi. "Tell Toumi that I am just going to have dinner with Uncle Ernest, but that the rest of the family are still on vacation. I am not complaining. Ernest is certainly the one in the family whom I am most pleased to see again." Toumi received a gentle fatherly warning as Duhem brought to a close his account of his visit with the Forgets: "Tell Toumi that little Marie Forget sits very nicely at table and eats well."

Duhem's frolicking with his little daughter on the beaches of St. Briac can easily be imagined. She was also the beneficiary of the loving attention of her papa who reserved for himself the right to put her to bed each and every night. But, as Hélène herself was to reveal years later, it was only in vacation time that papa and daughter belonged entirely to one another all day long. During the academic year her papa could not always be reached even before or after dinner, preoccupied as he was with his ever vaster researches. Little Hélène soon took on some of the traits, amusing as well as expressive, of her father's scholarly mien.

One was his style. Most amused was the father who told his colleagues at the University of Lille some of little Hélène's sayings. After telling how she had encountered a snail in the garden, she added, "I have pushed back its horns *absolutely*." One of those colleagues of Duhem was André Chevrillon, well-known literary figure of the decades preceding and following World War I, who joined the University of Lille in 1889 to teach English. In his lengthy reminiscences on Duhem, written (at Hélène's request) on March 1, 1934, Chevrillon also recalled Duhem's account of his way of admonishing little Hélène. It consisted in showing her a picture of Berthelot, the famous chemist and supreme power broker in academia. Eventually Hélène learned that Berthelot was a grave threat through much of his life to her father's career. Hélène possibly felt a lump in her throat as Chevrillon's letter led her back to a mother she had never really known: "Your father married while I was still in Lille. This is to tell you that I have known your mother — so lively, unaffected, and spiritual . . ."[6]

In the family correspondence, not at all extensive, Hélène figures several times in a series of letters which her Aunt Marie wrote between December 1894 and November 1895 to her grandmother. Marie, three years younger than Pierre, had great affection for her brother, especially since her twin sister, Antoinette, and their baby brother Jean, died in November

1872. After their father died in 1888, the widowed mother had increasingly sought solace and support in her daughter. The two went to live with Pierre in Lille until his marriage. After Pierre became a widower, Marie rejoined Pierre's household with their mother.

They went along with Pierre and Hélène when he was transferred from Lille to Rennes in the Fall of 1893. Aunt Marie was as fond of little Hélène as she was of her. But, of course, Aunt Marie had to think of her own place in life which was in the direction of a religious vocation. In Duhem's letters written from Belgium in September 1894 to his mother in St. Briac, his sister Marie is mentioned only as the subject of a conversation with a priest-friend, the Père Lefèvre, about Marie's fitness for the rigors of religious life. The Père Lefèvre took the view that it was counter-productive to try to prevent Marie from entering the convent. Duhem himself doubted that his sister's health was up to her plans. As to Marie's mother, who moved with Pierre and Hélène to Bordeaux in late October 1894, she could not bear the thought of being separated from Marie. Such is the background of the brief references to Hélène in the eight letters of Marie, mostly written to her mother, that survived in her brother's files.

In December 1894, Hélène must have been sick because Aunt Marie wrote from Paris to her mother: "I am tormented because of my little Hélène. I shall go to Notre Dame des Victoires to pray for her and for you." Notre Dame des Victoires, one of the most attended churches in Paris then and now, was certainly a favorite with the devout in the 2nd *arrondissement* where Marie and her brother grew up. Pierre Duhem never traveled to Paris without making a brief visit to that church. As a boy of nine he saw in that church the famed statue of the Virgin dressed up as Marianne by the *communards*. The letter contained a reference to the muff bought for Hélène and ended: "I long to cuddle my little Hélène." On May 20, 1895, Aunt Marie reassured the family in Bordeaux from Passy about some errands for Hélène "who should be very good and keep her rosy cheeks I love so much."

Marie was obviously under pressure both from her mother and her brother not to try religious life. Duhem's letter of May 28, 1895, to his mother, who at that time was with little Hélène away from Bordeaux, deals entirely with Marie's vocation. It began with the acknowledgment of the little note which Toumi attached to her grandmother's letter: "It gave me great pleasure." Little Hélène, by then well into her fourth year, may have already learned the rudiments of reading and writing. She was still to learn about the family struggles concerning her aunt's religious vocation which later was to play a decisive role in her life as well.

She may have been partly chagrined, partly perplexed when years later she perused that letter in which her father spoke of another meeting with the Père Lefèvre. The latter once more endorsed the wisdom of giving Marie full liberty so that she might find out through her own experience her lack of physical fitness for religious life. Duhem was obviously more in favor of the view of the Père Lacôme, a Dominican philosopher and admirer of his work.[7] According to the Père Lacôme, so Duhem reported to his mother, "Marie had, from the point of view of ecclesiastical law, no right to abandon you in old age." Duhem would not have been human if he had not thought of the advantage which the Père Lacôme's view implied for him, and especially for little Hélène.

Duhem also informed his mother in that letter that Marie was to arrive in Bordeaux two days later. It seems that Duhem could not persuade his sister to give up her plans. Marie's letter of June 18 to her brother dealt with her inheritance and revenues. In general she left everything to Pierre to increase his resources so that their mother "may buy dresses for little Hélène which I can no longer make. May she endow her with as much as possible; when she wants a toy it should be bought for her on behalf of her aunt." Marie knew that her mother would be disconsolate: "Would little Hélène help? She should learn how to find tender and spiritual things to say to her grandmother. I am comforted by the thought of a big moody girl being replaced by a little angel. I hope that she is good and deserves the nice drum. Since I lent you six francs for the gift to be given to the Monnets, please, buy that drum for your daughter because it cannot be easily sent by mail."

When it came to the specific settlement of Marie's inheritance and revenues, she was asking in her letter of June 25, for 10,000 francs as dowry for the convent. All the rest that would have come to her "was to be spent on Mama, Hélène, and the poor, especially the poor in Cabrespine." Hélène was mentioned briefly in Marie's letter of July 1, in much the same vein. By then the letters were largely about their mother who could not resign herself to Marie's departure. On October 31, Hélène was again but briefly mentioned: "Buy something for little Hélène, I would be so happy to satisfy one of her great wishes." Marie's rather emotional letter of November 24 to her mother ended with the request: "When your little Hélène puts her little arms around you, think that there are four arms and two hearts that press you hard and love you deeply."

Because her mother simply could not accept her departure, Marie discontinued her year of probation in the convent of the Oratorian nuns in Passy. It was a decision that bore heavily on Marie: In announcing on February 20, 1896, her leaving the religious life, she wrote: "I would have been so happy if you had wanted me to be so. May the good Lord forgive us all for our conduct and may little Hélène suffice to fill our lives."

Two days later, however, Marie informed her mother that although she would rejoin her with no resentment in her heart, she would ask in return "for a great freedom of action" because "my life ought to be filled and after little Hélène I want to occupy myself with much charitable work. . . . I want to let you know that I shall often go to the Assumptionist nuns from whom I have received so many benefits of all sorts and whom

I love so much that I cannot prevent myself from often visiting them. Tell little Hélène that Aunt will treat her very well."

Three months later Aunt Marie was visiting in Bretagne and wrote home on May 20, 1896: "All along the route Bretagne is colorful like a carpet. The meadows are all white daisies as if it had snowed. Hélène would be pleased to be in the midst of this harvest." Aunt Marie's letter, written very likely in early July 1896, indicates that little Hélène could communicate with her for a while only through letters:

> Aunt is very pleased with you. I hope you will be well-behaved and respectful. I thank you for writing to me. You should do it often. Aunt Marie loves you much and will send you many gifts, if you become kind to Grandma and Papa. You will now go to Cabrespine. You will play with the ducks and all the animals in the village; you will be very polite with Sophie to show that you are well educated. Sophie will tell you many stories you like and would very much like to hear. I too love my little sweetheart very much. I pray to Jesus to make of you a very polite little girl. Pray at times for Aunt Marie because you love her much, so much. I embrace you, my little dear doll, with all my heart.

The reason why little Hélène was to communicate only through letters for a while with her aunt is revealed through the latter's next surviving letter, dated December 1898. Written to Pierre from the convent of the Oratorian nuns in Neuilly, near Paris, it shows her in the midst of catechetical and charitable activities, "so varied and extraordinary in our order as if absolutely invented by St. Philip Neri for the actual moment." The letter in which Marie asked Pierre to release from her inheritance 10,000 francs as her dowry, ended with a reference to Christmas: "It so much recalls Hélène when she was one."

There was no reference to Hélène in Marie's next letter of January 18, 1899, in which the dowry question is raised again.

Hélène was, however, thanked for her sketch in the letter
Marie wrote her mother about the same time. The skill of
Hélène in drawing may have been better than average for a ten
year old. As will shortly be seen, she was instructed by a papa
who was a far better draftsman than are most amateurs. Marie's
letter also revealed that in the Order she was known as Mère
Marie-Dominique. It was as such that Marie appeared in the
obituary notice of her deceased mother who passed away on
August 26, 1906, at the age of seventy-six.

Education at home

For the years 1896-1906, Hélène is the main source of information about her life as a child who, by the way, was the recipient of a postcard from Lourdes dated June 18, 1898. An adult
friend (Anne Martin), with many ailments, told her about her
visit in the company of other sick to the famed sanctuary where
just an hour before her arrival a startling cure had taken place.
Catholic faith and devotion were to be the center of Hélène's
whole life. In writing her father's biography around 1934, she
provided charming pages about life in the two-story house, 18
Rue de la Teste, Bordeaux, where she arrived in November
1894 as a three-year-old and which she was not to leave
semipermanently until the age of seventeen. The only information not contained in those pages are a few photos of hers with
her father and grandmother; the entry of her name as a first
communicant in the register of Duhem's parish, Sainte-Eulalie,
and a letter of 1905 in which Duhem explains his plans to his
mother about Hélène's intermediate education. Last but not
least, there is a letter written to her by her papa who, from
1895 on, resumed his two-week-long hikes in various mountains of France once or twice during the summer vacation.

Done in non-cursive writing, with each letter carefully
drawn in the style of readers for young children, the letter must
have been written around 1896 or so:

My Toumi! Papa walks a great deal in the mountains with a big heavy sack on his back. He would love to carry you along. When you are big you will come with him and we will make sketches together. I kiss you. Papa Pierre.

These walks together in the mountains came during the summer vacations in Cabrespine just north of Carcassonne in the Montagne Noire. Duhem usually arrived there in early August and, apart from a two-week hiking trip in September, stayed until his return to Bordeaux in mid-October for the new academic year. For Hélène the vacations in Cabrespine were more than mere holidays. They were the times when, as she reminisced,

> Papa belonged entirely to his daughter and the daughter to her papa, and both were the much beloved children of the best of elderly relatives in the good hospitable house.

It is in that perspective of intimate togetherness with her father that Hélène saw her introduction into the delights, skills, and efforts of hiking and exploration:

> The outings were at first proportioned to the little legs but soon the little legs trotted as fast as those of Daddy. It was then, during so many happy years that they explored, up and down the hills, the entire region knowing the smallest paths, visiting the isolated hamlets and the outlying farms, enjoying all the beautiful panoramas which one finds from the peaks to be reached after a tough ascent through thorns and rocks, under the blazing sun, tired and thirsty.
>
> But at the top, what a recompense! The joy over an effort well done, over an obstacle conquered, the fresh air giving repose, a feeling of the infinite in the face of the faraway horizon! The ravished eyes of the two hikers discover an admirable panorama which the father explains to the child, indicating to her the peaks, so easy to recognize, of the distant Pyrénées emerging from the haze of the

horizon, while the Corbières with the hollow of the Alaric burn in the sun, and one is given to the amusing search for the silhouette of the towers of Carcassonne in the plains at the foot of the Montagne Noire.

Pierre Duhem raised his daughter a bit like a son (undoubtedly with a thought of that little Pierre whom he had wished for so much). With him one had to be intrepid, to fear no cold, no heat, no rain, to endure thirst when no springs were found along the route, to ignore precipices, and at times even to kill a viper, without trembling.

How many times, in the full month of August, immediately after the midday meal, at the hour of the cicadas, did he depart in the company of his daughter, to reach, in two hours' walk, a little village [Pradelles-Cabardès] on the slopes of the Pic de Nore. The curé, the Abbé Bernies, who since died as a curé of Limoux and canon of Carcassonne, wished to pursue philosophical studies. He used to find there at the rectory of Pradelles-Cabardès, two professors of the Institut Catholique de Paris, the Père Bulliot and the Père Peillaube. It was there, with them, under the shadows of a centenarian beech tree, that the founding of the *Revue philosophique*, of which the Père Peillaube was the editor, was conceived and turned into the planning stage.

In Bordeaux the duties of academic life did not allow for a similar uninterrupted flow of contact between papa and daughter. To be sure, little Hélène was to be near papa even when he worked, but she was not to disturb him:

At the end of the big table, weighed down with books and papers, papa's little daughter also had a place where she did her homework and learned her lessons. But she was not allowed to move around, let alone talk; the child worked in this recollectedness near the good grandmother who respected the meditations of her son. The temptation at times was very great to jump in papa's arms, to laugh a little, to ask him a question, as he got up and leaned with

his back against the fireplace, with a distant look in his eyes
. . . . 'Be quiet,' the child would hear her grandmother say,
'papa is searching for a theorem.'

But even in Bordeaux the meals and the evenings for the most
part were joyfully relaxed:

> Nothing was more lively in the house in the Rue de la
> Teste than the meals and the evenings. In the evenings
> Pierre Duhem used to read to his mother whose eyes were
> in poor condition. That was a real treat, because he used to
> read with a genuine skill which came from both a deeply
> poetic and artistic sense, able to do justice to the entire
> value included in the harmony of words, and from an
> extraordinary talent for imitating. On hearing him, one
> saw. When he read a play, the actors talked and moved,
> each with his peculiar character, as if made present by the
> intonation of his voice.

Both Hélène and her papa were deeply indebted to the selfless
care which grandmother kept giving them and the house for
some time even after she entered, in 1900, her seventies:

> She was the very soul of the house. Her face was a bit
> severe, with a look which at first intimidated and kept one
> at a distance. (Woe to the one who deserved a reprimand;
> her dark eyes could be vanquishing!) But, if one knew how
> to merit it, the same look softened and sparkled with
> serene goodness, as a smile ran across her gentle lips. She
> had the strength to keep her setbacks and sorrows in the
> secret of her heart and to recover, for that little one, the
> happiness which suits children. Her conversation was
> charming and lively. She joined a spontaneous informality
> to refined politeness, to the good manners of old times.
> Very active and a complete mistress of the house, she
> watched with unceasing care over the good order of its
> interior, the well-being of her beloved ones, and she did so

with the skill of the Bible's 'strong woman' concerning many a task requiring skill and effort, as once the custom had been. She also found time to instruct her granddaughter, assuming the ungrateful task of making her learn to read and write, and, to the end of her life, she would oversee her studies. Her solicitude, which handled all the cares, left her son with the quiet needed for meditation and work. As much as was possible for an unprofessional, she took interest in his projects responding from the depth of her heart to all his hopes and disappointments.

Grandmother was to be shown not only love but also respect. This was all the more an important part of Hélène's childhood because her papa astonished many a friend with his extraordinary attention to his mother's wishes. Whatever respect for tradition little Hélène imbibed from her father, it could only be reinforced by her grandmother's living in the past in more than one sense. She was drawn to the past by the memory of her husband and of two children who died at a tender age. The latter tragedy cast an air of sadness on her. She was also a conscious part of her ancestry of royalist bourgeoisie. There was, of course, the spirit of attachment to the Church which again meant for the Duhems not exactly the spirit of *ralliement*, inspired by the directives of Leo XIII who hoped for a *rapprochement* between French Catholics and the leading political parties of the Third Republic.

The traditionalist atmosphere of the Duhem home evidenced itself also in Hélène's education. Although compulsory elementary education became a law in 1886, the education of young girls could easily continue in a strictly private family framework. Hélène did not attend elementary schools. Her education was, until she was fourteen or so, a home affair run by papa and grandmother. The manner in which Hélène was to handle decades later her great life mission indicates that she received thorough training in French and history and a fair exposure to Latin. Later she learned some Greek to help her papa in reading the proofs of his great works in the history of science. At any rate, she was the type of intelligent child who absorbed new information with natural ease. An important factor in Hélène's education was her papa's readiness to talk with his mother not only about local and national events, but also about his own researches, especially the ones relating to the history of science. Hélène vividly remembered her papa's emotions as he came home with fresh bits of news about his various discoveries concerning the medieval origins of modern science and "hastened to share his excitement with his daughter in the evening." In general, to let Hélène speak again,

> Pierre Duhem was most communicative. He kept his mother abreast of his ideas, work, and projects. He loved to discuss with her topics — religious, political, and literary — which at that time created passionate interest everywhere. By listening to the two the little girl learned best.

Informal private education, done at home, could go only so far. Hélène was already fifteen when Duhem, in a letter written to his mother, explained why the so-called "Cours Désir" would be most appropriate for Hélène. Originated by Adèle Désir (1819-1875), who soon gathered around herself a group of dedicated women, the "Cours Désir" quickly spread all across France. It did not aim at preparing for universities, which at first were not easily accessible even for graduates of the new State *lycées* for girls. The "Cours Désir," as Duhem put it, "is given by women who in a sense form a religious order, but neither wear a habit, nor are constrained by anything that would pose a hindrance. The course is oriented in the direction I hope for; it has for its goal the formation not of school-teachers, but of cultured women at home in society."

By hindrances Duhem obviously meant the drastic implementation of anti-Church laws by the government of Combes in 1904 and 1905. Schools of all kinds together with orphanages, hospitals, day-care centers, old folks' homes, dispensaries, and soup kitchens staffed by the religious and clergy were closed amidst general uproar. As the Mitterand government was to learn almost a hundred years later (in the summer of 1986, when two million Frenchmen marched on the Champs Elysées and millions elsewhere in France to protest a much milder legislation aimed at curbing private, that is, mostly Catholic schools), France was more Catholic than most politicos dared to think. In a neighborhood such as the one around the Duhems' home in Rue de la Teste, even people with no religious conviction watched in horror as priests and nuns were thrown to the street by armed police and at times with the help of the military. In the village of Talence, just three kilometers south of the Duhems' home, which was then near the city limits, the cavalry had to be called out to implement the closing of the Catholic elementary school there — one of the tens of thousands of which the Church was summarily deprived in the name of "Liberté, Egalité, Fraternité." Near the Duhems' home the Carmelites of the Rue St. Genès had to leave their house in tense circumstances.

The events of 1905 were, of course, but the culmination in Bordeaux, as elsewhere in France, of measures taken against Catholic schools for some years. In July 1904, the Collège de St. Genès, just around the corner from the Duhems' home, had to close its doors and so did the Collège Sainte-Marie of the Marianists (who educated Pierre Duhem in Collège Stanislas in Paris). By then the big Jesuit collège in Rue Tivoli had been closed for three years. The Dominicans' house remained open only until 1903.

The year 1903 was also the year of Hélène's first communion. This could only heighten and broaden Hélène's religious awareness, also because it took place in Sainte-Eulalie, a focal point in Bordeaux of Sillonists. They were an activist group of progressive Catholics who to the bitter end hoped for conciliatory gestures toward the Church from the Republican establishment. On leaving Sainte-Eulalie after Sunday mass, Hélène could hear her father tease young Sillonists selling their newspaper, *Eveil démocratique*, with the remark: "What a pity you do not sell *Sommeil démocratique*. I would buy a copy right away." Hélène's attachment to the Catholic faith and presence was also strengthened by the completion in 1903 of a new façade for Sainte-Eulalie and by the renovation of its two medieval side portals — one for lepers, another for the pilgrims going to Santiago di Compostella.

From her father steeped in history Hélène learned incisive details about the Church in France just by going to Sainte-Eulalie every Sunday. Across the church there stood a stately building, originally a Catholic seminary, which, after having been turned into barracks by the Revolution, finally became a hospital served by nuns — a succession illustrative of *plus ça change, plus ça reste la même chose*. Sainte-Eulalie itself embodied both a vital past and a vital present. Its foundations led back to the 7th century with a chapel dedicated in honor of Saint Pierre, the patron saint of Hélène's father. They, with other parishioners of Sainte-Eulalie, learned that a certain Louis Stanislas Martin, the father of Soeur Thérèse de Lisieux, had been baptized there on October 28, 1823. A few years later, in the summer of 1912, Hélène and her father were reading the autobiography of the one whom the English speaking Catholic world remembers as the Little Flower.

In the Duhems' home the events of those troublesome years were discussed daily and with an animation that can easily be imagined. This is not to suggest that Hélène received simplistic viewpoints from her father. Although strongly anti-Republican, he kept his reservations about the *ralliement* urged by Leo XIII as well as the intransigent policy of Pius X. In both cases, Duhem was led by his clear realization of the limits of practical politics. As it turned out, leading Republicans, Jules Ferry in particular, roundly rejected the overtures from among the "progressives" within the French hierarchy. Against the intransigency of Pius X, Duhem held in focus the practical impossibility of securing private French Catholic colleges and universities in sufficient numbers to accommodate all the French Catholic youth aspiring to higher education. In fact, Duhem strongly urged young Catholics to attend state universities and seek employment there as teachers!

All these qualifications of Duhem's own intransigence could easily be lost on Hélène, just about to enter her teenage years. Towards their end, when she would have become more receptive to the finesses of her father's views, she was no longer under his daily influence. One illustration of Hélène's penchant for oversimplification is her reporting about her father's anti-Semitism, which we shall discuss later. Another is her failure to learn her father's diffidence when faced with political activism, whatever his strong feelings and views. Distressed by the possibility of anarchy, Duhem would have welcomed a strong rule, preferably through the restoration of monarchy, but he was too much of an egalitarian and democrat to welcome, say, any restriction on academic freedom. Thus while Duhem merely read, at times ostentatiously, the newspapers of the *Action française*, Hélène readily lent her name in the 1930s to the national organization of its women supporters. Not that she had ever engaged in political actions!

Anticipation of Hélène's future life is appropriate in one more respect in this recital of her childhood. Her father became a close friend in 1902 of Albert Dufourcq who arrived in Bordeaux in 1898 as professor of Church history.[8] The house of Mr and Mme Dufourcq soon became a second home for Duhem. Hélène, eight years older than Henriette, the oldest child of the Dufourcqs, quickly became an "aunt" to her, as well as to Mathilde and Norbert, born in 1903 and 1905 respectively. Hélène could see her father amuse those three with humorous drawings and call them "machurés." That word, used in the Lille area for miners (and other black-faced persons such as the mythically black three Kings of the Nativity story) was Duhem's way of speaking of the usually soiled faces of little children. In all evidence, the three Dufourcq children loved being called "machurés." On December 27, 1910, Duhem was sent a postcard from Paris with the following text: "The Machuré clan, gathered at 65 Rue Jouffroy under the graceful presidency of the High and Powerful Mademoiselle Hélène of Thiais, send most respectfully and affectionately their cordial best regards to the Squire of [the Rue de] la Teste." The signatories were M[adeleine] Dufourcq, A. D. [Albert Dufourcq], and their three children, Henriette, Mathilde, and Norbert, or the three "machurés." That the postcard also carried Hélène's signature was due to the fact that by December 1910 she had been away from her father's house in Bordeaux for some time, leading a quasi-independent adult life in Paris for most of the year.

2

Young Adult

Atelier Sainte-Agnès

On the postcard which brought to a close the preceding chapter the most obvious and dominating feature is Hélène's signature. Hers was a strong handwriting, almost masculine. Hélène's brilliant mind, blue eyes, blonde hair, facial features, and wiry frame suggest that she took more after her father than after her distinctly feminine mother. This may have resulted in some lack of self-assurance, hardly the trait of her father, for which she may have tried to compensate in various ways. Or perhaps she tried to respond subconsciously with her handwriting too to a father who, according to her reminiscences, unwittingly tried to raise her as a boy. Having been deprived of her mother at a very early moment in life, she did not experience the intangibly firm control which mothers alone can exert over their daughters.

Pierre Duhem, to say nothing of his sister Marie, may very well have spoiled young Hélène by trying to compensate for the loss of her mother. The result was a certain self-centeredness in Hélène's character coupled with the lack of strength needed for making important decisions. Possibly as she became more and more aware of her undeniable talents, she may have developed some resentment of the manner of her upbringing. Being educated at home could easily deprive her of the discipline of a daily routine that comes with going to school. She may have felt a conflict between her sheltered home-life and the life of other children, which may have been a part of her being deprived of a family-life centered on one's mother.

She felt such conflicts as she groped toward choosing a way of life for herself. Despite her great devotion toward her father, she wanted to be on her own, which could hardly be achieved if she chose to stay at home and take the place of her grand-mother as her father's housekeeper. Marriage may not have had much appeal for her. Her social life as a child and as a young teenager may have been restricted. At any rate, she was genuinely attracted by the self-fulfillment which her Aunt Marie found in religious life. Aunt Marie may in turn have thought of guiding Hélène, whose visits with her aunt in Paris became increasingly more frequent as well as longer during 1906-08, toward convent life. As Hélène recalled those visits in Paris, she was as pleased about being exposed to the capital's cultural riches, especially to its museums and art galleries, and about being introduced to the relatives and friends of her parents, as she was interested in exploring the possibilities of religious life.

Religious or convent life became a secular and civil life in most external appearances following Combes' denial of legal status to the Church in 1905.[1] Scattered nuns — Marie Duhem was one of them — grouped together as "laywomen" by renting, say, an entire floor of an apartment house, or a small section of their former educational or hospital estab-lishments. Marie Duhem, or Mère Marie Dominique, lived, when her mother died in 1906, in such a section of the large school-buildings still known as the Abbaye du Bois, near the intersection of Boulevard Raspail and Rue de Sèvres.

Under the circumstances new experimentation in religious life had been going on for some time. Some of these aimed at accommodating young unmarried Catholic workers, especially women, in residences with a Christian atmosphere. One such residence was the Atelier Sainte-Agnès in Thiais. Today the major source of information about it is a twelve-page brochure with photographs, whose general heading, "Monographie d'un Groupement Social Catholique,"[2] speaks clearly of its aim. In the brochure Thiais is referred to as a village of 3000 inhabitants, 12 km south of Paris, and with "fresh air" because it is "situated on a hill dominating the nearby Choisy-le-Roy and the Seine." The description was a far cry from the present appearance of Thiais that blends into the vast expanses of the densely-built Parisian suburbs, many of them referred to a generation or two ago as the *banlieues*. As late as 1930, many of them were without running water and proper sewage disposal. As to the "fresh air," the mushrooming of automobiles has made it a matter of wishful thinking.

There was in those *banlieues* plenty of need for Catholic social work of all sorts, including provision for living accommodations. Around 1908, the time of the publication of the brochure, the Atelier was already almost twenty years old. It originated as an evening club for young working women in Arc-les-Gray, a town in Haute Saône in the Jura, owing to the concern of Mlle Marie Thérèse de la Girennerie, daughter of General and Comtesse de la Girennerie. Because of her father's transfer in 1893 to Algeria as general inspector of French cavalry troops there, Mlle de la Girennerie transferred to Dole in the Jura this club which she had meanwhile developed into a small residence and workplace. The Atelier supported itself through the work of its residents, work which at that time consisted of sewing decorative pieces for military uniforms. Although the Atelier was a Catholic place, its residents wore no religious uniform or habit of any sort, "to the astonishment of many" as the brochure put it.

The creation of the Atelier earned for Mlle de la Girennerie the title of "Madame la Chanoinesse" by the Noble

Chapter of Maria-Schul in Brunn, an association of Catholic noblewomen patterned after the Knights of Malta and similar organizations. From all appearances, Mlle de la Girennerie had, through her parents, connections with high ecclesiastical circles. The book put together by her under the title, *Le Livre de l'apôtre* was not only published in 1897 by a prominent publisher (Victor Lecoffre, Paris), but also included commendatory letters from Cardinal Ferrata in the Vatican, and two bishops, Msgrs. Denechau and Bonnefoy.

A year later, in 1898, Mlle de la Girennerie moved the Atelier to Thiais, a "gentle village 12 km south of Paris," according to the brochure. About the cause of the move the brochure only mentions "circumstances," very likely connected with a further transfer of General de la Girennerie. In Thiais, the Atelier took quick and apparently strong roots. Between 1901 and 1905, four periodicals dealing with Catholic social work carried favorable reports about it as a worthy innovation. Hélène seems to have learned about the Atelier through her aunt, Marie Duhem, herself engaged in Catholic social work in Paris. The importance of the question, "Have you kept the letter in which Aunt Marie recommended you to Mlle de la Girennerie to be received in Sainte-Agnès?," in Duhem's letter of May 22, 1909, to Hélène, will be seen shortly.

As the Atelier was razed to the ground through urban renewal in the early 1960s, only the brochure allows one to picture it as Hélène found it at 1 Rue de la Bezonne in late 1908. The main building was a two-story brick residence. Between it and a work hall there stood a chapel. The work hall, a frame structure, also had two floors. The upper one served as a dormitory for the younger residents, whereas its ground floor, mostly glass-walled, contained a dozen or so sewing machines driven by an electric motor of 2½ horse power. According to the brochure, the ground floor of the main residence hall contained a large reception-recreation room to the right of the main entrance. On the opposite side were the dining room, kitchen, and bathrooms. The basement contained the laundry and storage space for wood and coal. There was, on the ground floor, a "special guest room for former residents of the Atelier who wished to come back for a visit even after their marriage." For, as the brochure pointedly added, "The Atelier Sainte-Agnès is not a nursery for celibates, it is not a walled-in institute, a cenacle with no radiance, but an establishment with a social purpose: Mme la Chanoinesse de la Girennerie guides her 'daughters' towards marriage."

The brochure contained references to various printed reports about the Atelier.[3] Partly through quotations from those reports the Atelier was described as a place where freedom was given to each resident to arrange everything according to her personal taste and a place of merry atmosphere created by the pictures and posters on the walls in the rooms as well as in the hallways. Those reports may have been written by Mlle de la Girennerie, in her late thirties around 1908, who did her best to convey the impression that the Atelier was a happy place where "one loves and is loved, and love is cheerfulness."

In Thiais, the Atelier supported itself by turning into finished products roughly tailored children's garments that were supplied by wholesale clothiers from Paris. According to the brochure, residents with years of practice could earn with their sewing 3 to 5 francs a day; the daily earnings of a beginner (mostly in the age bracket 13-16) was one half that sum. Most significantly, all earnings were held in common and disbursed according to individual needs. In the brochure, entitled "La vie heureuse," one also finds it stated that "the foundress contributes her share of work, because by staying with the young women who have joined her, Mme la Chanoinesse de la Girennerie has adopted their life, including their hard work." The brochure contained nothing specific about accounting.

The work of residents consisted in sewing eight-and-a-half hours a day — less than the workday authorized by law, as the brochure pointedly added. After rising at six, work began at eight and, with a lunch break, lasted until six. On Saturday afternoon work stopped at 3 to leave the remainder of the afternoon for general cleaning so that Sunday could be reserved for rest and recreation. Work connected with cooking was also shared by all.

Hélène found this place most congenial, partly because she was really interested in working for the poor, and partly because she could do her work leisurely and without strict responsibility. Most importantly, she found in addition to Mlle de la Girennerie, who from the first seems to have captivated her as a mother figure, several young women of her age, Cécile Paradis in particular, very much to her liking. A telling aspect of Hélène's joining the Atelier was her lack of fondness for sewing either by hand or machine. Clearly, there had to be an understanding between her and Mlle de la Girennerie that she would be a special resident in the Atelier. She, or rather her father, did in fact pay for her stay there. Her special status largely derived from her being the well-provided for only child of a well-known professor and author. Her close connections with the Chayets, a prominent Parisian family, could but be a further asset. For Mlle de la Girennerie it had to be obvious that such a recruit greatly enhanced the Atelier's social respectability. Finally, Duhem himself was inclined to see in Hélène's joining the Atelier a practical answer to a long-standing concern of his. That the Atelier was recommended to Duhem by his own sister, Marie, could but strengthen his confidence that he was right in approving Hélène's wish to live there.

From the moment Pierre Duhem lost his wife, a chief concern of his was to live until he would see his daughter safely settled in life. From the financial viewpoint the future seemed safe for Hélène. She inherited from her mother bonds and securities, carefully handled by her father. She was, of course, to inherit eventually her paternal grandmother's house in Cabrespine, with dozens of acres of land there. Compared with these assets, the royalties for her father's books could appear relatively minor at that time. She was also to become the beneficiary of her maternal grandmother's bequest.

Above all she was the daily object of her father's untiring attention. Witness are the letters which Duhem sent to Hélène every day, in spite of the fact that she was not always speedy or sufficiently detailed in her answers. "One could easier get a breath out of a dead donkey than a word from Toumi," complained Duhem on December 29, 1910. His reproach, "you have the habit of never answering the questions posed to you" (Feb. 18, 1911), was strengthened three days later with a modest boast: "With one exception, which occurred in the beginning of your stay in Thiais, I have not failed to write you a daily letter" (Feb. 21, 1911). Toward the end of that year (Dec. 2, 1911) he tried to get quicker and lengthier replies from Hélène by reminding her that he was writing her every day. A little over three years later (Jan. 3, 1915), he referred to his "little daily missives." Duhem was not on the defensive when a month later Hélène complained about the shortness of his letters. "I received," he wrote back, "only eight lines from you in eight days," (Feb. 14, 1915).

Without any doubt, Duhem greatly cherished the letters, however short and irregularly posted, he was receiving from his daughter. Unfortunately, only a very few of the many letters Hélène sent to him from Thiais are still extant. One, written on June 7, 1911, is in part a reflection on her papa's reference, two days' earlier, to an airplane race from Paris to Rome. Duhem also included the newspaper clipping of a sonnet which Rostand had just published[4] to commemorate the event that created as much stir then as did the launching of the first space rockets in our times:

> My dear Papa, I do not, as you can imagine, have every day leisurely walks in the woods to tell you about. Our day yesterday went by calmly and pleasantly as is often

the case with our days, but also happily because you were able to specify the date of your coming to Sainte-Agnès.

We have delightful weather — warm, to be sure, this is summer, but so beautiful and so radiant! — I think of you who are being cooked in the oven of Bordeaux and I suffer with you.

Yesterday I received a letter from Marguerite Estard and I have replied by return of mail.

Be assured, we are aware here of the race Paris-Rome In fact, the conversation turned around it almost all the time from morning till evening. Very early one morning some of us, on hearing a strange noise, got up and saw one of the airplanes flying overhead. — But I did not know about the poem of Rostand.

Our garden is even more beautiful than it was when you saw it. It is a corner lost in thick green foliage where one sees only trees — several of the flowers have already disappeared, but the honey-suckle smells sweet and the rosebuds are opening up.

I hope that your hay fever does not exhaust you too much. In any case I beg you not to overstrain yourself with work.

I think much of you and I kiss you from all my heart.

Hélène

PS I did not thank you for your postcard, and not even for the vacations of Cécile. I have already talked of it a little with Mlle de la G. — but I will broach the subject to her again. — Thank you.

On receiving such a letter full of sunshine Duhem could only conclude that Hélène was in the best place at Sainte-Agnès. The surprise contained in Hélène's next-day letter could hardly suggest that he was wrong in thinking so.

My dear Papa, I have waited until this very moment to let you have all the joy of a surprise, to announce to you my return. On Saturday, the 10th, you will see again your little Toumi. I shall leave from Sainte-Agnès in the morning and shall arrive for dinner in Bordeaux. — Therefore in a short while! — I am already almost there!!!!

I shall send you the train schedule tomorrow.

As my little dog will be a bit exhausted by the trip, I would like to have for her a good substantial soup. Rice cooked in water with salt, but well cooked. Naturally, the rice need not be of first quality.

I close because I have much to do here during the next two days.

I am very happy about seeing you soon and I kiss you tenderly.   Hélène

Duhem's next letter to Hélène was dated December 2. It seems that Hélène spent the rest of June and much of July with her father in Bordeaux, before the two departed for their summer vacation in Cabrespine. There Cécile most likely joined them for a few weeks. Duhem indeed was so intent to have the two friends together as to write to Hélène on June 8th that he and she "should join forces with Jeanne d'Arc to secure the restoration of the health of Cécile" from whom he had just received a charming letter.

Had Hélène's trip to Bordeaux, which was very sudden in view of her father's expected visit in Thiais, had behind it some emotional upheaval, it could hardly have failed to leave some trace in her letter. And the very fact that she planned to bring up Cécile's visit once more to Mlle de la Girennerie's attention indicates that her relations with her must have been very smooth at that time. Gone were the stormy months during which she fought off all advice and warning as to the lack of wisdom of finding in her a mother.

"My mother"

Hélène became indeed furious when her stay in Thiais appeared to be threatened by her own aunt, Marie Duhem, who, as was already noted, had in the first place strongly endorsed Atelier Sainte-Agnès as a suitable home for her. Sometime in March

1909 Marie Duhem began to express serious misgivings about
the Atelier to Hélène who quickly unburdened herself to her
father. At first Duhem reassured his daughter with a reference
to "the customary poor judgment" of his sister (Apr. 29, 1909).
But Marie Duhem kept pressing her judgment and before long
Duhem found himself caught between his sister and his
daughter. Aware of his daughter's impetuous character, Duhem
tried to mediate between the two. He called Hélène's attention
to the very strong ties between him and his sister: "My sister is
all that remains for me on earth, please do not make us part for
good." By then (May 19, 1909) Duhem suggested to Hélène
that she should not stay for too long at a time in Thiais and
that sooner or later she would have to leave it for good (May
5 and May 15). On the latter day, Duhem took note of
Hélène's undue attachment to Sainte-Agnès and suggested that
after his three-day visit in Paris he would accompany her back
to "our retreat in Bordeaux."

Being wholly captivated by Mlle de la Girennerie, Hélène
was not eager at all to return to Bordeaux, and certainly not for
good. Duhem might have been able to appraise his daughter's
emotional status in its seriousness had it not been presented to
him by his sister in a tone and in details that, through her
outspokenness, could readily become counterproductive. Had
Hélène not spent by June 1909 several months in Thiais, her
aunt would have found it less astonishing that in all of May she
was permitted by Hélène only once to go to Thiais from
Neuilly, in the western end of Paris, and that Hélène visited her
there only once. Being cut off by Hélène was just as displeasing
to Marie Duhem as was her brother's silence. The result was a
letter in which Marie Duhem spoke plainly to her brother:

> I have thought that you would be concerned (and you
> should have been), but you have replied that you had
> authorized a prolongation of Hélène's stay in Thiais. I
> think you are the best but also the weakest, the blindest,
> the most unwise of fathers. I am much worried and keep

my eyes open. It is pretty certain that in Mlle de la Girennerie we are faced with the finest kind of a schemer; and
you leave your daughter alone with a stranger who has all
the demeanor of a coquette, nay a queer (to say nothing
else) type, who is not under the control of any reputable
person.

After reporting that Hélène had stopped visiting her and that in
a practical matter (some embroidery) Mlle de la Girennerie sent
a rude note, written by one of her underlings, Marie Duhem
continued:

> Such is the so-called educator and mother who had told
> me that she would not do anything without consulting me;
> she now completely isolates that child. I showed my
> confidence in Mlle de la Girennerie by asking her to let me
> know why Hélène has completely changed towards us for
> some months now and to clarify this painful situation by
> giving the full truth. That lady answered me that my niece
> is jealous and that she would not forgive me for having
> denied her my portrait; she added other great faults she had
> found in Hélène; she does not recognize any quality in her;
> the poor thing gives all her heart, all her time, and is given
> nothing in return; they have made of her a slave, a jealous
> victim. . . . If Hélène is jealous, it is only because one
> instills that sentiment in her; she was so loving and gentle
> last year.

Marie Duhem wondered why Hélène would be jealous of her
social work. Was she jealous because Mlle de la Girennerie
could not bear seeing her own work collapsing while all was
going well with Marie Duhem's project done in collaboration
with Anne-Marie Récamier, daughter of Joseph Récamier,
Hélène's father's best friend? Marie Duhem hoped to wake her
brother up by reporting to him that, during her sole visit with
Hélène, she heard Mlle de la Girennerie tell all sorts of bad
things about the Récamiers: "As if she were a big fish, Hélène

swallowes it all. . . . I was livid on seeing Hélène believe all and say nothing in their defense."

Duhem could not be caught by surprise, at least in that respect. Apparently, in a letter to her father, Hélène herself had already criticized Anne-Marie Récamier in particular and the Récamiers in general for not being Christian socialists. Socialists they certainly were not; selfless Christians they undoubtedly were. In two long letters (May 9 and 25) Duhem listed evidences of the deep religiousness of the Récamiers of the previous two or three generations. Frédéric Ozanam, a saintly soul, was a Récamier,[5] Duhem reminded Hélène. As to Christian socialism, he recalled to his daughter that the very expression had been disavowed by Leo XIII.

Duhem took it in his stride that he would have to protect Hélène from being carried away with enthusiasm for a Christian apostolate reduced to social activism. He was startled by his sister's strong misgivings about the mistress of the Atelier Sainte-Agnès, about whom he received the following portrayal from her sister:

> Mme de la Girennerie is a woman who has not a penny and who makes use of a façade of social work and takes advantage of young girls by soliciting donations; she mainly lives by begging and by despoiling. Moreover, she lies and slanders; her language is that of a mundane woman; she entertains her young charges only with stories of scandals and vice; her apostolate is to be after men. That brother [of hers] who lets himself be kissed by her daughters! And that cousin [of hers] who is taken to Bordeaux while those young women are left unprotected at the critical hour? And that 'union of souls' adopted by her from the writings of Mme J. Goyau which [in the latter's case] lasted 10 years and produced 3600 letters, etc. etc.[6] Such is the life of the head of a social work. And who is the superior who authorizes and counsels all that?

Such were fearful, prophetic charges that may have served their purpose had they reached Duhem prior to the trip of Mlle de la Girennerie's cousin to Bordeaux; assuming, of course, that he visited with Duhem. Had such a visit taken place, it would have almost certainly showed up in Duhem's letters to Hélène. Duhem had been dead for a dozen or so years when the accuracy of Marie Duhem's sketch of Mlle de la Girennerie's character began to be fully vindicated by shocking events, some of which were foreshadowed for some time before Marie Duhem's death in 1929. She continued:

> If Hélène were twenty-one, I would make her realize that between that woman and her aunt one would be wise to make another choice than the one she is making. But she is only seventeen. I will say nothing; Mlle de la Girennerie may strangle me. One should break her [Hélène's] ties with Mlle de la Girennerie!

The latter, being exposed to Marie Duhem's overt displeasure, suddenly grew cold toward Hélène who became so upset as to have fainting spells. This was duly reported by Marie Duhem to her brother:

> Her idol, who has promised her everything, has not yet spoken to her for ten days. I advise you to look after her health, but not to act either immediately or suddenly; one should wait for the moment when another friendship would form. God be praised. She is still a minor. At twenty-one this might have turned her into a trump card never to be regained.

Marie Duhem seems to have thought of the possibility that once Hélène had come of age, she could be induced by Mlle de la Girennerie to crown her affection for her as her "mother" by turning her financial assets into a legal trust of hers.

That she was twenty some years younger than Mlle de la Girennerie could make it all the easier for Hélène to find in her the mother whom she never knew and, in her charges, the sisters she never had. Duhem, who was always most courteous toward women and who assumed the best intentions in others until gravely deceived, would have been most unwilling to see in Mlle de la Girennerie anything other than a selfless and enlightened religious educator. A great admirer of the army, Duhem must have also been impressed by the high military rank of Mlle de la Girennerie's father. At any rate, instead of breaking up, the ties between Hélène and Mlle de la Girennerie only strengthened. In that outcome an additional role may have been played by Duhem's bent on consistency. As he was wont in his intellectual work to follow through the logic of any considered judgment of his, so he was ready to be consistent with his erstwhile appraisal concerning persons and practical life. With respect to his estimate of Mlle de la Girennerie, Duhem stood by it in a way that could become a classic illustration of logic defined as the art of going wrong with confidence.

In all appearance, Duhem did not feel impelled to probe into that aspect of Hélène's attachment to the Atelier which would have shown Mlle de la Girennerie in a patently dominating role over Hélène. His failure to see this is all the more puzzling because he had plenty of opportunity to probe into the motivations of Hélène who spent the late summer and early fall of 1909 as well as of 1910 with him in Cabrespine. If he expressed any dissatisfaction with Hélène's being in the Atelier, it was because he was feeling lonely in Bordeaux. Hélène could hardly avoid saying that much to Mlle de la Girennerie, who in turn brought up the problem to Duhem. She must have been certain that Duhem would be gallantry itself. Duhem's letter of November 10, 1910, shows that the Atelier's mistress did not misjudge him:

Madame, I am neither miserable nor sad because of
Hélène's absence. My solitude is filled by the thought that
my child finds, at your side, the opportunity to make use
of her life actively and constructively and in a Christian
framework. Here, on the contrary, Hélène does not find
any objective to which she could devote herself with the
thought of fulfilling her calling. She is pained thereby and
I keenly suffer by anything that pains her. For a long time
I have understood that solitude will be one day my lot and
that Hélène undoubtedly would not find by my side the
means of following her vocation whatever it is. My gratitude for the hospitality you offer to my dear little one is
therefore unmixed and without any reservation. Please
accept the most sincere affirmation of this on my part,
together with the homage of my deep respect.   Duhem.

A month later, in his Christmas wishes to Hélène, he included
the entire Atelier Sainte-Agnès on the ground that all members
of a house should be happy if one was to be happy there. Yet
a week later in his New Year's wishes to Hélène he could not
conceal that doubts were not entirely absent from his mind:

I deposit these good wishes at the feet of the Lord so that
He may turn them into realities. . . . Almighty God may
grant you all that He, in His wisdom, judges good for you.
As a poor man of short views, I am not in the position to
know this correctly and what I may believe useful for your
good may, in fact, be your misfortune.

Duhem's high regard for Mlle de la Girennerie was further
strengthened when he learned that she had been invited in
February 1911 to the wedding of President Flory's daughter.
He took this also for a sign of the rise of the Atelier's social
standing. In March of the same year Hélène's healthy appearance prompted him to ask her to convey to Mlle de la Girennerie his gratitude. Ten days later, on March 21, he wrote to
Hélène: "It would be altogether strange if the agreement of

your and my opinion of Mlle de la Girennerie were to be mistaken."

Deeply attached as Hélène became to Mlle de la Girennerie, she could only be pleased by her father's refusal to take a hint even from his best friend, "Jo" Récamier. While in residence in Paris, Récamier, personal physician to the family of the Duc d'Orléans,[7] tried to be of service to Hélène. "He wanted me to give you my paternal advice," Duhem wrote to Hélène on February 13, 1911, "but you will do well to follow the advice of Mlle de la Girennerie." Apparently, Récamier kept insisting because Duhem wrote twelve days later to Hélène that regrettably his best friend was not familiar with Mlle de la Girennerie's "clear-sightedness." Récamier became involved in Hélène's welfare through two minor operations. After Hélène made a quick recovery, Duhem wrote to her on March 14 that Mlle de la Girennerie "should be given an M. D. for having called Récamier's attention to the matter right away."

Hélène failed to recover quickly from the second operation. Yet, although she felt "miserable" she was unwilling to leave Sainte-Agnès for convalescence with the Chayets in Mas de Marin. Duhem turned to Mlle de la Girennerie "to help Hélène overcome her martyr complex" (March 30, 1911). The complex had for its real object Mlle de la Girennerie rather than Sainte-Agnès. Hélène had her wish. Although very tired and pressed for time, Duhem came to Paris for Easter and stayed with Hélène for several days in the guesthouse "Meenehuis" which Mlle de la Girennerie recommended for him. In all appearance the place was very congenial. Not being in the middle of activities in Sainte-Agnès and being the indirect recipient of a special favor from its directress were two factors that greatly helped to make Duhem's visit a great success in the best sense. A month or so later, as shown by Duhem's letter of May 16, 1911, to Hélène, he still relished the deep conversations he had with her in the alcove of Meenehuis.

The subject of those conversations can easily be guessed. Duhem was most concerned about Hélène's turning into an adult well prepared for life as she was approaching the day of her coming of age in September 1912. In particular, Hélène was to be shown the deeper recesses of her father's inner life and family relationships. Only as the passing of years matured her could Hélène understand something of the depth of her father's feelings about his short-lived marriage and the signal injustices he had been subjected to in his professional career. Having lived in Paris for three years, Hélène could now better grasp the difference between the capital and the rest of France, and the meaning of her brilliant father's exile to provincial universities. Her being admonished as a small girl by a picture of Berthelot made more sense to Hélène in the measure in which she became privy to the more arcane details of her father's career. Maturity was also needed on Hélène's part that she might perceive something of the importance of her father's scientific, philosophical, and historical studies and of the priceless value of the growing pile of his manuscripts ready for publication. Had Hélène not shown an increasingly better grasp of such and similar matters, there would not have been, as will be seen shortly, precious references in her father's letters to her about his work, especially about the *Système du monde*. There were, of course, other topics touched upon in all likelihood in those deep conversations in the alcove of Meenehuis. One topic, that of Mlle de la Girennerie, even if it came up, was not a matter of dispute or doubt between the two. Hélène certainly could count on her father's approval of her enthusiasm for the directress of Atelier Sainte-Agnès whom she liked to call "my mother."

It should not therefore be surprising that Duhem paid no attention when he heard that George Goyau,[8] a former *camarade* of his in the Ecole Normale, and for years a champion of Catholic social activities, "hated" Mlle de la Girennerie. Duhem's attitude was all the more curious because in the same letter (March 9, 1913) to Hélène, he expressed his joy over the fact that Mlle de la Girennerie had been reconciled with her mother. Duhem failed to see that his comment, "what a pity not to be on good terms with one's mother," reflected on Mlle de la Girennerie's character. He did not begin to ponder, when about the same time he received word from a woman whose moral strength and sound judgment he held in the highest regard. She was Mme Dufourcq, the wife of Duhem's best friend, Albert Dufourcq, at the University of Bordeaux, who in the fall of 1913 moved to Paris with their children. She was most eager to see Hélène at Sainte-Agnès. There Mlle de la Girennerie made such a negative impression on Mme Dufourcq as to provoke some pointed remarks on her part. On reading Hélène's report about the incident, Duhem wrote back on March 18, 1913: "Keep telling Mme de la Girennerie how upset I am by the manner in which Mme Dufourcq behaved toward her. Am I to believe that the wives of all my friends have joined forces against her? Convey to her my regrets and my grateful respect."

Duhem possibly thought that Mme Dufourcq had been ill-disposed toward Mlle de la Girennerie by his own sister, who by late 1912 was back in Paris after an absence of about a year in a convent in Belgium. In her wishes for a happy 1914, Marie Duhem expressed to her brother her desire that contacts between aunt and niece be resumed. In his reply, of which he kept a copy in view of the importance he attached to it, Duhem was adamant:

> My dear Marie: You are not willing to take into consideration my counsels of prudence with respect to Mlle de la Girennerie. You ascribe them to excessive harshness. I wish you would not have to regret one day an excessive kindness on my part.
>
> You ask me if you can count on Hélène's return to you. The only reply to this question seems to me to depend on you alone. Hélène has a deep respect, a deep

affection, and a profound gratitude for Mme de la Girennerie. She is right because Mme de la Girennerie deserves,
in all respects, these sentiments. As long as your request to
meet with Hélène does not indicate a regret of the manner
in which you have acted toward Mlle de la Girennerie and
does not include a formal disavowal of the charges you
have brought against her, it is clear that your niece may not
resume her contacts with you. It is up to you to see
whether you want to do what is necessary to approach her.

In the concluding paragraph Duhem restated his intention to
respect his sister's wishes and rights with respect to the division
of their inheritance in such a way that she would never have
cause to reproach either him or his daughter: "I make no
reservation except in the matter of the relic of the Holy Cross
of our Lord. I have reminded and keep reminding you of our
mother's will that this priceless treasure should never part from
our family."

By then Hélène had long been fully informed by her father
about his major moves in the matter. They were two letters,
written to Marie Duhem in Belgium and to her superior there.
The choice Duhem offered to both was eminently fair: either
Marie would keep the relic in the convent with a written assurance from the superior that after Marie's death it would be
returned to the family; or the relic would be immediately
returned to him. In sending, copies of both letters to Hélène,
on March 17, 1911, Duhem asked her to "inform Mlle de la
Girennerie, who kindly advised me in this affair."

Duhem's gratitude to the directress of the Atelier was
repeatedly translated into acts worth recalling. One such act was
the contract which Duhem drew up in mid-January 1913 for
a re-edition, with J. Duvivier, of Mlle de la Girennerie's *Le livre
de l'apôtre*. That the contract form was sent by Duhem to
Hélène on January 21, showed her eagerness to be useful to
Mlle de la Girennerie, who in turn did her best to use Hélène
for her own purposes. Mlle de la Girennerie must have in the

first place spoken to Hélène of the Prix Agemoglu, awarded annually by the Académie des Sciences Morales et Politiques for "acts of virtue." Otherwise Duhem would not have written, on April 12, 1912, to Hélène: "You have been pressing me now for five months with this business." Clearly, Duhem was not particularly enthusiastic. Hélène had her way. Towards the end of 1912 Duhem informed his daughter that he had just completed his recommendation of Mlle de la Girennerie for the Prize. She received it in November 1913.

Duhem's move was characteristic both of his selflessness and growing influence. While he helped promote the cause of Mlle de la Girennerie, he did not lift a finger on behalf of his own election as one of the first six non-resident members of the Académie des Sciences. His election, that had been rumored since late 1912 and was a practical certainty since mid-1913, came on December 9 and was celebrated at Sainte-Agnès as if he had been a family member there.

Hélène did not become utterly exploited at the Atelier as long as her father lived because of his resolve to draw a limit, however tactfully. A case in point is his letter of December 2, 1913, to Hélène. There Duhem spoke of the problem of whether it would be advisable for him to write a review of a book which Léon Garzend, a priest apparently connected with the Atelier, had written in 1912 on the Galileo case under the title, *L'inquisition et l'hérésie.*[9] Duhem, though much impressed by the richness of documentation in Garzend's book, was concerned lest a review by him would draw on the author the ire of some heresy-hunters in the Church. The letter ended with a request that Hélène convey his concern to Mlle de la Girennerie, namely, whether she would think it wise to inform the Abbé Garzend about that possible outcome. Such was Duhem's tactful way of suggesting his displeasure about Mlle de la Girennerie's move aimed at involving him in an unnecessary trouble and for her own advantage.

Duhem certainly did not allow anyone, however useful and dear to Hélène, such as Mlle de la Girennerie, to come between him and his daughter. In fact, it was Hélène whose counsel Duhem sought whether he should visit her around Easter of 1915. By then the mother of Mlle de la Girennerie had been severely ill for more than a month and Duhem was afraid that his visit might be a burden on the Atelier under such circumstances, and especially if Mlle de la Girennerie's mother had meanwhile passed away. In speaking with Hélène about the legal problems posed by the death of her mother, Mlle de la Girennerie may have hoped to obtain some assistance from Duhem. But Duhem's reply to Hélène was no more than a reference to the recourse one has to make to a good lawyer in such circumstances (April 28, 1915). Earlier (March 19), Duhem asked Hélène not to bother about sending to him Mlle de la Girennerie's two small gifts by mail in view of his possible visit to Paris in a fortnight. Clearly, he had no sentimental longing for a gift or a letter from her though she could always count on Duhem's full respect for her own respective domain. When Hélène suggested to her father that Cécile, her closest friend in the Atelier, come with her to Cabrespine in the summer of 1916, Duhem insisted that Hélène first obtain Mlle de la Girennerie's assurance that Cécile needed no medication unavailable in that remote village (June 2, 1916).

Cécile's holiday visit in Cabrespine was only one of Duhem's contributions to the well-being of Hélène's associates at Sainte-Agnès. To Cécile, who was in charge of the petty cash at Sainte-Agnès, Hélène often handed over on behalf of her father sums varying from 100 to 200 francs. For Christmas, the Feast of Sainte Agnès (February 24), and for Easter, Hélène was the channel of a special sum to help everybody there to "celebrate." Signs of Hélène's happiness at Sainte-Agnès touched Duhem to the core of his being and prompted him to give a glimpse of his most carefully guarded sanctuary, the memory of his wife. In hearing from Hélène how youthful and

full of energy she felt at Sainte-Agnès, he replied: "This is one
of the things your mother wished for you. 'I want,' she used to
say, 'my children to have a happy youth. It puts its stamp on
one's entire life.' She was right" (Nov. 26, 1912).

Preparation for life

All that youthfulness and energy was to serve the young adult
in Hélène, able to handle her affairs and find her way in life.
Hélène's report of her going from Thiais to Rue Jacob in Paris
for lunch and returning by late afternoon to receive a visit from
Anne-Marie (Récamier), prompted Duhem's compliments: "A
true Parisian! The same would have taken eight days for anyone
in Bordeaux" (March 5, 1911). Two years later (May 20, 1913)
word from Hélène about visits and receiving visitors made
Duhem exclaim: "What an emancipation! What a coming of
age!" Hélène's spontaneous trip to Mas de Marin to attend the
memorial mass for her grandmother earned her the following
encouragement from her father: "What a big girl my Toumi is
now! She travels alone, stops in hotels . . . and does all that
with as much *sang froid* and *aplomb* as if she were a full-fledged
English Miss. And yet it seems that only yesterday she was
running alongside the imaginary Monsieur des Lilas-Roses, to
attack the enemy in the back of the garden. The little wheel of
life given to us runs its course very quickly" (May 9, 1916).

That Hélène could travel alone and carry out commissions
for her father in Parisian department stores was not, however,
the kind of maturity a single woman had to have in order to
stand safely on her own feet. A few months before coming of
age, Hélène received a stern reprimand from her father for
having spent on a dress an extravagant sum (a full month's
salary of a university teacher): "If you continue to order for
yourself dresses that cost 450 francs, I will have to make you a
ward of the court, once you come of age" (June 18, 1912).
Apparently Hélène had not improved in some respects since the
previous year when she received from her father this reprimand:

"You will always be the *bêteau-bêtouilleau*, the stupid little beast grandma Duhem used to speak of. Is it possible that simply through negligence and distraction you cause me so much concern? You, naughty child. Away with you!" To which were added the words: "I embrace you with all the tenderness which papas have for their toumis as Dickens' little maid used to say" (March 6, 1911). In the Spring of 1916 two monetary transactions made by Hélène caused considerable dismay to her papa whom she did not consult (April 11 and May 20). In the second case there was apparently more involved than mere inexpertise: "You are more naive than I thought and less the nice soul I supposed you to be." As to the first, Hélène's error was a blessing in disguise. The Russian shares she sold were to have no value within a year or so. Duhem foresaw the misjudgments she was to make when he wished her Happy New Year for 1913 and referred to the free decisions she would have to take from there on.

As far as decisions were concerned, Hélène seemed to be spared from having to make really important ones as long as her life alternated between an eight-months' stay in Sainte-Agnès and a four-months' stay in Cabrespine. In both places she was under the watchful eyes of someone considerably older than she. The two places were, however, very different for Hélène as far as the cultivation of her intellect was concerned. Whether during meals in the ancestral house in Cabrespine, or during long walks in the mountains around it, or on occasional trips from there to other parts of the mountainous south of France, Hélène was the constant beneficiary of her father's wit, wisdom, and erudition. Had she not had a brilliant mind, she would not have absorbed from conversations with her father the measure of articulateness she needed in order to fulfill her great task in life of which at that time she could suspect nothing.

On the contrary, Sainte-Agnès was for Hélène an intellectual wasteland, though a wasteland of her own choice, which was difficult to explain to others. Duhem himself chose not to attempt an explanation as he was making his New Year's visits demanded by etiquette, so his letter of January 13, 1911, informed Hélène. The wives of his colleagues naturally inquired about "Mademoiselle Hélène, your daughter," reported Duhem. "Is she continuing her studies in Paris? — 'Yes, Madame,' I prepare in thought my answer, 'she learns to piece together trousers for little boys.' — But they would not understand it. Therefore I bring up something that would lead to my favorite topic, the weather. Once there, I am inexhaustible and so are all my interlocutors, men and women."

In Duhem's daily letters to Hélène, which are by far the chief source for the period of her life now under consideration, Hélène is found only once asking for a book for her own entertainment (May 23 and 27, 1916). The book in question was a work by Racinet.[10] This is not to suggest that she was not reading at Sainte-Agnès where she obviously had many more hours of leisure than the regular residents. But her reading there may have been largely related to devotional literature. Her playing the piano, about which her father pointedly asked her (Dec. 19, 1910), does not seem to have been regular. Unlike her father with a vast production of impressive landscapes, Hélène's paint box (referred to in Duhem's letter of April 9, 1911), was not, in all evidence, used intensively.

Hélène's mind continued, however, to receive precious seeds as her father kept informing her about the major steps through which his masterwork, *Le système du monde*, approached the stage of published reality. When Hélène learned from her father's letter of March 23, 1911, that a priest, Père Lalanne, fell asleep almost immediately after he began a lecture in his public course on "Copernic," she needed no further explanation of what that "Copernic" was about. She could freely chuckle over the further detail that the priest in question did not wake up even after the lecture was over.

As a young teenager Hélène was given ample share in her father's excitement over the vast vistas of the medieval origins of modern science that suddenly emerged on his mental horizon in late 1904. Her father shared with her his gropings toward an enormous project: a revolutionary rewriting from until then unexploited original sources (including long-forgotten medieval manuscripts) of the history of the exact sciences from Plato to Copernicus. Her father's commitment to the project was no news to her. In his letter of Feb 14, 1913, he spoke of his hesitation about going to Paris because he had to devote all his time to "Copernic." Her reaction to the news in her father's letter of March 25, 1913, that "Copernic" would be subsidized by the Ministry of Public Education, must have been the same as that of her father: the enormous effort would not remain buried in manuscript form. She must have cringed at the same time, because that same letter also contained the ominous remark that Catholics would remain unappreciative of his works on the history of science.

Yet what a joy it must have been for her when, on May 31, 1913, she received word from her father: "The first galley sheets of 'Copernic' have just arrived." Her joy could only increase when a year and a half later her father suggested that the completion of his great work was no longer a matter for the distant future: "By November 1914 I will finish the volumes on the Middle Ages. Only the volumes on the Renaissance remain to be written." On the same day, March 15, 1915, when Duhem wrote the last lines of the medieval part of "Copernic," Hélène was notified also "of the three piles of manuscripts in the bottom shelves of the book-cabinet, all complete and enough for five years of printing." This meant that since the manuscript of the third volume had already reached the printer (Feb. 14, 1915), eight volumes of the *Système du monde* had been completed by March 1915. Undoubtedly, Hélène must also have heard through conversations with her father about the growth of those manuscript piles and about their location. Apparently, as will be seen, the same information was not given to many others.

That the publication of volume IV took place in early 1916 is clear from the word which Hélène received on April 19, 1916, from her father about his having presented a copy of that volume to the dean of Bordeaux University. Hélène also learned about her father's eagerness to see the volumes come out as quickly as possible and in spite of the shortage of paper due to wartime conditions. On May 27, 1916, Duhem shared his joy with his daughter over the availability of paper for volume V: "Hermann asked me to send its manuscript to Barnéoud, the printer. I gladly do it in order to make a little room at the bottom of my book-cabinet." No small credit was due for the progress in printing to Mr. Hermann, who had early on recognized the value of Duhem's historical researches and had thrown his support behind him although aware of officialdom's opposition to Duhem. On the part of Duhem, a signal expression of his esteem for Mr. Hermann was given in his letter of June 2, 1916, to Hélène. The subject was not the *Système du monde* but a copy of a work by Racinet which Hermann was able to locate: "The best you can do, in my opinion, is that you frankly ask Mr. Hermann, who is an honest man, whether he suggests that you accept the available copy or whether he thinks that it is better to wait for another."

These details about the *Système du monde* were to have great significance for Hélène's future life, a significance unsuspected by her at that time. For the moment the same details about her father's work were a reminder of his solitude. Not that Duhem wanted to make his daughter feel uneasy on that score. But she could hardly fail to feel a lump in her throat as she read on occasion in those letters that her father had not seen a soul for two days. One wonders whether Hélène, although already nineteen, had really grasped the richness of her father's remarks on solitude as he explained to her why he was not keen on going to Paris often: "Nothing is more painful to me than to feel myself drifting homeless in that city where I passed all my childhood and all my youth. I am surprised that nobody understands this. You see, without being alone, it is still less painful to be alone all alone, than to be alone in a crowd" (March 9, 1911). Less philosophical but no less gripping was Duhem's report on June 22, 1913, that the Dufourcqs would soon move to Paris: "In the future I will be a bit more alone in Bordeaux than in the past." The same is true of Duhem's description of his daily walk. As a Bordelaise, Hélène could easily picture the streets in question but it must have been less easy for her to read her father's comment "On early afternoons one meets nobody even along that route."

Whatever edge there was in such references to solitude, it was quickly taken out with a reference to "Boy" as a life companion. Hélène's pet dog, Boy, was first taken along by his mistress to Sainte-Agnès, but was returned to Duhem by March 1911. From then on, Duhem's letters to Hélène contain some humorous references to Boy (including some delightful sketches), but none so touching as the one in his letter of March 12, 1911: "As to little Boy, who when he is taken for a walk, wants to cross each sidewalk and enter each door, I too had one like him in my youth; only he had two paws and was called Toumi." The full emotional weight hidden between these lines could hardly be fully sensed by one who, like Toumi or Hélène, was not yet out of her teens. On reading about her father's references to his bouts with hay fever that tormented him from late spring until early fall, Hélène must have taken comfort in her father's wiry frame and endurance as well as of his apparently successful defiance of medical care. She probably did the same on reading in his letter of May 29, 1914, the lines: "Last night I was seized in my right leg with a cramp of extreme violence. Today I had much pain in walking. Luckily, this will be over by my forthcoming trip to Paris." One had to be a medical doctor to diagnose Duhem's predicament as something that put at grave risk not only his leg but also his very heart and with it the great lifework he had set for himself.

Bits of advice

Yet for Hélène's future life this was a most portentous bit of information in her father's letters about himself. Insignificant in comparison were the vignettes, or stories included there, now and then, about society, religion, churchmen, and, last but not least, about the war. Being vignettes with emphasis on a single aspect of a complex matter, they would not have been easily put in perspective by Hélène even if she had not been given to impetuosity in thinking. She was, of course, sternly warned by her father when carried to a patently extremist conclusion. On learning from her that she showed contempt for German prisoners of war whom she encountered in the Toulouse train station, Duhem wrote back: "I do not approve of your comportment. Vanquished enemies are entitled to our pity. And just think of our prisoners of war. How painful it would be to them to be insulted by Germans. Don't do to others what you would not wish to be done to you!" (Dec. 16, 1914). Not that Duhem failed to recall to Hélène big and small wrongdoings of the Germans. Once he even concluded: "May Kaiser Wilhelm II be accursed!" (Dec. 27, 1914). The resolve to outlast the enemy had to be strengthened in all possible ways.

The patriotism which Hélène absorbed from her father could hardly have been more robust. But when it came to practical judgments about this or that patriotic movement, the problem could be too complex even for one with far better enlightenment than the one which Hélène could, for instance, derive from her father's allusion to the Action Française in his letter of May 19, 1913. The occasion was the putting on the Index of all post-1905 issues of *Annales de la philosophie chrétienne* for whose editor, the Père Laberthonnière, Duhem had considerable sympathy. In that brief allusion the Action Française was described as the target of intriguing ecclesiastics, such as the Ultramontanists, their Jesuit allies in Italy, Pius X himself, and of Catholic intellectuals jealous of Laberthonnière.[11] The Action Française became involved in all that intrigue, so Duhem made it appear, through its reaction to Laberthonnière's exposure of the atheism and amorality of one of its leaders, Maurras.[12] Did this mean, Duhem seemed to ask, that the Action Française was thoroughly anti-Christian or that its unabashed patriotism was hopelessly tainted by rank paganism? Such a conclusion could be just as inconceivable for Hélène as it was to not a few Catholic bishops in France and even for some time after Pius XI had condemned the movement in 1928.

When in that letter Duhem called Pius X a "misérable," he certainly had no worries that such sharp criticism of the highest church authority would in any way weaken Hélène's loyalty to her Catholic faith. Then as before and ever since, French Catholics had no problem in being both very devout and sharply critical, a mystifying paradox to many non-Catholics. As a deeply devout Catholic, Hélène could easily grasp the significance of her father's references to his reading the autobiography of Soeur Thérèse de Lisieux. The last phrase of the passage to be quoted from his letter of June 12, 1912, suggests that Hélène recommended the book in the first place to her father who then reported back:

> I have finished yesterday evening Sister Thérèse of the Infant Jesus. I am under the charm of this small book. It was wonderful to see how she shows a way along which, without becoming a Carmelite, without abandoning the profession in which God placed one, one can become a great saint. In that book there are marvelously deep thoughts on charity. We should take this small book with us to Cabrespine and read it again under the chestnut trees of Granel.

Behind the critical remarks about this or that member of the French hierarchy which Duhem included now and then in his letters to Hélène, there lay a progressivist attitude which will surprise those who have readily swallowed the stereotype about his "ultra-Catholicism" and "extreme religiosity." One such cleric was, rather naturally, Cardinal Andrieu, Archbishop of Bordeaux. He was moved there in 1908 from Albi to implement the resistance of Pius X to the virulent and violent anticlericalism which the Third Republic had adopted shortly after the turn of the century. Prompted as those remarks were by distinctively progressivist aspects of Duhem's Catholicism, they could only strengthen such aspects in Hélène's thinking. Such an aspect was Hélène's fondness for Christian social action. Also, she advocated a greater role for women. Otherwise Duhem would not have added, "and you talk of feminism . . . ," as he reported (Dec. 8, 1910) to Hélène a new academic honor accorded to Mme Baudeuf, who had earned her doctorate under his mentorship in 1907. Very progressive and therefore very contrary to official Church policy was Duhem's acting as president of the Catholic Lay Association. By excluding all priests from its administrative organs the Association was able to reopen some Catholic schools without involving them in the conflict between Church and State. A part of this program was the formation of a Catholic Student Association at the University of Bordeaux of which Duhem was a founder and Hélène an honorary member.

Touches of progressivism which Hélène would assimilate from her father did not, of course, include enthusiasm for novelties. On receiving a Kodak camera from her father Hélène also received a note of reservation. With the camera there came also an attachment for making close-up portrait photos. "Just to take snapshots makes no sense," wrote Duhem to her on April 28, 1914. Hélène, who by then had many opportunities to watch her father draw impressive landscapes, must have heard him refer to the enormous difference between a good drawing and a snapshot of the same scenery. Undoubtedly it was the graphic vividness and richness of detail that drew Duhem toward Dickens whom he used to read aloud at home in the evenings when Hélène was a child.

Duhem's attachment to Dickens around the turn of the century was not a vote for novelty. Dickens' works had been in eclipse even in his own land for several decades before Chesterton threw a powerful light on his perennial value in 1908.[13] Hélène would guess her father's attachment to the perennial as opposed to the novel as she was informed by him of the appearance of Francis Jammes before the Association des Etudiants Catholiques of the University of Bordeaux on March 19, 1914. Jammes presented an anthology of reflections by modern Catholic poets on the six days of creation. Duhem did not fail to reflect on Jammes' performance:

> For an hour and a half, in a snuffling voice, with errors in pronunciation, and on a lullaby tone, that bore treated us to absolutely incomprehensible delinquencies both in prose or in verse — by him, by Claudel, by Rimbaud and other poets of the so-called Catholic Pleiades. Ah! the jokers! Many people with common sense chuckled up their sleeves and had much trouble not bursting into laughter. But there were also many dupes who applauded.
>
> After the conference, as I was waiting for the audience to leave, which it did slowly, I used the opportunity to convey my contempt for these jokers; one must not let youth be captured by these types. Many students shared my opinion; "this is cubism in poetry," one of them said.

Such graphic vignettes could forcefully shape the opinions which Hélène was to form on such and similar matters. No different was the case with Duhem's occasional remarks in his letters to Hélène on high society, on the poor, on Jews, and on the great moral erosion which for him was a harbinger of social anarchy. All those topics are touched upon in brief incisive remarks in the letters in which he reported to Hélène about his visits with Chevrillon. A former colleague of Duhem in their days at the University of Lille, Chevrillon, a prominent name in French literary circles, was spending several months near Bordeaux to be with his oldest son, a ten-year-old boy, who needed care in the famed sanatorium of Moulleau on the Atlantic coast. As Duhem wrote on December 24, 1912, with Chevrillon were also his wife and two younger children:

> Chevrillon's wife — very petite — has no Jewish features at all, although she is a Sorges girl, daughter of a rich Portuguese banker of Jewish origin. She is without any affectation, very preoccupied with works of charity — one of her sisters founded in the poor sectors of Paris six working places for unemployed young women. We have discussed these questions at length. . . . Chevrillon seemed to be very happy to meet an old friend again. He absolutely wanted me to come back next Sunday.

Duhem's next noteworthy report to Hélène about his visits with Chevrillon was from Feb. 28, 1913:

> At the Chevrillons I have found a nephew and a niece of his wife, Mr. and Mrs. Charles Ferdinand Dreyfus. I have never seen a type more perfectly Jewish than this big boy; there are in the Louvre Assyrian kings who have exactly the same profile. To be sure, he did not say more than those kings of granite. After lunch I went with Chevrillon to the beach of Molleau. Chevrillon told me a lot of stories about the stirring of ideas among the descendants of Taine, Renan, etc. All these people turn to Catholicism, to the ethical beliefs of our fathers. The fear of anarchy seems to me to be in them the beginning of wisdom. At the Chevrillons, ardent Dreyfusards, one hears the practicing on the piano of the Marseillaise and of the Farewell song. It is certain that something is happening in France.

Half a month later Hélène received the following word about the Chevrillons:

Chevrillon tells me lots of stories about the world of free-thinking intellectuals, a world in which people like the Painlevés live. What he tells me should make one tremble. The rottenness of that milieu, in which Christianity has no influence any more, goes beyond all that I could imagine. As to the Chevrillons, theirs seems to be a total disgust for their world. They are visibly turning toward Christian ideas. Chevrillon himself does not consider them in a supernatural perspective, but from the natural viewpoint he sees in them the only salvation for society. Mme Monnet told me in fact that Chevrillon's wife is on the road to conversion. I do not know whether she is now converted but her words often would suggest precisely that.

The Chevrillons were soon back in Paris and Mme Chevrillon was eager to visit Hélène at Sainte-Agnès. "I share your good impressions about Mme Chevrillon," was Duhem's reply on May 31 to Hélène's report of their meeting.

The foregoing letters suggest much about Duhem's attitude toward Jews. It was as multifaceted as Jews were of many different kinds. Certainly alien to that attitude was personal hostility toward anyone just because he or she happened to be a Jew. Had Duhem harbored any such hostility, he could not have dissimulated it to the extent as to lull into lifelong illusion such a perceptive and very liberal Jew as Jacques Solomon Hadamard. A famed mathematician, Hadamard remained Duhem's trusted friend ever since he met him as an upperclassman at the Ecole Normale in 1883. Those ready to dismiss this as a "lame effort" to exculpate Duhem from the charge of anti-Semitism make, by implication, a plain fool of such men as Hadamard. The first president of the Ligue du Droit d'Hommes, Hadamard was a brother-in-law of Captain Dreyfus and a colleague of Duhem at the University of Bordeaux in the very years 1895-97 that saw almost every Frenchman passionately taking sides either for or against Dreyfus. Duhem, who unlike most academics, never concealed his convictions however unpopular,

must have been able to present to Hadamard his views on
Dreyfus in particular and on Jews in general in such a way as
to weaken not a whit their ties of friendship. Of that friendship,
Hélène, herself an ardent anti-Dreyfusard and "anti-Semite,"
was to become a beneficiary.

As any perceptive Jew, Hadamard could but appreciate the
chief reason behind Duhem's "anti-Semitism," namely,
Duhem's resolve to protect the substantial Catholic ingredient
in French culture. That ingredient was particularly threatened
around the turn of the century by the agnostic crusaders of the
Third Republic among whom Jews were prominent and
numerous. As to typical Jew-baiting, such as the charge that in
their business-deals Jews are systematically fraudulent, the closest
to that in Duhem's letters to Hélène is a remark about the
insensitivity of "Jews and capitalists" for the plight of poor
workers (March 12, 1911). The remark was prompted by
Hélène's report about the hourly wages of seamstresses in Paris.
Clearly what bothered Duhem was not the profile of exploiters
but exploitation itself.

In a large part it was the ardent defense of that cultural
ingredient that produced a certain strain between the Duhems
and some of their relatives among the Chayets. When in June
1916 Maurice Chayet, one of Hélène's cousins, accepted the
post of secretary to Léon Bourgeois, president of the Senate and
a chief anticlerical, he received from Duhem a sharp lecture
which must have been very much to Hélène's liking. The
closeness of Hélène's thinking to that of her father was a telling
indication in Hélène's reference to the Paris Commune of 1871
at the outset of her father's biography. It was, however, hardly
from her father's letter of March 18, 1914, that Hélène first
learned about his views of that historic event:

> My Toumi. March 18. Anniversary of the Commune of
> Paris. You did not see it. Paris was in the hands of bandits
> whose minister of finance, Eudes,[14] was strictly upright.

While he functioned as a minister his wife continued to do her laundry in the public washstands. When he was shot, she took the few State papers held by her husband to the government in Versailles, as instructed by him. Today, as we are not governed by bandits, the minister of finance is a top millionaire who cheats scandalously and when a journalist lays that charge to him, the minister's wife shoots the journalist.[15] You see that without yet being old, I have seen things capable of making me awfully skeptical of politics and also of the definition of bandit and non-bandit.

This drawing with very sharp lines was typical of Duhem and also did justice to his keen sense of logic and equity. Whenever he saw either of them at stake he reacted with no fear, with no consideration of what others might think of him. As his remark about Eudes shows, he was ready to give credit where it belonged regardless of ideological background. Some such traits will appear in Hélène's drawing a book-length portrait of her father. Those who find Duhem's foregoing sharp lines facile generalizations and patent exaggerations may easily become guilty of spreading a smoke screen if in return they dwell on the amenities of the *belle époque*. Behind those amenities there could be seen, not only in March 1914 but also earlier, the fearful silhouettes of the four horsemen of the Apocalypse with the one called War in the van. They were invited by corrupt politics on all sides and soon shattered the lives of many millions. One of the victims was Hélène's young adult life, carefree and dedicated at the same time.

Her dedication to help the underprivileged was made carefree by the security which her father's loving concern assured her. Her privations were not noteworthy as the war kept going on. At the end of the summer of 1914 she could safely remain in Cabrespine, far from a capital facing a possible repetition of the debacle of 1870. As an only child she did not have to agonize over the fate of brothers in the trenches. But sad news about cousins and friends came frequently. She kept receiving brief but heartrending accounts from her father who did not spare her the shocking details of trench warfare.

But some time after the battle of the Marne, life reacquired many appearances of normalcy in Paris and even more so farther to the south. Thus the routine of the two Duhems' lives kept its major rhythms centering around the summer months spent together in Cabrespine. Duhem's letters of July 1915 and 1916 to Hélène in Paris conveyed an increased longing on his part for her presence. In the summer of 1916 Cécile Paradis joined Hélène and her father in Cabrespine. The two had already been there for some time when she arrived on the morning of Tuesday, August 8, at the railroad station of Carcassonne. She was met by Hélène and the two went to a hotel to let Cécile recover from an over 20-hour train ride. The next day, Wednesday morning, they took the stage-coach to Cabrespine. They were met by Duhem in Villeneuve Minervois, three hours' walk for him over the mountains of neighboring St. Martin. With the coach the same distance was covered in less than an hour. The three were in Cabrespine by 10:15.

Such details are from the diary, 22 large octavo pages, written by Hélène of Cécile's visit. Almost every day there was an outing, short or long, recounted in a few phrases in the diary decorated for each day by a little drawing, humorous or scenic, by Duhem. Cécile discovered ruins, insects, snakes, people, dialects, and enjoyed the warmth of a home in addition to the good country air. She also discovered the indefatigable hiker in Duhem.

Wednesday, August 30, the next to last day described in the diary, included for Hélène and Cécile a little walk down the road to St. Martin with exploration of some of the cavernous holes in the calcareous terrain. They hoped to surprise Duhem a little farther up the road but he apparently came back on a different and longer route from his hike. The next day Cécile went to mass and, although fatigued, she took a walk to the end of the village and back. "In the evening Cécile is seized by a strong chest pain," was the conclusion of the entry for August 31. Cécile's affliction turned out to be mere fatigue. It explains the last line in the diary, "Vendredi, 1ᵉʳ Septembre," and the sole line for that day. Obviously, the first day of September was not a day of vigorous exercise, or a day of "allégresse" for at least two residents of L'Oustal des Alègres, the local name for Duhem's mother's ancestral home.

The following day, chest pain, and an excruciating one, found its true victim, Duhem himself. Twelve days later, he did not survive another heart attack. Life for Hélène as a young adult, serious as well as carefree, was over.

3

From One Shock to Another

An ominous fortnight

For the three residents of L'Oustal des Alègres the second of
September, 1916, a Saturday, began like another routine day of
vacation. Hélène very likely thought about Cécile's vacation
diary in which text and illustrations were already three days
behind. Much, of course, depended on the mail which on any
day could bring to Duhem an urgent request from publishers
and editors and keep him from leisurely projects. At any rate,
Hélène and Cécile very likely did not go for a hike in the
company of Duhem who seems to have decided on an arduous
outing. It must have been a real exertion, otherwise he would
not have had great difficulty in returning home. His condition
was certainly unusual, but possibly no cause for alarm. A
summer or two earlier Hélène had seen her father with a much
more haggard face than the one with which he reappeared on
that Saturday in the late afternoon. Then Duhem, the intrepid
hiker, had merely lost his way. Low clouds and thick fog kept
him for a day and a night in the mountains. Although exhausted by hunger and cold, he had still been able to relish the
eventual embarrassment of two gendarmes who found him and
had first taken him for an escaped convict.

This time there was no fun and his true condition was worse than sheer exhaustion. Still, Hélène could seek comfort in the thought of her father's will power. It had helped him cope with intermittent severe abdominal pains ever since he had contracted rheumatic fever as a young teenager in the cold waters of the Breton seacoast. Once more Duhem made a brave effort to prevent those around him from noticing his extreme discomfort as he quickly retired to his upstairs bedroom. In the quiet of the night, Hélène, whose bedroom opened to the other side of the hallway a few paces farther away from the staircase, would certainly have heard her father's groans had he not done his utmost to muffle them as much as possible. Only in the morning, as she made ready for breakfast downstairs and passed the door of her father's bedroom, did Hélène notice his sobbing inside, a sound she very likely had not heard before.

Upon entering, she found him on his bed wracked by pain. To her complaint that he had not called for her earlier, he gave the gallantly lame excuse that he did not want to disturb her and Cécile's rest. To this he added: "I am waging my war." He did not want to make his own suffering appear even remotely comparable to the trials of those in the trenches that had by then been uppermost in his mind for more than two years. While Hélène could be impressed by such patriotism, her attention was not to be drawn away from what she saw with her own eyes. Her papa's convulsing face was more than reason enough for calling for a doctor. The nearest one was an hour's coachride away in Villeneuve Minervois. It must have been nearly noon when the doctor arrived and diagnosed the obvious: cardiac seizure. The doctor must have asked about possible past symptoms and perhaps Hélène recalled that little note which her father had sent her in late May 1914 about an immense pain in his leg that had made walking for him most difficult. This time his being severely restricted in his walking by the doctor was the most difficult medicine for Duhem to swallow.

Hélène had a clear understanding of all this, though not of Duhem's own understanding of the gist of the diagnosis. A fatal repetition of the seizure was a distinct possibility at any moment. He clearly realized that from then on he was to be ready for death in a special way. He was not, however, to live as a moribund the remainder of the life-span allotted to him. Above all, Hélène had to be reassured as much as possible. She immediately wrote to Mlle de la Girennerie who hastened to express her concern and good wishes. The thrust of Duhem's reply, of which only a part survives, was most likely another recommendation of Hélène to Mlle de la Girennerie's kind attention and good will.

Hélène hoped for the best. She could not help realizing that her eventual return to Paris was dependent on her father's return to Bordeaux for the opening of the new academic year in late October. But even in this case her routine was to change. She used to stay for an additional week or two in Cabrespine, following her father's return to Bordeaux, to close up the house for winter and spring. This time she was to return to Paris through Bordeaux. Even if her father made the best recovery, he could not be allowed to take a full day's journey alone, first by stagecoach and then by train, with a night's stay either in Carcassonne or in Toulouse. A return to Bordeaux would have been, in all likelihood, a first for Hélène in perhaps five years, quite a change from her routine. Sooner than she expected she was to return there — and alone.

For the time being she could take comfort from her father's incredible resiliency. Instead of staying in bed he made the most of the short walks which the doctor allowed him. Hélène now had to be by her papa's side, not only during those walks but on many other occasions. For the first time in her life her papa leaned on her and not she on her papa. In a few days the villagers saw a new Duhem and a new Hélène, as he was allowed to walk 200 yards daily. He used it for a resumption of his daily visit to the Post Office, near the *mairie*, off the central square, Place de l'Eglise, where the daily war bulletins were posted. Hélène could now see her gravely weakened father waging his war again: with his weakened voice and haggard face, he tried to put in the best possible light the often cryptic bulletins. It was not an easy task: the terrible toll which the war took of the male population was, unlike in big towns, always all too obvious in a small village like Cabrespine. Dejection and defeatism could raise their ugly heads at any moment under blows that struck at close range. On seeing her father's undaunted optimism, Hélène could but grow more hopeful about her father's recovery. In that heroic mood Hélène could also take in stride her father's intermittent remarks that he had hoped to have in her a boy who would fight in his place in the trenches. .

Another sign that suggested a non-ominous outcome was the indomitable mental energy of the patient. He sought reassurance that his voice would fill the auditorium in which he had been giving his public course on "Copernic" for the previous seven years. Still another such sign was his readiness to discover interesting subjects for study — simple plants, moss, and wildflowers — in the courtyard and immediate neighborhood. Vigor of life reappeared in Duhem through his being a born naturalist. Last but not least, he could still draw. That he did not take up the easiest challenge, namely, to add further small sketches to Cécile's diary, suggests that shortly after the second of September Cécile returned to Thiais. Duhem now had to choose from among the views available from the windows of his house or from its front yard and garden. One of those views was the spire of the village church.

Whatever pleasure Hélène could derive from those sketches, her chief satisfaction at that point must have been her father's rapid recovery. Ten days after his cardiac seizure he was allowed to walk three hundred yards. He should have felt elated that he could do this "at a snail's pace" but he was deeply frustrated. Hélène, at his side, could not fail to notice his concern about the future, a concern registered in what may have been his last letter. There he said goodbye to "the long walks in our beautiful mountains. This had been each year my great happiness and my chief relaxation. The doctor has just come to say: No longer."[1] He, and perhaps Hélène too, must have realized that, if this goodbye meant anything, restriction for threefive hundred yards or even more was not "for the moment." Many other moments had to pass before the snail's pace could be replaced by a walk at a normal pace. But there were more ominous factors to take into account. One was the war, with its constant expectation of further tragic news from the trenches. Younger relatives, sons of close friends, younger colleagues, such as Dufourcq himself, former students of the University of Bordeaux, especially from the ranks of the Association des Etudiants Catholiques, were a daily anxiety for Duhem. Then, most unexpectedly he himself became war news, and in a most distasteful way, on the front page of the largest provincial French newspaper, the *Dépêche de Toulouse*.

The incident deserves a re-telling for two reasons. One allows an important glimpse into Hélène's impetuous character, ready for rigid, almost inflexible reactions. Her father did his very best to return with a loaf of bread the viper's bite administered to him by Mr. Huc, the editor of the Dépêche. Militantly Freemason and rabidly anticlerical, Mr. Huc decided on character assassination, the favorite weapon of unconscionable newsmen. He did so when he was informed by an intermediary that Duhem would not honor his son's request for some information relating to medieval intellectual history. Duhem could have, of course, simply referred to the fact that as a professor of the University of Bordeaux he was only obligated to honor requests of that type when made by his own students. Being frankness incarnate, he did not hide his utter displeasure at the prospect of helping the son of such a crusader as Mr. Huc. Disregarding the ideological truce accepted by clericals and anticlericals, Republicans and anti-Republicans, for the duration of the war, Mr. Huc kept up with his divisive tirades in which Duhem saw a crime against the nation.

Mr. Huc therefore lived up to his billing when he reserved a seventy-line column in the center of the front page of the September 10th issue of the *Dépêche* to denounce Duhem as an embodiment of sectarian intolerance and preface this with the headline TOLERANCE. To make his blow even more devastating, Mr. Huc placed just above that column a gripping photograph showing French soldiers marching to the front lines. Such a blow could not have been repaired even if Mr. Huc had been willing to do what even more consciencious newspaper editors would not agree to. They would not publish on the front page and within a few days a rebuttal by the unjustly accused. What they usually offer in the way of reparation is a brief note (buried somewhere in the "gutter") which, even if noticed by all, cannot undo the harm. Of course, readers of newspapers have, as a rule, a very short memory which is heavily counted upon by editors as they indulge in their often arbitrary presentation of the news. But character assassinations are rarely forgotten and certainly none too quickly. In fact, they leave a trace of suspicion even in most of those who, on account of their acquaintance with the person in question, do their best to disregard the charge.

At any rate, Duhem did not try to defend himself. On the contrary, he assured the City Librarian of Toulouse, who had, in the name of Mr. Huc, requested the favor on behalf of Mr. Huc Jr., that the latter would be given a positive reply. The one who took strong exception to this course of action was none other than Hélène. She must have been rapping the table with her fingers as her father reminded her of Christian forgiveness. Hélène's readiness to take uncompromising extreme positions and views was not news for her papa. As was already noted, sometime before she left Bordeaux for Thiais, she voiced incomprehension when she saw her papa give the customary alms to a beggar whom he had just caught faking blindness. It was more Christian, Duhem reminded his daughter, to accompany the reprimand with some tangible expression of charity. Hélène's rigidity was also to be softened with a similar reference to Christian forgiveness and resignation when she urged him to take strict action against her aunt who was evasive about the foremost family treasure, a small relic of the Cross. On an another occasion Hélène's outrage at the high price charged by some wholesalers of flour in Paris had to be tempered by Duhem with a reference to the essentially unreformable character of human nature. However, such examples of advice were just as ineffectual as was the tone of resignation in which Duhem reported to Hélène, early during her stay in Thiais, "the strange behavior of very good Catholic families who failed to realize that their place is among the *camelots du roi*," that is, among the committed Royalists.

For the moment Hélène could hardly pay attention to the wisdom of being conciliatory. She could see, and this is the second reason for re-telling the Huc incident, the enormous emotional toll which it took on Duhem. She could not help noticing the immense distress inflicted on her father whom few things affected so strongly as matters relating to patriotism. Any charge, however slight or implicit, of unpatriotic behavior would have been most difficult for him to bear even in normal circumstances. It would have been simply a miracle if he could have lived down a nationally advertised charge made against his patriotism in wartime and only a few days after he had suffered a heart attack. Pent-up emotions must have kept him in their relentless hold for the next day or two. Physically, he seemed to be progressing. On the morning of September 14, Thursday, he was in the sitting room on the ground floor right across from the kitchen, waiting for Hélène. She was to accompany him to the *mairie* to read the latest war bulletin. As he was waiting, he worked on a sketch of the view of the church spire seen from his house. As Hélène entered she made a remark about further bad news probably to come. There was indeed plenty such news in the summer of 1916. While the Germans seemed to have been stalled at Verdun at an enormous cost, the French counter offensive on the Somme, almost as costly, did not produce comparable results. Clearly, had Duhem's heart not been doubly damaged by physical failure as well as by the extraordinary emotional stress of the Huc affair, which was still being read in Cabrespine and in the region, he might have taken in his stride Hélène's remark which, however innocent, appeared to him defeatist. As he began to list reasons for optimism, his face suddenly contracted under the impact of enormous pain. He expired in a few minutes without being able to say a word.

Hélène's frantic call for help to the servant was quickly passed on to neighbors, old and young. One of them, only sixteen at that time, was still around when this author visited in Cabrespine in the Spring of 1985 and could vividly recall from a distance of sixty-nine years, the lifeless body on the sofa with its head hanging sideways. It was only later that the *curé*, the *maire*, the *notaire*, the schoolmaster and others began to ponder the cause of death. They still talked of it twenty years later. The present mayor of Cabrespine heard, as a precocious twelve-year-old around 1936, some of them state firmly that Duhem had been killed by the *Dépêche*.[2] Hélène had no leisure to ponder this or that hypothesis. She must have been numbed by the shock inflicted on her by her father's sudden departure.

Comforted by father's old friends

Fortunately for Hélène, she could not suspect that her father's sudden departure from life opened the way for another blow to hit her within less than two decades. For the time being she had to absorb the shock of a death whose seriousness she must have increasingly felt with every passing hour. At the same time she could take no small comfort from the sympathy shown to her from all sides. As she sent telegrams to relatives, friends, and colleagues of her father, as she made arrangements for the funeral, as she prepared the house to accommodate as many as it could, as she asked others for similar accommodations, she was given countless signs of the good will which plain country folks are signally capable of giving. The poor peasants and artisans of Cabrespine, among whom her father's generosity and kindness were a legend, gave to the deceased the very center of their cemetery, a spot usually reserved for a large crucifix. Led by their *curé*, the Abbé Louis Blanc, who was to remain their beloved pastor for another quarter of a century, the villagers of Cabrespine formed the overwhelming part of the funeral procession that started from the church following the solemn requiem mass sung late Saturday morning, September 16th. If any relative stood by Hélène, it was either a Chayet uncle or aunt from Mas Marin, near Tarascon.

Even if the times had been normal, the academic world could not have sent enough representatives to a funeral in a remote countryside in the middle of September, still vacation time for French intellectuals. Hélène's telegram to the University of Bordeaux found no major university functionary in town. The circumstances of war kept away from the funeral even such close friends of Duhem as Albert Dufourcq and Joseph (Jo) Récamier, both of whom were at the front. Edouard Jordan, professor of medieval history at the Collège de France and one of Duhem's closest friends, was the only academic able to rush to Cabrespine. Jordan, son of the famed mathematician Camille Jordan who was among the first to recognize the talents of young Duhem, was in the best position to give Hélène specifics about the help which she could expect from her father's real friends in academia. This was true in particular of the attention to be given to the priceless manuscripts of the still unpublished parts of the *Système du monde*. Hélène, in turn, must have been Jordan's source about some details concerning Duhem's last days and moments that appear in his obituary of Duhem.[3] But precisely because in that obituary emphasis was given to the absence of activism in Duhem's political views, it provoked, as will be seen, Hélène's displeasure.

In the bleakness of the days immediately following the funeral Hélène must have received special comfort from the letter which Jo Récamier wrote from his unit of field ambulance where he served as a surgeon.

My dear Hélène,

Your telegram touched off in me, as you can very well imagine, a profound sadness. During his youth, your father's health gave us worries at times but since then he seemed to have gained strength and nothing, it seems to me, could make one think of a sudden death.

Now a friend has disappeared for me, a friend of forty-five years, the oldest and dearest friend, and I feel a void which allows me to understand what you yourself must feel. But the great loss relates especially to France and religion. Your father has acquired, through the universal esteem which was gradually accorded to him on account of his incomparable erudition, a powerful influence that few men possess.

His writings certainly exuded conviction and often, in the moments of doubt and fear, it is to his faith, well-reasoned and incompatible with any doubt, that I take recourse. His mere presence [in thought] in our camp was an encouragement and I am certain that it acted in the same way on many students and old schoolmates.

He could have served the science of his country and the Catholic faith for many years yet, but God wanted, sooner than we expected, to give him the reward in which he believed and which he had so magnificently deserved.

As for me I firmly hope that, if there endures between the living and the dead the sympathy which existed in life and in which our religion allows us to believe, my old friend will not forget me and his saintly prayers will help me to accept what remains for me to undergo in this life.

> I beg you to believe in my deep affectionate sympathy
> and in the very large share which I take in your sorrow.

Within a week there came the first expressions of sympathy from prominent representatives of officialdom. Radet, dean of the University of Bordeaux, wrote on behalf of himself and his two daughters a letter which witnessed Duhem's stature in the Faculty both as a scientist and as a man:

> Among all the dear colleagues your father was one of those who inspired greatest admiration and lively friendship. He had the twofold superiority, so rarely united, of character and talent. I have been proud of the affection he always showed me and I am unable to become accustomed to the idea that we shall not again exchange our impressions of events and men as we did so many times and which we did even more frequently as this terrible war was going on. It is no less cruel to think that his great patriotic soul will not witness the end of the conflict. France and French science have suffered an irreparable loss. And how we all feel that which you yourself have lost! To be sure, an intangible inheritance, which will only increase, of an already illustrious name belongs now to you. But who will render you the tender care with which he surrounded you?

Hélène was hardly surprised by the spontaneous outpouring of genuine friendship from Radet's letter. She knew the depth of sentiments which her father inspired in all those who met him with unfeigned sincerity and fairness, occasional as their meetings could be. In view of the fact that there is not a single reference in Duhem's letters to Hélène to Msgr. Chartain, Canon of the Bordeaux cathedral, he must have been such an acquaintance. He wrote no sooner than he had learned the sad news:

> I come to offer you my deeply felt condolences. I did
> more than admire your father. I have felt for him a very

affectionate sympathy and he let me disclose it to him. I even believe that I was not far from being ranked as one of his friends. Each time, and this often happened, that I had the great pleasure of hearing him talk, it was always you who were the first topic, always before his studies and our projects. His fatherly heart then opened and he let me readily see all that tenderness which he had toward his daughter.

This is an enormous loss for you, Mademoiselle. For another reason it is also an immense loss for us. Personally, I harbor a perennial gratitude for him because of all the benefit deriving from the prestige of his work, of his devoted co-operation, and of the good example he has given to the youth of this city. My heart impelled me to tell you this while I keep praying with you. Accept, my dear mademoiselle, my respectful greetings.

The condolences written by G. Darboux, perpetual secretary of the Académie des Sciences, were less personal though, as will be seen later, not without much bearing for Hélène's personal future. After a brief recall of his long-standing support for Duhem, Darboux wrote:

Recently I have repeatedly contacted the Ministry of Public Instruction and persuaded Mr. Bayet, director of Higher Education, to accord an important subsidy to his great work, *Le système du monde*. Unfortunately, we shall not see the completion of this great work which was to have ten volumes. I hope that Duhem left behind material to permit the publication of volume V.

Darboux' concluding words, "I am at your disposition," received their reply through Hélène's remittance to the Académie des Sciences of so vast an amount of manuscript material as to assure the publication of all ten volumes of the *Système du monde*. Obviously, no one was more elated than Darboux who was most instrumental in obtaining a second Petit d'Ormoy

Prize "for the late Pierre Duhem in support of the publication of his work, *Le système du monde.*"

Among the very first written expressions of sympathy was a letter from Mme Baudeuf (née Hélène Bayard), professor of physics at the girls' *lycée* in Bordeaux and Duhem's last doctoral student:

> I have just learned from the newspapers of the immense loss suffered by French science in the person of the admirable man and great savant who was Monsieur Duhem.
>
> His death is a cause for grave mourning to all his former students, to all those who took so keen a pleasure in listening to him and who followed his courses with inspired admiration. Alas, how ineffective is this pain we all feel to relieve your sorrow!
>
> Nevertheless, allow me, Mademoiselle, to tell you that inasmuch as you are his daughter, you have many un-known friends who would be happy and proud to be useful to you in any way that may ever be within their power.

While Hélène had not met Mme Baudeuf, she certainly knew Lucien Marchis who discovered physics for himself when he first attended Duhem's courses in Lille and who in turn was immediately spotted by Duhem as a promising young talent. Soon after Duhem arrived in Bordeaux, he secured there a teaching post for Marchis. Connection between Duhem and Marchis was further strengthened by the latter's vast doctoral thesis. Marchis must have met more than once young Hélène, who would have felt kindly toward him even if he had no other attractive qualities than that of being an esteemed and trusted younger colleague of her father. But Marchis became Duhem's special pride when in 1908 he was called from Bordeaux to the Sorbonne as the first occupant there of the new chair of aviation science. Hélène's recollections of Marchis were very likely further strengthened by a meeting or two or by occasional notes during her first six years in Thiais. Otherwise Hélène would not have poured out her soul to Marchis following the receipt of his first expression of sympathy. In reply to Hélène's letter, Marchis wrote on September 30th:

> My dear Mademoiselle,
> What a Calvary is yours! I have vividly sensed it in your precious letter. I have no doubt that you do not lack courage, but you must have needed it enormously and you will be in great need of it in order to bear that terrible blow.
> Since you live in the outskirts of Paris I am glad to tell you that my house in Paris is yours and my wife and I will be very glad to have you there.

That fondness for Duhem on the part of his doctoral students meant also fondness for his daughter was also clear from the letter of Eugène Monnet. A chemistry demonstrator at the Institut Catholique of Lille when Duhem arrived there in 1887, Monnet owed as much to Duhem as the latter owed to Monnet and his wife. Duhem's sympathy for Monnet helped him to overcome his diffidence in his abilities and to earn his doctorate in Bordeaux a dozen years later. Duhem in turn owed to the Monnets the opportunity to meet his future wife in their house. By the early 1910s Monnet was in the laboratory of mineralogical chemistry at the Collège de France. At the time of Duhem's death he was working in an ammunition factory in a remote valley near the Spanish border. Such was the reason for his letter of condolence being dated on All Saints Day, November 1:

> On reading the dreadful telegram the words were dancing before my eyes. I thought I was reading them wrong. It took an effort on my part to surrender to the evidence.

I thought of your cruel loss and I shall never be able to tell you adequately the share I take in it. But what a loss for us, for the many admirers he had in my entourage in Paris!

We knew that a chair was reserved for him in the Collège de France. To his future colleagues this was like the rise of a new horizon. I have heard one of them say what a beautiful conclusion of their career it would be for them to listen to that master. It appeared to them that a corner of the veil of truth could be lifted only by Duhem. Around me — I cite only Matignon[4] — only your father was taken for a savant. To have Duhem in Paris was a dream not only for me, it was also the dream of the most distinguished physicists and chemists I know. I had arranged all my plans to stay at the Collège de France when I learned that the selection of your father for a chair in the Collège de France had been approved as high up as the Ministry of Public Instruction.

Yes, the loss is great for you, Mademoiselle, but it is so great for us that but for a special effort I would be crushed, completely dominated by our own loss.

Today, which is the commemoration of the dead, I stopped for the first time in my work and I focus all my thoughts on the departed, beloved ones, but it is the thought of Duhem that dominates all other thoughts of mine and more than ever I feel the void gaping in front of me. It was discouraging for the laboratory to receive the news. Where to find another like him?

I sent you a telegram from Marignac but my work kept me at a very remote place, otherwise I would have been the first to rush to be near you.

Hélène could but wonder concerning the kind of chair that had been "approved" for her father in the Collège de France. She kept urging her father to visit Paris more often, precisely because she knew better than most that he had, from his student days on in the Ecole Normale, a moral right to teach physics in Paris. Hélène also knew of the rumors — so many keen disappointments to her father — about his being called to Paris, either from Lille, or from Rennes, and especially from Bordeaux. She was nine when her father made his first and last formal request to that effect to the Ministry of Public Instruction. She also knew that there had been moves shortly afterwards to bring her father to Paris as a professor of the history of science in the Collège de France. In 1913 she was informed by her father about the plans to make him dean of the faculty of philosophy at the Institut Catholique de Paris.

That no such moves would have been considered by her father was also very clear to Hélène. At home and among friends, Duhem repeatedly stated that Paris would have him as a professor of physics or Paris would not have him at all. The news from Monnet was therefore not so much a comfort as a reason to feel deeply frustrated. The news added another dimension to the loss she suffered by her father's death. Had it not happened, it would not have been a mere dream on her part that one day her residence in Thiais would be but a tramway and metro-ride away from her father's apartment in Paris. For Hélène considered the Atelier Sainte-Agnès as her final station in life. A proof of this is Dr. Récamier's second letter to her. That letter is all the more significant because in it Dr. Récamier put Hélène on guard against a possible loss of the "little fortune" which her father had secured for her. Only the cause of that possible disaster was wrongly conjectured by the good doctor:

> My dear Hélène,
>   Thank you for your affectionate letter which I could not promptly answer because we are at this moment in complete disarray, not so much because of the wounded to be operated upon as because of the number of dead.
>   Certainly, if one can be sure of the eternal happiness of a Christian who has just died, one can be sure of that of your father, and whenever I think of him, and I do at

every moment, it is to ask him to help me by his interces-
sion and not to pray for him.

At an age such as mine, fifty-five, friendships like the
one that united me to him cannot be replaced, the empty
place cannot be filled, and the rupture is profound. It is
curious to think that as long as I knew him to be in
Bordeaux or in Cabrespine near you, I did not suffer
because of his absence from my life, whereas now that I
know him to have departed from life I would like to
communicate to him each thought I have; and as you see
it well, it is the loss of a brother I constantly experience.

Few things have been published about him in the
papers. The best I have seen is the little article by Fliche[5]
in the *Journal des Débats*. It is absolutely necessary that
something more complete should remain about him. I
wrote to Edouard Jordan in that connection; he wrote me
a long letter in which he described the moving funeral of
your father, his body surrounded by the peasants who
loved him and especially by the *curé* who preached.

Edouard Jordan was deeply moved. He loved your
father for as many years as I did and he loved him profoundly. He seemed to me ready to write a biographical
notice of your father (in the archives of the Ecole Normale,
I believe[6]) and I think he will do it very well. If you also
think so, it would be a good idea to write to him to
encourage him. If you prefer another Normalien classmate
of your father, tell me so and I will persuade Edouard
Jordan not to do anything. He has the advantage of being
a friend and of having the opportunity to consult with his
father, Camille Jordan, who is the president of the Académie des Sciences for this year, about your father's scientific
work.

Reflect on all this and write to Edouard or me,
whatever the case.

Undoubtedly there will be published analyses of his
scientific work but it is necessary that a brochure help one
feel his heart and the cohesiveness of his life; it is precisely
this that people like Fliche or Jordan might do better than

others. At home I have hundreds of letters from him but the only one with interest for the public would be a letter on the basis of his religious faith he wrote me last year. I have sent a copy of it to Edouard Jordan and if another person would collect his documents I would copy it again. That letter is so dear and neat that on reading it I seem to hear him talk to me.

My dear Hélène, you are now the mistress of your life and I know that Mme de la Girennerie is another mother for you. Consequently I find it natural that you have tied your future to Thiais. But be on guard against the malice of men. I think that after the war the anticlerical campaign cannot reopen in full, but, believe me, the weapons will not be laid down. Therefore watch carefully lest your little fortune be confiscated by the kind of theft which the government has in so many instances perpetrated against religious orders.

Another thing. You have found in Thiais a family and great happiness. I do not know at all the family of your late mother and I don't know what support you would find there in case of necessity. But don't forget that as long as the *brother* of your father lives, his house is yours and that he would have no greater joy than to be useful to you as he keeps thinking of his [late] friend. Don't forget that. As long as the Thiais project continues, this is irrelevant but if it ever were to fail you, then this would be the time to think of your old uncle if God still keeps him alive.

Au revoir, my dear Hélène, may God protect you. Very affectionately yours,   J. Récamier

Working from Thiais for father's work

"If the Thiais project were ever to fail you . . . ," such was precisely an eventuality unthinkable for Hélène. And what thoughts, if any, may she   have had on reading Récamier's cryptic line about another seizure of the goods of religious congregations by anticlerical politicians and the possible loss of her "little fortune"? Did Hélène realize that this was possible only if her "little fortune" became tied to the Atelier Sainte-Agnès? Did she perceive in that cryptic line of her father's best friend a veiled warning lest she give the directress of Sainte-Agnès some power over her "little fortune" as a token of her unbounded confidence in her as her "mother"?

In all likelihood Hélène found food for thought only in those of Récamier's suggestions that related to the various ways of saving for posterity her father's intellectual bequest. She seemed to be keen on that subject during the first half of the fourteen more years she was still to spend at Sainte-Agnès. It was, of course, difficult for her to do full justice to such requests as the one that came in the letter which Henri Bénard, lecturer in experimental physics in Bordeaux, wrote to her on December 23, 1916. Bénard wanted to perpetuate Duhem's memory in the physics laboratory that had been under Duhem's directorship by suggesting that the small library which Duhem organized there for students be enriched with a full set of reprints of all his articles: "I will classify them and have them bound by subject if you can satisfy this desire of mine." Bénard also asked for the negative of a well-known photograph of Duhem so that a large print on glass might be produced as a chief décor of the laboratory. Bénard was ready to make as many small prints from the negative as Hélène and others might need.

As Bénard's next letter of April 8, 1917, indicated, his collection of Duhem's reprints was enlarged by a set donated by Vézès. The negative in question had to be obtained from a Bordeaux photographer. That Hélène sent only one reprint to Bénard finds its explanation in the most cumbersome aspect of the difficulties that befell on Hélène following her father's death, namely, the removal of all that was in her father's residence in Bordeaux. By the time Bénard's request for the reprints arrived, Hélène had already separated the items she was to keep from the ones to be given to relatives and others. A special concern of hers was the fate of the still-to-be-published manuscripts of the *Système du monde*. Hélène did the best she could by depositing them with the Académie des Sciences. She also set apart about two-hundred volumes from Duhem's scientific library and donated them to the University of Bordeaux.[7] All the other items, save those to be given to relatives and close friends, were confined to the storage firm, Maison Manuel, as early as October 24. Listed in their inventory were 26 boxes and 8 cases of books. Among the furniture listed there were three book-cabinets and a case of paintings. The termination date of storage, January 22, 1917, and the cost of 641 francs, was followed by a reference to the transportation of all items to 1 Rue de Bezonne, Thiais, the official address of Sainte-Agnès. Their arrival there by early February is attested by a bill of 828 frs paid by Hélène on February 16th.

The various documents settling Hélène's inheritance were also executed in Paris by the Notary Public firm, Blanchet, between October 28, 1916 and May 1917. Quite possibly Hélène sent some pieces of furniture, such as her father's large writing desk, from Bordeaux to Cabrespine, but no bill kept by her indicates this. At any rate, even the items she ordered to be transported to Thiais must have posed a considerable problem there. Only a few pieces of furniture could have been accommodated in Hélène's room in Sainte-Agnès and their presence there made her even more conspicuous in comparison with others, mostly young working women. Other items including reprints, scientific correspondence, etc., had to be stored either in the basement or in a utility shed.

As long as the moving had not been completed, and for some time afterward, Hélène was powerless to honor requests such as the one made by Bénard for a full set of reprints, no matter how worthy the cause. But even after she was able to form a reasonable idea of her suddenly and vastly increased possessions, Hélène was not in accommodations and surroundings appropriate to promote the cultivation of her father's memory. Her lack of higher education put her further at a disadvantage to capitalize on the publication in November 1917 of Volume V of the *Système du monde* or on the numerous commemorative articles published on Duhem in 1917-1920.[8]

At any rate, she seemed to be confident that her father's friends in the academia would not fail to cultivate his memory. Several of them could have indeed published in one or two of the major newspapers an appeal for copies of Duhem's letters and received an effective response. Why such a step failed to be taken by Marchis or Jordan or someone at the University of Bordeaux, or at the Institut Catholique in Paris, is difficult to explain. In that respect the name that particularly comes to mind is, of course, Récamier who, as was seen, did not fail to think even in the din of war of the eventuality that someone would set himself to collecting, as he put it, "Duhem's documents." Another who comes to mind is Blondel who, on hearing of Duhem's death, wrote to a friend: "Who will now be concerned with the manuscripts and correspondence of poor Duhem?"[9] Editors of conservative newspapers and periodicals and their political allies also failed concerning Duhem. While they were eager to get some mileage out of Duhem's death, they soon forgot him. As always, here too, they were more interested in winning skirmishes than in fundamental strategies, such as proper publicity given to painstaking scholarly research, so necessary for securing reputable and sound positions in the never-ending ideological contest.

All these and others could not ignore that with the passing of each year the project of collecting Duhem's letters would run into ever greater obstacles and frustrations. In view of the strong post-war patriotic consciousness, nothing would have been easier than to put the same project in the perspective of conserving the French intellectual heritage. Nothing was done, in all appearance, to exploit the postwar euphoria of French Catholics. They could only be elated on seeing resumption of diplomatic ties between France and the Vatican, certainly a major reversal of anticlerical forces. Catholic intellectuals should have seized on Duhem's vastly documented discovery of the medieval theological origins of that very science by which the secularist world had been swearing for some time. But, as will be seen, French Catholic intellectuals remained conspicuously insensitive to their great opportunity for turning the tables on their chief cultural antagonists and keeping those tables turned on them by a systematic cultivation of Duhem's great discoveries in the history of science. Actually, some French Catholic historians of science were to ally themselves with Alexandre Koyré, who as a historian of science aimed above all at discrediting Duhem's principal conclusions concerning the medieval roots of the science of Galileo and Newton.[10]

In the light of all this, the sudden passing away of Darboux in 1917 should seem a major blow. During the five months that separated his death from that of Duhem, he not only obtained the Petit d'Ormoy Prize for the *Système du monde* but he also set up a committee to evaluate the publishable character of its manuscripts left by Duhem. That the committee expeditiously reported about the eminently publishable character of those manuscripts was an indication that Darboux was a doer of things. As an admirer of the talents and accomplishments of Duhem since the latter's student years, Darboux could have easily made an appeal in the name of the Académie des Sciences to any and all in possession of letters by Duhem. After all, since Duhem was a member of the Académie des Sciences, his manuscripts and letters were to find, as had been the case with uncounted other members, a natural repository in the Archives of the Académie.

It was not, of course, to be expected that Darboux's personal fondness and professional appreciation of Duhem would also be as alive in Picard, Darboux's successor as perpetual secretary of the Académie des Sciences. Not that Picard had not done his best to carry out in a most creditable manner his official duty to Duhem's memory. In preparing Duhem's eulogy, Picard did not fail to contact Hélène in order to receive detailed information from her about her father. Or, as Picard wrote to Hélène on August 23, 1920:

> By planning to read a commemorative essay on your father in a public session of the Académie des Sciences I would like to ask you whether you could give me information or lend some documents that would enable me to portray vividly the great and noble stature of the one whom you have so painfully lost. I did not know him intimately but perhaps his correspondence and family souvenirs, if you would kindly lend them to me, would help me to fill that void and to present the man and the *savant* in the truest light.

Picard's letter, sent from the observatory of Abbadia in the Pyrénées, found Hélène in Cabrespine. In her reply Hélène asked for time on the ground that the documents were at Sainte-Agnès in Thiais, as can be surmised from the next letter of Picard written on September 3. He hastened to reassure her that he could easily wait for the documents until her return to Thiais because he planned to read the eulogy only toward the end of the next year. Picard also indicated that he would eventually ask Hélène for information about her father's parents, his childhood and marriage, "as well as of his manner of working." In his letter of November 6 to Hélène, Picard expressed his wish to have a meeting with her after he had finished the first draft of the eulogy. Picard also asked for the names of some of Hélène's father's best friends. Picard's letter of December 3 acknowledged the receipt of various documents, among them a copy of Jordan's biographical essay. He also registered gratitude to Hélène for the suggestion that he get in touch with Dr. Récamier. On January 10, 1921, Picard wrote: "I thank you very much for the very interesting documents you have just sent me. I carefully keep this precious deposit. I hope to be able to utilize it in order to bring to life as well as possible your father's image."

Clearly, Hélène was achieving an increasingly great familiarity with the many personal documents in her possession. Fortunately for her, her father kept his scientific correspondence in envelopes arranged in the alphabetical order of his correspondents. She was in the position to give valuable information to Picard about this vast material. That she personally took at least some of the material requested by Picard from Thiais to Picard's office in the Académie on Quai Conti, across from the Louvre, is suggested by Picard's letter of April 5, 1922. There he expressed his embarrassment for being so late in asking Hélène to come and take the documents she had put at his disposal. He also asked Hélène whether she had received copies from the publisher, Gauthier-Villars, of the nicely printed eulogy. He also expressed his readiness to donate to Hélène, on behalf of the Académie, the copper plate from which Gauthier-Villars made the prints of Duhem's photos in that essay.

That no reference in that letter was made to the manuscripts of the *Système du monde* may appear ominous in retrospect, but was not necessarily a disturbing sign at that moment. Hélène perhaps remembered at that point the reply, "Everything will be published eventually," given by her father as she once complained about a publisher's procrastination. In that respect she was to learn a unique lesson in patience. For the moment she could still relish the glow of that late afternoon of December 12, 1921, when an overflow audience heard Picard read his long eulogy of Duhem under the great cupola of the Institut de France. The audience most likely included Marie Duhem, some of the Chayets, the Jordans, the Récamiers, the Dufourcqs, and a small delegation from the Atelier Sainte-Agnès headed by Mlle de la Girennerie. Tears may have flooded Hélène's eyes as she heard Picard express his hope for the full publication of the *Système du monde* and conclude with the words: "France lost in Duhem a good servant, the Académie one of its members that brought it most honor."

As the honored guest, Hélène could now graphically feel, in the highest academic setting, what it was to be the only child of a pre-eminent father. She, of course, may have been overly impressed by the prolonged applause that followed the eulogy and by her being congratulated by leading academics. Once more they were readier with exquisite phrases suggestive of generous support than with self-effacing collaboration. Most likely present was the elderly Hermann and his son, Jules, soon to succeed him as director of the firm. Neither of them, and certainly not the latter, would have thought at that time that toward the end of the 20th century the greatest achievement of Hermann et Cie would still remain the publication of the *Système du monde* in all its ten volumes.

The older Hermann, whom Duhem esteemed for his honesty, displayed this quality in his letter of March 30, 1917, to Hélène concerning the publication of the fifth volume of the *Système du monde*. He informed her that the proofreading had been done by Mr. Doucet [Doublet], professor of astronomy at Bordeaux and by a professor [Rougier] at the University of Aix, but the typesetting, because of the shortage of personnel caused by the war, was going slowly. Then Hermann turned to the principal topic:

> As to volumes VI and VII, I have not received the report of the commission set up by the Académie des Sciences, but I have no doubt it will be favorable. There remains the question of the Ministry's subvention; if Mr. Darboux were alive, this would pose no problem, but Mr. Darboux is dead. This is a great loss for you and a very painful loss for me. You will certainly obtain the Prix Petit d'Ormoy. You certainly have a right to a pension given by the Société des Amis des Sciences; you have a right because of the fine works of your father who rendered eminent services to science, who during almost all his career received a modest recompense, and who spent so much of his money to carry on with his studies.

Hermann offered to take various steps. He was ready, provided Hélène approved, to pay a visit to Mr. Picard, soon to be named perpetual secretary of the Académie des Sciences and one "who holds your father in high esteem." Hermann expressed readiness to make inquiries at the Académie des Sciences morales et politiques, through one of its members, Charles Benoit.[11] Although Hermann disclosed to Hélène that he was not on the best terms with his late brother, the father-in-law of Benoit, still he felt he could visit Mr. Benoit who spoke highly of Duhem's last two books, *La science allemande* and *La chimie, est-elle une science française?* "If he is ready to take the necessary steps," Hermann continued, "I will offer him a copy of what has so far appeared of the *Système du monde.*" He also offered to contact a childhood friend of his, Lyon-Caen,[12] of the same Académie. But, he added, "I want you to know that he is Jewish." Obviously, Hermann must have heard of Hélène's sympathies for the Action Française, a movement where patriotism often went hand in hand with Jew-baiting. Still, had she been the kind of anti-Semite who resents, let alone hates, anyone simply because of his or her Jewishness, Hermann would have hardly offered to contact, on her behalf, a prominent Jewish woman, Henri Poincaré's widow, who happened to be also the sister-in-law of Emile Boutroux.

A contract recalled

Adolphe Hermann had already been replaced by his son Jules as head of the firm when Hélène had to be contacted in 1923 concerning the plan of A. Boutaric, professor of chemistry in Dijon, to bring out in an updated edition Duhem's *Thermodynamique et chimie.* Two years later, on July 10, 1925, Jules Hermann informed Hélène that he had received the revised text from Mr. Boutaric and that he had hoped "to sell a good number of copies of the new edition."

Much of the letter related to the fate of the future of the *Système du monde.* In reply to an inquiry of Hélène about some manuscripts she thought she had deposited with him, Hermann reported that, during the aerial bombardment of Paris in early 1918, he had returned, for safekeeping, the manuscripts of volumes VI, VII, and VIII to the Académie des Science. Its committee, set up by Darboux to evaluate the manuscripts left behind by Duhem, must have found them eminently publishable, or else they would not have been handed over to Hermann sometime in 1917. In all evidence, both the Académie and Hermann foresaw the resumption of publication at an early date.

It was precisely that intention which Jules Hermann wanted to convey to Hélène, though with an important proviso:

> I propose to resume publication as soon as possible. This is where matters stand:
>
> You know that I am bound by a contract with the Ministry and that, if I publish the rest, I must furnish them with 250 copies [of each volume] at a great a cost (given the depreciation of the franc); I would lose a vast sum if I carried out the contract. Therefore I must obtain the annullment of the contract of 1913. I think this will be easy because the Ministry merely wants that the subvention in question not be spent.

Since in his next communication to Hélène, Jules Hermann pointedly remarked that he had re-read, obviously at her urging, the contract in question, it may be most appropriate to reproduce it here in full:

> Between the signatories, Mr. Pierre Duhem, professor at the Faculty of Science of Bordeaux, on the one hand, and Messrs A. Hermann et Fils, on the other, the following has been agreed upon:
>
> Messrs Hermann et Fils undertake to publish a work by Mr. Duhem, entitled, *Le système du monde, Histoire des*

Théories cosmographiques de Platon à Galilée. The work will comprise ten volumes in large 8° of about 500 to 550 pages each; it will appear a volume a year and the first volume during the year 1913.

Six hundred copies will be put on sale of which fifty will be on Holland paper and five hundred on ordinary paper of good quality; in addition fifty copies on Holland paper will be given free to Mr. Duhem to be used by him as his complimentary offerings. Messrs Hermann will assume the cost of publication in its entirety. Mr. Duhem will not receive any royalty for the first four hundred copies sold, but will have the right to forty percent of the sale of all copies beginning with the four-hundredth-and-first copy sold.

The right of translation can be granted only through a common accord between Messrs Hermann et Fils, on the one hand, and Mr P. Duhem on the other. The sum forthcoming from this accord will be equally shared between the author and the publisher.

As an exception, one hundred more copies will be put on sale of the first volume than of the rest, that is, seven hundred copies.

Signed   A. Hermann et Fils

The contract, drawn up in two copies by the publisher in Paris, became legally binding on both parties as Duhem added his signature below the lines:

> Text seen and approved
> Bordeaux, June 21, 1913.

An extraordinary contract it certainly was as far as the author was concerned, both with respect to the amount of most original scholarly research and to the rate at which it was to be delivered to the publisher. The latter's financial risks were largely non-existent by the date Duhem signed the contract.

Apart from the considerable funds released by the Académie des Sciences towards the publication of the first volume, the Ministry of Public Instruction obligated itself to purchasing 250 copies of each volume.

Quite different was the case ten or so years later. Funds were not available while prices were steadily on the rise. Any publisher of scholarly works could therefore expect understanding though hardly to the extent to which Jules Hermann wanted it. The next paragraph of his letter of July 10, 1925, puts him in a strange light:

> I could easily assume the risks of publishing a very small number of copies [of each volume still to be printed], if the purpose is just to honor the memory of your father, but in no way to include questions of author's royalties and deals with booksellers. If I consider the publication of the complete work from the viewpoint of my risks and perils, I want us to agree at the outset that there will be no question of author's royalties for the *Système du monde*. I would simply give you a few copies [of each volume]. Moreover, I would not be able to print on Holland paper. With the Dutch guilder being 9 francs instead of 2 francs and 10 centimes, Van Gelder's paper is beyond the means of a French publisher.

Hermann gave the impression that he considered the matter settled as he went on to ask for a photo of Duhem to be inserted in volume VI. He appeared to be dictating the terms as he expressed his hope that there would be no Greek texts in the remainder of the work. In his final note he stressed again the financial problems of the publication of a work whose author was no longer alive and therefore the cost of hiring competent proofreaders had to be kept in mind.

Hélène's feelings about all this must have been a sort of a shock, though not strong enough to amount to a shock treatment. While she was still asking for a prompt payment of royalties for copies of the first five volumes, she did not seem to grasp Hermann's resolve to present her with an ultimatum and press on with it. In his next letter, dated July 25, 1925, Hermann subtly warned Hélène: "I don't know whether you have really grasped the sense of my previous communication regarding volume VI and the other volumes of the *Système du monde*." Once more he registered his plan to ask the Ministry to annul the contract and to publish the volumes in question in a few copies. Within that framework he expressed readiness to look for some subvention from Mr. Picard. His last two sentences were a threat introduced with flattery: "In any case I do not want to take any step except in full accord with you. One, however, must not assume that the publication of the remainder of the *Système du monde* should involve any risk for the publisher." Clearly the son's attitude was a far cry from his father's appreciation of being a main publisher of Duhem's works. As he took up, in his letter of July 13, 1916, to Duhem the matter of sales of *La chimie, est-elle une science française?*, the older Hermann noted: "Even if I lose a little money with this work, I have gained enough money with the other works of yours I published."

Hélène's reaction to the younger Hermann's resolve to remain absolutely protected of financial loss, must have contained words of indignation, because, in his next communication to her (Sept. 5, 1925), Hermann protested his friendly dispositions: "I will not be upset in talking with you on the subject of the *Système du monde*. . . . Please, kindly set therefore a date either at your place [Thiais] or here [in my office], by giving me an advance notice of two or three days." Then Hermann expressed his hope that Hélène's health left nothing to be desired, as if his stance could not have been for her the cause of a serious depression if not plain outrage.

Curiously, the scholarly world showed no surprise, let alone indignation or outrage about the total lack of news concerning the fate of the still unpublished parts of the *Système du monde.* The Père Théry, editor of *Recherches d'histoire médiévale,* could in 1926 innocently ask the Académie des Sciences about the whereabouts of Duhem's manuscripts. With no pressure from the academic world, the publisher could confidently continue his tactic of giving not a hint that he would consider the slightest modification of the terms he had set. Over-confidence once more proved to be its own undoing. Hermann did not suspect that he would provide Hélène with something to seize upon as he briefly listed his terms on September 8, 1926. In fact, he gave himself away with the very first point in his "new" proposal to reach a solution: "reprint photographically the first volume in order to have copies to sell." On reading this it dawned on Hélène that the first volume must have sold out. "Donc épuisé!" — she jotted in black ink on the margin of the letter. But then where were the royalties, amounting to 40% of the sale of about 200 copies of that volume? What about the status of copies of volumes II-V?

The second shock

The contest was no longer offense versus defense if not mere defenselessness. Still Hélène was not energized enough to go on the offensive. Her energies were lulled by the illusory security she had at Sainte-Agnès. She was also preoccupied with the opportunity of buying in Cabrespine the house adjoining the ancestral home. She made the purchase in 1928. Her resources were comfortably large. She could live well without the royalties from her father's books. Not that she forgot the *Système du monde.* To an inquiry of hers, Picard, perpetual secretary of the Académie des Sciences, sent on June 11, 1929, ·the following reply: "There was no visit from Hermann. I wish very much that all difficulties standing in the way of the publication of your father's volumes be surmounted and I would be happy to contribute in some way to that effect." Could this mean that contrary to his statements made in his letters to Hélène, Hermann did not really mean to visit Picard or others who could have helped? Was Hermann hoping that ultimately he would wear down Hélène's resolve and condemn the remainder of the *Système du monde* to oblivion? Could not he count on the tacit collaboration of the world of scholarship?

He might have started celebrating had he been privy to Hélène's apparent disarming herself once and for all. Not later than in early 1929, so it seems, she gave some power over her entire bank account to her "adopted mother," Mlle de la Girennerie. Luckily, her real mother did not abandon her from heaven, though, as is usually the case with heavenly interventions, here too they first came as apparently irreversible disasters. Mlle de la Girennerie had for some time been away from Sainte-Agnès when Hélène began to receive legal notices requesting payments on the sale of the Château Brannay near Sens. Not being able to consult with Mlle de la Girennerie, she departed for Cabrespine for the summer only to be confronted there with a sergeant-at-arms who served her notice about the confiscation of the ancestral house as collateral against installments still to be paid.

Worse, she was summoned to pay those installments on behalf of "Monsieur et Madame Duhem." The latter turned out to be Mlle de la Girennerie, the former a fictitious person, to assure further credibility to her transactions with Hélène's money. In order to make the down payment for the Château, possibly the future home of the Atelier Sainte-Agnès, she withdrew much of the money (about 20,000 francs) from Hélène's bank account, a fact which Hélène found out too late. In her despair Hélène turned to the Chayets but with no result. However, her papa's best friend in Bordeaux, Albert Dufourcq, came speedily to the rescue by satisfying the legitimate financial claims of the former owner of the Château. As the new owner of the Château, through the Dufourcq's generosity, Hélène had on hand more of a burden than an asset. But at least she was safe in her house in Cabrespine.

All this happened between two communications from Hermann to Hélène, dated, May 22, 1929 and June 11, 1929, respectively. In the first, sent to Thiais, Hermann stated that the officials of the firm "would be very happy to have a discussion with her" concerning her "desire to pursue the publication of the *Système du monde*." Hermann then expressed his readiness to receive her on any of the following Saturday afternoons in the offices of the firm. In the second letter, Hermann spoke about his visit to Picard and expressed his hope, that following his next steps at the Ministry, the publication might get under way. Hermann must have known that once more he had succeeded in postponing real action.

Equally procrastinating was his reply to Hélène's request for a complete statement on royalties. Meanwhile she was sent 2,000 francs as royalties due to her for other books of her father. Hermann could hardly know the extent to which now Hélène needed to count every franc. She had been back in Cabrespine, and for good, as well as for her own good, together for the good of the world of scholarship. But as always, the good had a price tag on it. She had to discover her life's mission, a mission to be full of struggle, frustrations, disappointments, before it could gain its true fulfillment.

4

A New Purpose in Life

Hélène Pierre-Duhem

Full awareness about her life's vocation may have come to Hélène rather quickly. To translate that awareness into specific programs of action demanded time, the chief matrix for ideas to germinate and mature. Hélène's correspondence shows, from 1933 on, no trace of reluctance, however subconscious, to devote her energies to the cause of her father's intellectual bequest. As the months and years went by she found herself more and more engaged in a struggle that required of her heroism without heroics. Hers was not a battle to be won by one or two spectacular engagements. She had to refight her battle every day for many days to come in the face of regularly recurring rebuffs and setbacks.

She would not have been human had she not hoped for a reasonably quick victory as she kept visiting her father's tomb in the very center of the little cemetery of Cabrespine, a mere five-minute walk from her house. Years earlier she had the tomb covered with a rose-hued marble slab with her father's name on it. The slab was to carry only one other name, hers, some forty years later. Now, in the spring of 1933, she ordered a slab of granite to be erected over the tomb.[1] On one side of that slab of granite, hewed from the neighboring mountains which her father loved to explore, she had the names of his parents, sisters, and brother engraved. A year or so later she conceived the idea of perpetuating her father's memory in the church by a marble plaque to be placed on the wall next to the pew which he was accustomed to occupy. The curé, the Abbé Louis Blanc, gladly consented and even drafted a text for the inscription. For a more suitable text she turned to Albert Dufourcq, her father's best friend in Bordeaux and a renowned church historian, who started his scholarly career with a critical study of the Acts of the early martyrs. The text, composed in Latin and French, is best reproduced here because it testifies to Dufourcq's deep devotion to the memory of his friend:

In Memory of Pierre Duhem,
Illustrious professor of the University of Bordeaux,
Excelled by virtue no less than by learning,
Friend of the poor, model of the rich,
Wanted to assist rather than preside,
Loved truth more than friends,
Chastiser of errors, kind to those who err,
Had no enemies, except the enemies of truth,
Covered with merits, forgetful of himself,
Received renown, while fleeing honors,
Worthy of being crowned by Christ in heaven.[2]

For a reason, which became very pressing by the end of 1935 and is very pertinent to this chapter, the inscription remained a mere text on paper. By then Dufourcq had already given his devoted assistance to Hélène for at least two years in the great task of implementing her life-mission. Hélène carefully kept his letters, together with copies of the more important communications of hers to him. As a result it is possible to reconstruct in detail the steps, many and often painfully frustrating, which Hélène had to take to fulfill her heroic mission. Dufourcq's letters to Hélène show him to be committed no less zealously to the cause of Duhem's memory than was his protégée.

A good starting point is Dufourcq's letter of October 12, 1933, to Hélène, which begins with the statements: "I thank you from all my heart for not having forgotten your promise. Thanks to you, a photo of your papa already glows in my study in Chilho; and soon, still thanks to you, in my study in Paris. May it convey to me something of the powerful radiance of the one whom it represents." The rest of the letter is about the publication of Duhem's *La théorie physique* in its third edition, a month or so earlier, by Rivière in Paris, an unexpected event in which Dufourcq saw much significance: "The lasting success of *La théorie physique* profoundly impresses me. The fashion, I believe, is today in favor of theories which your father combatted. Still the book where he summed up his thought keeps selling: what a token of truth!"

Indeed the second edition of the book, enlarged by Duhem's famous essay, "La physique de croyant," kept selling ever since it was first put on sale in 1919, four years after it had been printed. A letter written by Marcel Rivière to Hélène on April 2, 1917, explains the delay. In August 1914 Rivière and almost all his personnel were mobilized. The yearly statements of sales sent to Hélène between 1919 and 1933 show that a total of 1100 copies were originally printed and that in January 1933 there were only 52 copies left in stock, or about the half of the average yearly sale.[3] The book which was priced at 8.50 francs in 1914, was now sold for 30 francs, with 3 francs of the price going to the author, or rather, Hélène.

On a closer reading of the contract Duhem had signed with Rivière in 1914, Dufourcq advised Hélène not to contest the publisher for having taken the initiative, without prior consultation with her, to reissue the book. Hélène was, however, to make it clear to the publisher that she was the full and exclusive heir to all rights belonging to Duhem and therefore entitled to a new contract. In particular, Hélène was

to insist on the twenty-five complimentary copies specified in
the original contract. Far more important than Rivière's ready
compliance with these stipulations was, in Dufourcq's eyes, the
use of those copies: "You yourself shall distribute them in your
father's name. And this discreet publicity, coming from you,
cannot help being efficacious. Should you be perplexed in
choosing the twenty-five recipients, please contact d'Ocagne or
another of your father's friends still alive."

In the letter, written from the Dufourcq's ancestral home
in Chilho, near Labastide Clairance in the Pyrénées, Dufourcq
gave news to Hélène about his three daughters, Henriette,
Mathilde, and Louisette.[4] The first two (already married) had
first come as little children into the life of Hélène, the young
teenager. Dufourcq's closing words were about the family's
return in a week or so to their home in Rue de Bellechasse,
Paris, a street not too far, Dufourcq pointedly noted, from
Rivière's offices. "If necessary, I could go to see him. Keep me
advised. And do not hesitate to write to me. I will always have
the necessary time to try to help you. Would that Mlle de la
Girennerie leave you alone so that you may concentrate on the
Système du monde!"

As to Mlle de la Girennerie, she showed up in Cabrespine
with some of her "family" in Sainte-Agnès, but Hélène showed
her the door. Nothing was to sway her from the task she had
now set for herself. She reflected more and more on the best
strategy to secure for the *Système du monde* the future it deserved. In this latter respect she was enormously helped by the
affection shown to her by the Dufourcqs. In early August 1933,
the very same Mme Dufourcq, whom she had some twenty
years earlier rudely dismissed for her warnings about Mlle de la
Girennerie, came to Cabrespine to take her to Chilho for
vacation. Hélène's long note of thanks, written on September
3, contains the following section:

You all have been so good and so tactful that all the thanks of the world would be plain banality. I prefer to say not a word and keep in the depth of my heart the memory of your hospitality that must be a cause of rejoicing for my dear papa in heaven. When he was all alone in Bordeaux, it is in your home, in the midst of your children, that he again found joy and comfort. It is in that home of yours that his orphaned daughter now finds the same consolation and support. May God bless you, dear Madame!

In the same letter she apologized to Mme Dufourcq for a faux-pas she committed while serving lunch for her in Cabrespine. It concerned the kind of plate in which she served fruit, a faux-pas for which she was, on her return, "rebuked by Jeanne," that is, by Jeanne-Désirée Paradis, daughter of a drapery manufacturer in Calais and her best friend from her days at Sainte-Agnès, who came to live with her in Cabrespine. As Hélène showed Jeanne, also known as Cécile, the diary she kept in Chilho, memories to both must have come back about Cécile's first visit to Cabrespine when Hélène's father drew the illustrations for the diary which she kept for Cécile. This time the illustrations were provided by Norbert Dufourcq, whom Hélène first had known as one of the "machurés," and who, twenty years later, following his father's death, became his substitute as Hélène's chief support and adviser.

The most revealing part of Hélène's letter is her signature. She not only signed her name, the first time so it appears, as Hélène Pierre-Duhem, but she did it in a way practically indistinguishable from Duhem's own signature, drawn in straight, broadly flowing, manly lines.[5] Therefore it must have been during those days in Chilho, during the restful conversations she had with all the Dufourcqs, that she took full consciousness of the fact that, as long as she lived, the fate of her father's work hinged on her. Her father's great intellectual monument the *Système du monde* could not be left half unpublished. She also wanted to rescue her father's true features from distortions, the work of his well-meaning early biographers. As she discussed these two plans of hers in friendly intimacy with the Dufourcqs in Chilho, she could hardly suspect the role to be played by her account of her father's life in promoting the full publication of his great work.

First campaign for the Système du monde

By the time of her visit in Chilho, more than a year had gone by since she had started pressing Jules Hermann to resume the publication of the *Système du monde*. It is easy to imagine what her reactions were on reading Jules Hermann's bittersweet letter of February 13, 1932. It came to a close with a note about the coming payment of royalties in the sum of 944 francs, accrued up to December 31, 1931, together with an advance payment of 1000 francs for royalties in 1932. Within ten days she received the sum of 1994 francs. Apparently, Jules Hermann wanted to cover himself in advance against charges of having been notoriously remiss in his contractual obligations. Much of the letter was about Hermann's report of a conversation with the Ministry of Public Instruction about the subvention, which, it is well to recall, his father preferred not to include in the original contract. The substance of the conversation was that the Ministry was ready to replace its old commitment with a new one (obviously to take account of the steady weakening of the franc). Hermann, however, was not eager to conclude a new agreement with the Ministry. "We had to adjourn the matter because this would have resulted in tying down a considerable capital in a critical time for publishers. This is why we did not feel it necessary to obtain a prompt reply from you. You may, however, be assured that we have at heart to take up the publication of the *Système du monde* as soon as the financial situation clears up."

More than a year later Hélène received to her inquiry about the steps of publication the reply of Jules Freymann, one of Jules Hermann's three successors, in which she was asked to

"wait still, because in spite the scientific interest of the manuscript and our devotion to the memory of Mr. Duhem, we
cannot at this moment consider publication." Among the
reasons listed by Freymann was the economic crisis, certainly
serious in the spring of 1933 in France as well as abroad: "The
exportation is almost nil, foreign universities that purchased the
first volumes of the *Système du monde* have no funds for
purchasing works with no immediate interest; as to the
subscription of the Ministry, it would be limited to the
purchase of a certain number of volumes at a price much lower
than profitable." Freymann also reported that Picard, perpetual
secretary of the Académie des sciences, saw no hope for a
subsidy from there. The only good news was that the manuscripts were "in the vaults" of the Académie des sciences,
protected "from all indiscretion." In case of an improvement of
the economy, Freymann promised only that the question of
publication would be reconsidered again. He gave no hint that
he considered the publication as his contractual duty.

Freymann's next two communications to Hélène were
about some works of Pascal and a book she asked Hermann to
sell on her behalf. By then the Fall of 1933 had come. Not
being able to make any progress with the publication of the
Système du monde, Hélène pressed for exact figures about the
sales of its already published volumes. Freymann's letter of
October 30 postponed answer on the grounds that Hélène
failed to make it clear whether she wanted exact or approxi-
mate figures. Hélène's reply must have revealed much of the
true nature of her interest in the publication because, in his
reply of November 23, Freymann admitted to having been very
touched: "I admire, as always, your devotion for your Father
and I assure you that I am making a special effort to implement
your and our wishes at the earliest."

Part of Freymann's effort was to use his next trip to the
South for a meeting with Hélène, if she could come to
Carcassonne. Meanwhile Freymann had a visit from Dufourcq

who informed Hélène on December 15 in a long letter entirely devoted to the *Système du monde*:

> I have seen Hermann, or at least one of his three sons-in-law, this morning. I want to tell you right away that I gained a good impression. I hope that the *Système du monde* will be published in full, without costing you a penny, and I hope that it will bring you some money.
>
> I was very worried this morning in entering the office. Indeed I felt as if I were encountering a Boche.[6] The old Hermann is dead, his son [Jules] is dead. What is left are three married daughters and therefore three sons-in-law. The business is divided in three parts, each daughter with an equal part. Of the three sons-in-law the one I met is effectively the director.
>
> He is . . . Mexican. He paints. He adores Leonardo. He said he is resolved to publish Duhem, because of Leonardo. Long live Leonardo! The old father-in-law and his son have left behind the finest disorder. The contract of your papa with Hermann is lost. . . . Do you have the copy of the contract and the statements of sales and some other information?
>
> If yes, please send them to me — and indicate what you wish.
>
> If no, here is the plan of the Mexican.

The essence of the plan was that Hélène would not be paid any royalties for sales prior to the moment. Hermann in turn would engage in publishing the entire work and pay Hélène 20% in royalties for the sales of all volumes, including the new edition of the first five volumes, each volume being printed in 500 copies. Dufourcq was in fact so hopeful as to broach to Hélène the question of proofreading. He hoped that she would do it, while he would check the Latin and Greek passages, and that Hadamard or d'Ocagne[7] would help out with the scientific formulas if any. "Hermann's son-in-law will write you tomorrow or day after tomorrow. Compare what he writes to you with what I have written to you. Don't be afraid to ask me all the necessary explanations and to write to me and write again. The matter is of such importance! My impression is good. The son-in-law in question is young, with a flair. He told me he is resolved to finish the work."

Dufourcq further voiced his confidence by adding that "the good Lord is stepping into our business." Still, some mundane businesses were to be handled by Hélène and before Easter. One was some property tax due for the Château of Brannay, the other a recovery of 20,000 francs from Mlle de la Girennerie. Yet the really important business was of a very different kind. Only in retrospect could Hélène see much significance, and indeed an eery significance, in the fact that contrary to a brief note about the new contract to be promptly sent to her, it just failed to come. Hélène must have been rightly anxious and decided to act on the basis of the information she had received from Dufourcq.

Her letter, sent by registered mail on December 27, contained a copy of the original contract and a reference to a letter sent to her on May 23, 1917, by Camille Jordan of the Académie des Sciences, in which she was assured that the manuscript of volume VI had been handed over to Hermann. "I hope that you have those manuscripts safe in your hands. My earlier letters in which I asked you about this, were left unanswered. I would be very grateful if you kindly replied to these various questions so that we may arrive at something specific." As a postscript, Hélène also wanted exact figures about the copies of the first five volumes still in stock.

Once more a registered letter seemed to put things in motion. Two days later Freymann sent Hélène a long reply in which he referred to the confusion left behind by his late brother-in-law and again expressed his hope to meet Hélène in person around mid-January in Carcassonne. He expressed his desire to have a clear new basis and emphasized the advantages which the new contract would have for Hélène. She would receive 20% royalties for all copies of all volumes, beginning with the first copy and not a 40% royalty beginning with the 400th copy of each volume.

The next paragraph contained, however, that very delay in making things effective which had by then for almost ten years been the crucial characteristic of Hermann's dealing with Hélène and would be, unforeseen by her, for another twenty years. "The plan I submit to you is my personal idea which I have not yet submitted to my associates, but I am sure that they would accept it." If the plan was so secure, why could it not have been acted upon promptly? It was not for some time yet before Hélène started asking this kind of question of herself as well as of Freymann. For the time being Freymann prevented such questions from arising with his remark that following that meeting of theirs in Carcassonne, "many things could be settled conveniently and provide me with the means to have the proposals I have made to you to be accepted by my associates and [assure] the quick publication of the remainder of the *Système du monde.*" The only factual specific contained in the letter was that "the entire manuscript was in the Académie des sciences in the hands of Mr. Picard. Please, be reassured, I understand your worries." Here again was a detail that could have given much thought to Hélène: Could a publisher be really keen on a manuscript if after so many years he failed to bring it into his own office? Yet it was that very keenness which Freymann professed in the same letter after striking the old chord of ever more serious economic difficulties: "The economic situation becomes more and more difficult and, believe me, I am making this proposal — which, if you accept, will involve the setting aside of a rather considerable sum in view of the means at our disposal — because I sincerely admire your perseverance as well as your father, and for the honor of collaborating in the publication of one of the intellectual monuments of our times."

Things still looked rather promising in early January, 1934 when Dufourcq received word from Hélène about her readiness to accept the annulment of the original contract. Still, now that the original contract had been found by Hélène, Dufourcq could no longer be sure about Freymann's insistance for a new contract: "I fear," Dufourcq wrote to Hélène on January 7 "that something contrary to your interest is at work. Yet I immediately feel sorry for my doubts. My Mexican appeared to me a man of his words; my impression of him is favorable. Even you say that you are satisfied with the annullment of the original contract. This is what has been decided; this is what would satisfy him and accelerate matters. This is obviously your goal. . . . The publication of the *Système du monde* will be a great joy for you, and for me too, I confess." Dufourcq's satisfaction had another angle as well: "Living here in Paris, I see or hear that certain people are happy — the imbeciles, they hardly see beyond their noses — thinking that the monument of Duhem will never see light." He thanked God and had a special word of thanks also for Hélène because "you persist and succeed in continuing and bringing to completion the gigantic work!"

The next two months witnessed indeed a round of insistent steps on the part of Hélène and Dufourcq. The latter visited Freymann on January 12 and prevailed on him to draw up a preliminary contract which he forwarded on the same day to Hélène. He urged her to "keep that paper carefully until both parties had signed the final contract." Then he tried to reassure her on a point which, obviously, troubled him as well: "Something will at first sight bother you. You agree to have no business, in the future, with the [copies of the] first five volumes still to be sold. This provision is to Hermann's advantage, a reason, for which, I think, he had asked you to annul the contract signed by your father." Dufourcq took the view that in the future to receive royalties of 20% for all copies of all volumes was not a bad deal. He advised her, however, to allow at most a maximum of one year delay between the publication of the new volumes.

A snare for the Système du monde

Three days later Dufourcq advised Hélène to ask once more for a complete inventory of copies sold prior to January 1, 1934 and of copies still in stock at that date. In doing so, Dufourcq must have responded not only to his good sense but also to some suspicions of his. Indeed, within three more days, his suspicions turned into astonishment. He discovered that a set of the five volumes of the *Système du monde* was selling in Paris for the sum of almost exactly twelve hundred francs, or about seven times the original price! This meant that in terms of the original contract Hélène should have received for the sale of only three sets royalties equivalent to the total yearly royalty which Hermann had sent to her at the end of the previous year.

"We have luckily escaped!" Dufourcq wrote to her on January 19. "Indeed I was right in suspecting that you were mistaken in renouncing the contract signed by your father from the very moment you had found its original copy." On reading this Hélène could at best think that her friend's memory was not too accurate as it was he who had urged her in the first place to agree to the annulment of that contract. At any rate, she could but heartily respond to Dufourcq's advising her to do "the most important and most urgent thing," namely, "to go to the church and light a candle in honor of the Blessed Virgin in the corner where your father used to pray. It is he who saved you! and me too, who let you do it, without enthusiasm, to be sure; me, nevertheless, who let you go ahead."

Dufourcq also apologized for having advised her to go ahead quickly, because the matter was urgent. He now wrote: "Don't fail to go ten times slower." He, however, felt confident that now "we have the Mexican pinned down." He asked her to insist, until new word from him, on being held to the contract signed by her father and demand full account of the sales. "Full light should be put on the subject, and all the more so because they want to prevent you from seeing clearly. Double your diffidence. It is certain that they try to cheat you . . . in the name of Leonardo!"

Nothing of this was suspected by Freymann who on the same day of January 19 sent to Hélène a letter in which, after some incidental matters, he briefly informed her that she would soon receive from Dufourcq the draft of a new contract. On the same day Picard too wrote her a brief note, assuring her that the detailed table of contents of the manuscripts corresponded exactly to the text on the folders that contained the various parts of the still unpublished parts of the *Système du monde*. Exactly a week later, on January 26, the bookseller Guillaume Budé, of 95 Boulevard Raspail, sent his reply to Dufourcq who had placed orders for various books on church history together with a check for 600 francs. The postscript of Budé's reply read as follows: "The work of Duhem costs 1190 francs. We can send it to you when you want it. We have an incomplete series which we are trying to complete at this moment. As soon as we have found the missing volume, we shall let you know." Dufourcq now knew through tangible and incontrovertible evidence what he had suspected for some time.

Three days before that, on January 22, Hélène informed Freymann that she had received the draft of the new contract from Dufourcq ten days earlier:

> I wanted to take my time in order to examine it at leisure. On a closer reflection I truly doubt I have the right to modify the text of the contract finalized and signed by my father. I confess that the very thought of it has always troubled me and I believe this was also the case with Mr. Dufourcq. A contract has been been agreed upon between your father-in-law and my father; why not to adhere to it? For my part I no longer feel the right to modify or annul what has been concluded by my father and I am certain

that you, who admire his work and zealously profess to complete its publication, will understand my scruples and my filial respect about actions that have my father's approval and signature.

In the rest of the letter Hélène returned to her request made five months earlier about a complete inventory of volumes already sold and still in stock both in France and abroad. "Since you, Monsieur, show all the possible devotion, for which I am most grateful, on behalf of the *Système du monde*, I don't doubt your readiness to give me rapid satisfaction, since you have, in response to my letter of September, written to your clients and you must by now have their answer."

Five days later, Dufourcq wrote to Hélène: "The Mexican has just left my home. I tried to make him feel that we see the situation clearly but still hold him to be an honest man. He admits that he wants a new contract, because he cannot, at the same time, pay all he owes you and do volume VI." With this Freymann made it abundantly clear that the sum in question could be considerable. This is precisely what Dufourcq felt and, as a result, continued: "I insisted that he send to you the inventory of what he has in stock as soon as possible and inform you about what he owes you. That is a figure I am curious to know." It hardly reflected well on the bookkeeping at Hermann that Freymann, according to Dufourcq, asked him to convey to Hélène his request to send him a full account of royalties she and her father had received. It should have been all too clear to Freymann that Pierre Duhem had not received a single penny from the sales of the *Système du monde*. Obviously, Freymann tried to put the burden where it did not belong and thereby postpone any real action.

All this could but push Hélène towards thinking about a new publisher. Dufourcq, however, urged caution: "The wisest thing is," Dufourcq wrote to her, "not to force a break with Hermann for at least the time being. . . . To complete with

him, if at all possible, the publication of the *Système du monde,*
seems to me the best course." It is not difficult to imagine that
Hélène must have gone through days of despair if not agony,
days all the more grim as they had to be spent in complete
isolation in a far-away village.

Yet little if any of her feelings transpire in her letter of
January 31 to Freymann in which she proceded according to
the advice given her by Dufourcq. In conformity with her
letter of January 23 she reiterated that the original contract was
for her "untouchable" and asked for its "faithful and integral
implementation." She expressed her hope that Dufourcq had
informed him about her own financial losses that forced her to
press her creditors for payment. She then reminded Freymann
that she had already made the same points on October 30. She
now suggested that Freymann would pay her, and immediately,
through the Société générale of Carcassonne, four-fifths of the
total due to her and the remainder once he had received the
booksellers' reports. As to the royalties she and her father had
received from sales of the *Système du monde* it was a simple
matter: her father had not received a penny; she reminded
Freymann that she had received only two payments, in 1932
and 1933 respectively, facts that should be easy to verify from
his own bookkeeping. Payment of the sum due to her, she
concluded her letter, "must precede any further discussion
concerning the publication of volume VI."

Freymann's response of February 6 should have taught
Hélène that he could easily find means of avoiding the real
issue. He now reminded Hélène of two letters sent to her in
1925 and 1926 by Jules Hermann. He hoped that Hélène
would provide copies of her replies that could not be found in
Hermann's records. To add insult to irony, Freymann now
asked Hélène to send him a copy of the original contract.
Freymann simply ignored the fact that Hélène had already sent
a copy to him months earlier.

Hélène now could say, and she did so a day later and
without the slightest exaggeration, that she was astonished. She
reminded Freymann once more of his letters of September 22
and October 30, concerning his request for an account by his
booksellers. She concluded her letter with a request for
payment by return mail to the same bank in Carcassonne. She
also wrote to Dufourcq who on February 11 advised her to
inform Freymann that she had not found copies of her replies
to Jules Hermann in her dossiers, without suggesting that she
had not kept drafts of her letters. She should insist, kindly but
firmly, on prompt payment. Most importantly, she should state
that she did not give permission to Freymann's request made in
his letter of September 8, 1926, for a photographic reimpression
of the first five volumes. "Your style should always be extremely polite even when, and especially if, you think that they want
to defraud you."

Dufourcq now foresaw the very thing which he knew
Freymann had as his chief weapon against Hélène. It was a
weapon often used by publishers remiss on their obligation and
feeling confident that in almost all cases the royalty due to an
author is far less than the money he would have to spend in
bringing matters before a commercial tribunal. "I am afraid, as
you are, that all this will end before the tribunal. Let us do
everything to avoid a lawsuit without ruining ourselves and
compromise thereby our cause in the eyes of the judges whom
we should face." Dufourcq did not want to hide the seriousness
of the situation. "If by early March we do not see clearly,
perhaps it will be wise to confide the whole affair to a lawyer
connected with the commercial tribunal." Of course, this
would mean "new expenses and new frustrations. If a miracle
is needed that we be spared of all that, let us ask for a miracle
from God! Prudence and prayer, more than ever!"

In the rest of the letter, Dufourcq, as was recalled in the
previous chapter, sketched the grimness of the political situation. He spoke of the unconscionability of the Daladier-Frot-

Blum clique "to treat France with choloroform" instead of preparing her for the worst. Hélène's own helplessness, coupled with that of her beloved France, could but make her feel doubly depressed in her little village locked among hardy mountains bound in fog and snow.

In his letter of February 19, Freymann showed once more what he was capable of in the way of procrastinating in the guise of claiming rights that were not his. He made the payment demanded from him by Hélène dependent on her first sending him a copy of her answers to the letters Jules Hermann wrote to her on July 10, 1925 and September 8, 1926. In reply, Hélène asserted on February 21, that she did not remember having replied to those letters and that she was sure she had not given permission for a photographic reproduction of the first volume. She rather demanded a report on the exact number of copies printed in that way. She could easily imagine what Freymann would feel on reading her reference to her satisfaction over the fact that the original copy of the contract had been found in the offices of Hermann et Cie.

There followed on March 7, a registered letter in which Hélène asked immediate payment. It finally came on March 17 in the amount of 5,379.80 (five thousand three hundred and seventy nine francs and 80 centimes)[8] for all copies sold until December 31, 1933, together with a detailed list of sales. Hélène would not have been the daughter of a great mathematical physicist, had she not checked the data in Freymann's statement.

In informing Dufourcq about her own calculations she must have sounded furious because he suggested to her: "Convince yourself that you deal with honest people and speak accordingly, but act as if you faced swindlers." That Freymann finally came up with payment indicated to Dufourcq that he felt himself to be on the defensive. After advising Hélène to protest the photographic reproductions in strong terms, Dufourcq urged patience and confidence: "Let us proceed step by step. I believe that with God's help, we are on the right course. Let us persevere with a smile on the lips and with eyes wide open!"

On April 10 Hélène informed Freymann that she was entitled to an additional 7,010 francs and demanded payment by May 15 in view of her own serious financial situation. It was now clear that not only volume I but also volume II was reprinted photographically. Hélène hastened to remind Freymann: "Allow me to remark that since I have not replied to the letter of Jules Hermann asking for permission to reprint photographically volume I, this should not have taken place. As to the photographic reproduction of volume II, no authorization whatsoever has ever been requested from me. I am certain, Monsieur, that with you this would not happen again, and that if you consider such reimpression, you would ask in advance for authorization, on which I insist absolutely."

Toward a showdown?

Matters seemed to be heading for a showdown. Unfortunately, Hélène did not keep a copy of her letter of May 10 to Freymann, a reference to which provides the starting point of his letter of May 26 stating at length the official view of Hermann et Cie on the photographic reproduction of volumes I and II.

> 1. Hermann et Cie takes the view that the contract with Mr. Duhem, with regard to author's royalties, has expired with the sale of the last copy and that such will be the case in the future for each remaining volume, without implying that we renounce our future rights.

> 2. While it is true that we cannot provide a proof of your agreeing with the photographic reproduction of the said copies, you, and you yourself stated it, cannot recall having replied to two letters of Mr. Jules Hermann who asked for authorization and of which letters we have sent a copy to you. We are astonished that you did not believe it to be

your duty to reply to two letters which evidenced great interest in the diffusion and continuation of your father's work.

3. The 40% royalties which you mention and which are in the contract, relate only to copies from #401 on to the end of the impression foreseen and the total sum of those 40% royalties correspond, if applied at 10% to all copies, to about the same amount, the one which we have offered in our liquidation, and we do not see on what ground you take your stand in requesting a royalty of 20%.

The expenses of that photograhic reimpression were, as you yourself admit, undertaken by us only in order to prevent the stopping of the sale of other existing volumes, and therefore we are certain that your father would have been grateful for that gesture of ours and we are surprised that you disagree.

4. In memory of Mr. Duhem and in order to terminate a situation for which we are but indirectly responsible, we shall satisfy your demand concerning the interests on the royalties as you demand, but as we do not want to create a precedent for the future, we shall withdraw from sales all the copies of the two photographically reproduced volumes in our possession. In so doing we shall re-establish matters as they were at the moment when Mr. Jules Hermann wrote to you and asked for that authorization which you say you had refused by your silence.

Please be so kind as to tell us whether you maintain your viewpoint so that we may send you the sum you have requested.

On reading all this Hélène must have felt some remorse of conscience about the less then exemplary zeal she showed in the 1920s about her father's work. Still this did not mean that she had lost ground. In her reply of June 7th to Freymann she

rightly reminded him that "the contract between Hermann &
Fils and Pierre Duhem will terminate only when integrally
carried out," that is, "when the manuscript of my father has
been fully published in the form specified in the contract. I
suppose that we are in perfect agreement on that subject. In
consequence I will be much relieved if you tell me when you
plan to start producing volume VI." Hélène was not to be
defeated on the question of royalties either. She still found
some errors in the statements sent to her.

Instead of the seven thousand francs, demanded by Hélène,
Freymann felt obligated to send, on June 23, a check for only
five and a half thousand francs. The last paragraph of the
covering letter showed something of Freymann's next move to
secure further delay. He first spoke of the difficulty (rather
unconvincing) of bringing together all the directors interested
in a decision relating to such a major work as the *Système du
monde.* Then he stated the firm's willingness to publish as soon
as possible the entire work, provided "we can bring together
the conditions present at the beginning of the enterprise." He
spoke of conditions, not of contractual specifications. While
most likely he could not find a copy of the letter in which A.
Hermann expressed his wish to Duhem that the ministerial
subvention be not included in the contract, it was enough to
read that contract, so clear and brief, to see the absence there
of any subvention.

Since this was all too clear to Hélène, she could feel
furious over Freymann's latest diversionary tactic and she vented
her feelings to Dufourcq. "My dear little friend," wrote
Dufourcq to her on July 3, "I understand your indignation. But
as Bismarck used to say, 'indignation is not a diplomatic
attitude.' One has to act." Then Dufourcq began to analyze
Freymann's letter of June 23 to her. The situation was now set,
Dufourcq thought, by Freymann's twofold resolve: not to go
ahead with the printing of volume VI now, and not to yield his
right to another publisher ready to print it. "Your idea," he

wrote to Hélène, "of informing the perpetual secretary of the Académie des Sciences seems to me excellent. Bring his attention to Hermann's two refusals and to the enormously successful sales of the *Système du monde*. Then ask for advice and support. Cannot the Académie intervene with a publisher in a manner that is convenient to it?" Further Dufourcq advised Hélène to make a list of her father's friends still alive in order to sollicit their help.

Since it was early July, no really new steps could be planned about the situation as things now stood with Freymann. That nothing was indeed done is clear from the absence of documents for the rest of the year. Hélène clearly sought relief in concentrating on the biography of her father. Dufourcq's next extant communication to her, dated December 14, 1934, is indeed about his contribution to that biography. He also suggested that perhaps Chevrillon would find a publisher for it. Dufourcq thought that only after the coming plebiscite on the future of the Saar would it be advisable to take new steps about the *Système du monde*. He therefore suggested to Hélène to resume contact with Picard and ask Hermann for a schedule of immediate publication by sending him a copy of your father's contract. "Dare him to refuse to implement the contract! Make him come up with written proposals, all precise, to print all the volumes still in manuscript and right away! One must not wait any longer." Rarely did the waiting turn out to be so long as in this case.

Things did not move forward at all. Dufourcq had to admit on January 21, 1935, that Picard's reply was "stupefying." Eight days later, Dufourcq voiced hope that Chevrillon, a member of the Académie Française, might be a good contact there and perhaps at other learned societies and foundations. Dufourcq obtained a rendezvous with Chevrillon but no help. In the same letter of February 8 Dufourcq broke the bad news that his own publisher, Plon, had just had a disastrous financial year and that unless Rivière had come up with a good offer,

Hélène should shift her attention from the biography to the *Système du monde*. Indeed, her attention had, during the previous two years, been often absorbed in planning and writing that biography. Whatever anxieties and perplexities that work caused her, it also served her as a means of revitalizing her sense of purpose.

5

Portrait by a Daughter

Faults to be corrected

As her long letter of March 21, 1933, to Dufourcq shows, Hélène planned a book about her father as he really was. The idea of such a book originated in the early 1920s with Duhem's sister who, as Hélène wrote to Dufourcq, "was dissatisfied with a biography of good intentions though very inaccurate, that appeared shortly after papa's death and was copied more or less by other biographers of his." The biography in question was the long Notice written by Edouard Jordan for the Association Amicale des Anciens Elèves de l'Ecole Normale Supérieure.[1] Marie Duhem therefore put together her own account about her brother and left it to her niece with the request to be published eventually. Her aunt's reminiscences, Hélène continued,

> were meant to give of her brother a faithful image, which she had already found distorted. I must confess that I have found papa absolutely in these lines [written by my aunt, which contain also] my grandmother's reminiscences about his youth and infancy. They are for me a true treasure. My aunt wanted their publication. Now, can this account, though precious to the family and intimate friends, have an

interest for the public? Who, apart from you, Monsieur, can be a benevolent judge of this question?

But the real question, posed by Hélène indirectly to Dufourcq, did not relate to her plan of printing her aunt's reminiscences about her brother in sufficient number to allow a "fairly large distribution." The real question was whether Dufourcq agreed with Hélène's plan of adding several paragraphs to Aunt Marie's portrayal of her brother. What was to be said in those paragraphs? One paragraph was to be "on the Christian, another on the professor, the creator of a new science, with his vocation of intellectual apostolate." Hélène's next phrase shows that she had already begun researching her father's vast scientific correspondence: "I am sending you the copy of a letter of papa's to Van't Hoff whose work he fully admired. Is it not his own dream which he paints with so much warmth?"[2]

Then Hélène turned to the very nerve center of her strategy to re-establish her father's memory in its true features:

> You will recall as I do, with deep sadness, that the official potentates, who barred his road to Paris and organized a conspiracy of silence about everything he had written, made that dream impossible to realize. And I think that these potentates ought to be perhaps called (impossible to do in an official biography) by their very names: Lippmann and Berthelot.

The purpose of this was not a personal vendetta but the vindication of true French science, the very thing which Duhem meant to protect in his battle against Berthelot and his vast coterie. Hélène rightly sensed that her papa's anti-Berthelot stance was but part of a larger picture of his patriotism. This is why Hélène wanted to add still another paragraph, devoted to Duhem, the Frenchman:

I do not have to tell you the extent to which papa was a patriot, because you are one as much as he was. But the biography I am criticizing presented him as one with no political convictions and made him appear, in his youth, sympathetic to "Christian democracy." This is *monstrously* false. Papa was not a democrat; on the contrary, he was a perfect Christian. As to that political atonality of his, that too is false. To be sure, he never engaged in political activity because, for good reason, he thought that there were better things to do. He was absolutely anti-republican. If he did not do politics, he practiced patriotism: admirer of Drumond, reader from the very start of the *Libre parole*, anti-dreyfusard, one of the first to give his name to *La Patrie Française* — all this seems to me to be items to say aloud, because they show him eager to combat all ideas he considered to be false, and in all domains. One might add that he was an 'anti-rallié.'[3]

All these details about Duhem belonged to the years of Hélène's childhood. Was she therefore an unreliable witness? She did not hesitate to answer: "I was very young, but I avidly listened to his conversations with my grandmother, to his comments on what he read in the newspapers; all that remained engraved in my memory when I was a child." What she did not realize was that objectivity was difficult even for a trained historian, let alone for her, an amateur in scholarly matters, worshiping her papa's memory. Clearly, she overshot the mark as she added that "on reading my aunt's reminiscences about her brother, you, Mr. Dufourcq, will notice that my aunt wrote in a manner altogether impersonal; I think that in what I plan to add to her account I could do the same, that is, to efface myself before so interesting a subject."

Two brief items in the remainder of her letter are worth recalling. One conveyed her relief at being free of her worries about the small château near Dijon. The other was about a new biography about her father published by Bloud & Gay, to be discussed shortly. She was naturally eager to obtain a copy. On seeing it, she could be assured that there was now an added reason to write her account about her papa. As will be seen, the eventual sale of the château provided her with much needed money which she readily put into publishing her portrait of Duhem as the eminently *French* savant.

The making of that portrait had its ups and downs. She was elated when Dufourcq sent her his reminiscences about Duhem in Bordeaux. She felt that Dufourcq's lines showed "sympathy (in the etymological sense of the word) and comprehension," a word she underlined. In addition to her own gratitude, she spoke of her father's gratitude towards the Dufourcqs: "While papa was alive," she wrote to Dufourcq on December 23, 1934, "you have never let a great feast of the Church (Christmas, Easter, Assumption, etc.) go by without sending him a few words. He was deeply touched and was happy to be approached by you in those days of Christian cheerfulness. He was moved to the heart when you wished him well on his feast-day, a gesture no other friend of his had done previously. He had become indebted to you for many signs of attention, joy, and expressions of friendship. Providence was indeed good to have placed you on his path when the going became more and more arduous." Not unexpectedly, the letter quickly turned to the projected biography. Hélène suspected that Mr. Villars, partner in the firm Gauthier-Villars and a classmate of Duhem in Stanislas, might find the text too outspoken. She recalled her father's view that Gauthier-Villars produced the best-printed books on mathematical physics, but that his former classmate, who published several books of his, did not place them in the foreground of his shopwindow. "I am afraid," Hélène concluded, "that he is too pusillanimous not to be frightened by your outspokenness and mine."

Scientific instincts

Contrary to Hélène's expectations, Gauthier-Villars would have been ready to publish the life of her papa, but only at an exorbitant cost. Then, suddenly recalling that Dufourcq published his books with Plon, she turned to Plon and received a promising reply. However, very unpromising did she appear to herself with respect to a major facet of the biography she was writing: Could she draw her father's profile as a scientist with any reliability? The question weighed on her all the more as she knew very well the importance which her papa paid to that point. Yet, on reading her long letter of October 27, 1935, to Dufourcq one cannot help being struck by the accuracy of the observations made by her, less than an amateur in physics. Her apparent lack of competence pained her all the more as by then she had received Plon's reply in which much satisfaction was expressed about her manner of painting her father as a human being, a Frenchman, and a Christian. Yet Plon also wanted her to portray her papa as "a man of science and an innovator at that." The scientific point was not touched upon in the positive reaction of Dr. Récamier, who was able to read the manuscript a few weeks before his death.

Thinking about the scientific part of her papa's life left her utterly perplexed. She poured out her perplexity in the next three pages of her letter to Dufourcq. What she wrote there, with not even a formal high-school education, reveals the stunning measure of her intellectual incisiveness, obviously an inheritance from her father:

> I did not try to hide from myself that to recount the life of papa, without talking of his scientific work, which dominated him completely and to which he had entirely subordinated all his life, was to write a mutilated biography. A scientific competence, which I lacked, was needed. When I racked my brains for a collaborator in that scientific part, I felt I was up against views and judgments alto-

gether contrary to the thought of my papa. The actual
physics, as far as I know it, follows a path wholly different
from the one papa traced and where no one wanted to
follow him. I have found it written that 'physics would
have wasted its time on the road where papa put it and that
it would have never arrived at the discoveries celebrated
today' (J. Perrin, de Broglie, etc). It is claimed (Fabry of
the Institute said it) that papa 'passed his life in writing the
grammar of a language which nobody speaks any longer'
and that 'he needed a voluntary blindness to deny the
reality of atoms.'[4]

I cannot, of course, be a judge, but I remember that
papa spoke to me — and how often! — about the atomistic school as an absurd thing, revolting to good sense and
logic. Experimental evidence had, so it seems, refuted him,
but how to interpret the experiments? And what sort of a
theory — conforming to his doctrine — would papa have
constructed in order 'to save the newly observed phenomena'? Ah, Monsieur, how much I wish I were in the
position to answer this question and rescue from willful
oblivion that precious work which represents the solitary
effort of an entire life!

However, you understand that in the course of
recounting that life, I would not risk to set forth, even in
a veiled form, such an opinion. I am therefore alone with
my absolute incompetence. I know that the readership of
Plon does not want, it would rather resent, those mathematical formulas without which one cannot talk about
papa's work in theoretical physics. In order to show him,
as Plon wants it, in his capacity of innovator — and this
explains the opposition he encountered on the part of those
caught in routine thought — one needs to appreciate not
only his works but also the state of physics prior to him.
One would also need to know the work of foreign scientists, because in Holland, in Poland, in Germany[5] his work
was not ignored as it was in France. One would need to
know the path traversed by his thought from the *Potentiel
thermodynamique* to his great *Traité d'énergétique* which he

regarded — he himself told me — the culminating point of his work. Was not there in his thinking an evolution from the moment when, as a disciple of J. Moutier, he definitively formulated the laws of energetics?[6]

I hoped to find that out and I don't know whether he was an antiatomist from the start. He had already explored several branches of physics in the light of the principles of thermodynamics, when one day he noted that he had a predecessor in an obscure British physicist, Rankine. I was very young then, but I remember his despair on that day. He believed he had said nothing original in his works. His examination of Rankine's work during the next few days reassured him. By being ready to do justice to his predecessor, he saw what he himself had contributed. From that moment on he abandoned the term 'thermodynamique générale,' which he previously used to designate his method of theoretical physics, and adopted the term 'énergétique,' a term of Rankine. I think that, in fact, he was the true creator of Energetics. Rankine laid down its principles or guessed their fruitfulness. But papa, after rediscovering them, was the only one to apply them, and successfully, to all branches of physics without ever finding them wanting. He therefore had confidence in reasoning based on those principles and judged them by their rigor to be helpful in avoiding the shallows of false theories.

I would be more at ease in the domain of the history of sciences, because there the discoveries of papa were achieved, so to speak, under my very eyes, and we spoke of them every day. And since you are there, you will not refuse, after reading my manuscript, the advice that would help me to avoid saying stupid things.

Such were her memorable reflections on receiving from Plon a letter, full of promise as well as reserve. "I pray to God," she wrote to Dufourcq, "to inspire you with good advice for me. Am I wrong in taking Plon's letter for an encouragement to

improve my manuscript, to turn it into something worthy of
my dear and admirable papa?"

For an assurance she needed more than, say, a prominent
physicist's word that her father's views were of lasting value. To
begin with, it would have been impossible to find such a
physicist in the early 1930s. Then as before and now, to recall
the graphic simile of the American physicist, S. P. Langley, who
a hundred years ago did valuable research in the analysis of the
infrared spectrum, physicists could act "like a pack of hounds
. . . where the louder-voiced bring many to follow them nearly
as often in the wrong path as in the right one; where the entire
pack even has been known to move off bodily on a false
scent."[7] Of course, the game just caught in the early 1930s in
the physicists' net, the neutron and positron, gave to many of
them the illusion that atomism had witnessed its supreme
conquest and that nothing else was left to look for. Only the
passing of another four to five decades, with further penetration
into the subatomic realm, could bring some of them to suspect
that what the physicists catch with their enormous accelerators
are not so much "particles" but energy resonances and that
their systematization is an exercise, however unconscious, in
Duhem's very energetics. And precisely because only history
could give this insight to those who were unwilling to heed the
voice of sheer logic, Duhem was doubly in the right.

There was no physicist at that time either in France or
abroad with enough authority to give the assurance so badly
needed by Hélène. Then as now physicists could not appreciate
the difference between atomism and atoms. Atoms could hardly
be a fiction to a Duhem who was among the first to demonstrate radioactivity as part of his physics course.[8] What he
firmly held to be a fiction was atomism, enshrined for all
classical physicists in Newton's words about absolutely hard
particles created in the beginning by God.[9] Although Leibniz
had already pointed out that such atoms could not physically
interact, physicists went on adding many pages to the illogicality

of atomism. Maxwell spoke of atoms as manufactured by God and Kelvin took his vortex atoms, wrapped in the regalia of mathematics, for plain reality. Some time before Duhem became a historian of physics and had rescued physics from taking for its origin Galileo's coming for a "Deus ex machina" event, he had provided instructive pages about that science-coated cavorting in illogicality which is atomism.

As to post-Duhem historians of science, they were the last to give assurance to Hélène. Many of them were waiting for a liberation from Duhem's findings about the medieval (and theological to boot) origin of Newtonian science. Their deliverance came when Galileo's science became the sudden avocation of A. Koyré whose chief aim was to demolish the very thrust of Duhem's thought by leaving him with all the unessentials.[10] No comfort could come to Hélène from philosophers of science, rapidly falling under the sway of logical positivism which ultimately deprived them of a coherent picture of science. They became cultivators of mere words, such as paradigms, research programs, revolutions — all of them without an unambiguous definition. Still worse, no help to Hélène could come from those very few Catholic intellectuals who took a more than cursory look at the history and philosophy of science. They became, almost to a man, betrayers of the great heritage left behind by Pierre Duhem. They found that it was far easier to be in cahoots with some sworn enemies of Christian culture in the highest chairs of academia. They all should hang their heads in shame on seeing Hélène take the right track as if she had inherited a scientific instinct.

Heroism repaid

Not that she would have been able to articulate at length her reference to the physicist's task "to save the new phenomena." Indeed, she had to fall back on her "untiring endurance for the sake of all that concerns my papa." That endurance, a chief aspect in her turning into a heroine, she needed physically as well. She lived in a remote village that became connected to the rest of the region with a road suitable for automobiles only in the late 1920s. Only a few houses had electricity and possibly none of them those comforts, based on running water, without which daily life would be unthinkable in the civilized world today.

Her letter of November 25, 1935, to Dufourcq begins precisely with a brief but revealing reflection on the "pleasures of country-life" which Dufourcq extolled as being most helpful to her work. Those pleasures, Hélène replied, in a graphic account of her daily toil,

> exist only in the imagination of the city folks. In addition to numerous and almost daily interruptions, because it is rare to do absolutely what one planned, I have been taken up towards the end of this Fall by work in the field and by planting trees that required my continual attention all the time. One had to make most of the last few beautiful days. The cold is severe in our mountains, one has to hurry to do things in their proper time before the cold's arrival. We still have another week of 'hard labor' [corvée] ahead of us. After that I planned to write to you in all tranquillity when this letter of Massis, in this morning's mail, spurs me to write to you of what I was thinking while planting my trees and I now ask your advice.

Meanwhile Henri Massis, editor of the conservative *Revue universelle*, asked Hélène to let him publish a chapter from her projected book, news about which must have been making the rounds for some time. As she informed Dufourcq, she was in the process of doing the final revision of her manuscript and hoped to be able to send a section of it to Massis. Undoubtedly good advance publicity was assured to the book by the appearance, in the April 15, 1936, issue of the *Revue* of a part of the manuscript amounting to about thirty printed pages. The part contained Chevrillon's letter on Duhem and the latter's letter to the Père Bulliot on the teaching in Catholic universities of the history and philosophy of science.[11] For the moment Hélène had to make haste of a different kind: "I am now on my toes. I have work to oversee in the fields just when I need quiet days to complete this small work which is so close to my heart. Nothing is more fragmented as our poor time. One has to be clever not to lose a bit of it."

In the same letter Hélène also spoke to Dufourcq of her idea to ask the mathematician Maurice d'Ocagne, of the Académie des Sciences, to write a preface to her biography. In his reply, written four days later, Dufourcq began with judging the idea "excellent" but at the bottom of the same page he added, what could only be dispiriting for Hélène: "If d'Ocagne declines, there remains no one!" D'Ocagne promptly agreed, news of which made Dufourcq write, on December 9, to Hélène: "We only have to thank God, and you, who had that great idea which did not occur to me at all." Dufourcq urged Hélène to send a copy of the manuscript to d'Ocagne so that he might write an appropriate preface. "Who knows whether he would be willing to intervene with Plon? Everything could but please Plon: the preface, as well as d'Ocagne's title of membre de l'Institut, and his renown as mathematician . . . ." Dufourcq expressed his own readiness to intervene if necessary, adding that he had no word whatever from Plon about his own ninth volume.[12]

In early February, 1936, Dufourcq still had not received the galleys of volume 9, let alone of volume 10, of his work. As it turned out, for Plon the year 1935 was not good financially. It became evident that Plon would publish Hélène's work only if she were to contribute 8,000 francs to the cost of publication to protect Plon from major risk. Dufourcq was cautious in matters of money. He even suggested that perhaps Massis would publish the entire manuscript in installments which later could be turned into a single volume. It was, however, a Hélène now profoundly devoted to the cause of her father that Dufourcq had to face. His letter of March 2, 1936, began with the question: "Can you produce that advance of 8,000 francs which Plon demands?" The question showed that care as Dufourcq did for Hélène's finances, he respected her financial privacy. He also voiced sympathy with the emotional part of the subject, though again he sounded cautious:

> I understand your father. And I am with you in that you, only child and heir of Duhem, feel the urge to give about your father *your* testimony and that of your family and friends, because certain aspects of his character have been distorted by others — nothing more legitimate, nothing more opportune. But as your old friend I must also recommend to you not to be imprudent. Before signing the contract, examine your heart, review your budget. We are in full revolution. The worst is not improbable. Wisdom demands that you should have money on hand, and all the more so as many expect a new bank crisis following the election.

More to the point was Dufourcq's postcript: "But if you had already said 'yes' to Plon, there is nothing to discuss."

Actually, things seemed to go far better than Dufourcq suspected. It suddenly seemed, of which more later, that even the fate of the *Système du monde* had taken a major turn for the better. Hermann gave a signal about its intention to reissue other books of Duhem, out of print, especially the Leonardo studies. There also appeared in Abel Rey a powerful supporter of the great cause, as Hélène's letter of February 8, 1936, to Dufourcq informs us. For Hélène the only sad item, for the moment at least, was the news about the passing away of her mother's oldest sister, Martha Balthus. She leaves behind, Hélène wrote to Dufourcq, "a husband of eighty-four, very saddened. Luckily he has with him one of my cousins, unmarried, very devoted to her parents. Theirs was a Christian household, par excellence. God was served there first, and I think that my aunt will find her reward in Heaven. She was very much united to my mother and nursed me when I was very little. Neither of us has forgotten the other and we loved one another very much. Another void on this earth: Heaven is more full of people for me than this world!"

The last and no small hurdle in the way of signing the contract with Plon was the publisher's stipulation that the sum of ten thousand and forty five francs be paid by the author in three installments. One third of that sum was due on the signing of the contract, another third on the receipt of the first proofs, and the third on the receipt of the final proofs. "The sale of [the Château] Brannay," she wrote to Dufourcq on February 27, "would allow me to devote that sum to the memory of my dear Papa! — I have to confess to you in this connection that, by foreseeing this expenditure, I did not execute the plan about the inscription I thought to place in the church of Cabrespine and for which I was asked a fabulous price. I carefully kept your very beautiful text, reserving it for a later day in the belief that the burden of each day should suffice to it and that it was more pressing to print these precious reminiscences which it was given to me to collect on Papa." She showed noteworthy determination in another matter as well. Her letter came to a close with the words: "I try not to be too upset by the anguish felt over the actual situation. The dissolution of the Action Française does not make me lose my confidence: one does not dissolve except what lets itself be dissolved and the human will is stronger than all persecutions. May God help us!"

On the sixth of March Hélène signed the contract which called for the printing of 2,200 copies, including the author's 50 copies and the 150 copies destined for publicity. If after three years the book's sales were so small as to suggest it would not be out of print in another five years, the publisher would hand over any number of copies to the author, with the provision that she could not sell them until all copies in Plon's possession

had been sold. Hélène's sole correction in the contract came at
the very end: "The book's title is not <u>Pierre Duhem</u> but: <u>Un
savant français, Duhem</u>." The patriotism of her papa had to be
evident even on the title page.

Un savant français: Pierre Duhem

That Plon, a publisher catering above all to a Catholic clientèle,
published the book made it almost inevitable that most of its
immediate readers were familiar with Pierre Humbert's book on
Duhem, published four years earlier by another Catholic
publishing house, Bloud & Gay.[13] The readers may have at a
first look been struck by the fact that both books were divided
into five sections. This was just about the only similarity
between the two books. With meager documentation, Humbert
dealt with Duhem the man, the physicist, the philosopher, the
historian, and the teacher. Concerning the last four points,
Humbert's summary of the essentials could certainly be infor-
mative to anyone with no easy access to the essays published a
decade or two earlier by scientists like Picard, Vicaire, Jouguet,
Houllevigue, Manville, and Hadamard; by historians like
Jordan, Dufourcq and Fliche; and by theologians like the abbés
Garzend and Berniès.[14] Only in connection with Duhem the
teacher did Humbert provide a few original though brief
details.

Concerning Duhem the man, Humbert heavily relied on
Jordan's account which had so much upset Marie Duhem.[15]
Had Maurice d'Ocagne, the prominent mathematician and
member of the Académie des Sciences, been asked to write a
preface to Humbert's work, he would have hardly been
prompted by reading its manuscript to say what constituted the
high point in the preface he wrote to Hélène's book. The latter
was in a sense a series of graphic and poignant vignettes about
a life full of grave lessons for posterity. With a mastery of
understatement this is what d'Ocagne meant to convey after he
had surveyed, in eleven pages, Duhem's scientific work:

Faced with that colossal work — at once scientific, philosophical, and historical — one cannot avoid being seized with a profound admiration for its author; one indeed feels the desire to follow that great mind across all the vicissitudes of his life on earth and to do so in the certainty that one shall gather beautiful and salutary lessons. Such a prospect is made real for us, thanks to the filial piety of Mlle Duhem, by the publication of this book which she devoted, in so touching a manner, to the memory of her father, by drawing either on her own memories and those of the family, or on those of qualified witnesses about the illustrious physicist. Never shall we be able to tender her a properly vivid gratitude.

Presenting a long chain of vividly and authoritatively told vicissitudes was the filament that gave a unity to Hélène's book. Beneath its chronological structure, that presented Duhem first in his childhood, then as a collegian and a Normalien, and afterwards as a professor in Lille, Rennes, and Bordeaux, there lay a recourse to facts that sent a gripping message to any but a jaded scoffer. Duhem's childhood was recalled largely through the reminiscences of Marie Duhem, about whom Hélène wrote at the outset: "My aunt Marie Duhem wanted the life of her brother to be retraced with an exactitude by those who have known and loved him, so that there may remain a faithful picture of him." In the same breath Hélène also disclosed that her aunt wanted to write the entire life of her brother but an "implacable sickness and death prevented her from carrying on with her narrative."

It was the same emphasis on exactitude that set the tone of Hélène's introductory references to her other main sources, and in particular to Récamier's account of Duhem's youth: "The last message I received from him, at a time when he was no longer able to write, was to assure me that he had found everything very exact and that the opinions and the thinking of his friend were rendered in conformity with truth." In speaking for herself, Hélène put the moral of her father's life and work into the perspective of the times:

> In these times of ours, times so troubled, so torn apart, times that obviously try to find themselves, it is not perhaps without relevance to recount that life of such perfect unity, of so great a balance, and to show how that mind — which, enamored of logic, fathomed the method of physical theories and followed the efforts of the human intellect across the ages — stood with respect to the Catholic *Credo* and to the great problems of patriotic duty and of politics.

Hélène would have been most discouraged had she been given a view of the times half a century later. Since politics is no exemption to the rule symbolized by the panther's proverbial inability to change his spots, only the naive would take the decibels of democratic slogans for a reality of equality, fraternity and liberty for all. Worse, compared with the state of affairs half a century ago, society has gone even farther down the road towards that anarchy which repeatedly raised its ugly head in France around 1900 and around 1935, two dates closely tied to Duhem's career and to the appearance of his life-story by his daughter.

From among the many observers of this fearful process it is appropriate to call upon a historian of science who can hardly be suspected of sharing Duhem's espousal of that Credo and his attitude towards the political process and many other tenets and precepts very dear to him, except, of course, his devotion to scholarship. And since it was Cornell University that showed on this side of the Atlantic the first appreciation for Duhem's reinterpretation of physical chemistry, just as appropriate should seem that the historian of science in question, L. Pearce Williams, is a professor at Cornell. That he found for his succinct appraisal of the present times an outlet in the pages of the *New York Times*, a chief organ of ethical relativism, crowns the appropriateness of quoting his words. They were prompted by a faculty debate touched off by the attack of a professor (D. Kagan) on the putative morality of civil disobedience:

> What Kagan, I think, was arguing was that there is no "moral" universe to which citizens can now appeal that provides an adequate basis for disobedience to the law. I find it strange that liberals, who insist upon the ultimate relativism of all moral values, suddenly appeal to a "higher" morality (which they are careful not to define) when it suits them. All that went out with the Victorians, and we now inhabit a society in which all moral opinions seem equally valid. . . . The point, of course, is, as Kagan clearly stated, that we live in a consensual society in which we often have to do things we don't want to do, or even think are wrong, because we have agreed to abide by majority rule. Destroy that argument, and the result is not freedom but anarchy — a condition which the United States seems rapidly approaching.[16]

Instead of the United States, one could simply speak of the affluent Western World. In addition, a historian of science should have been aware of the fact that his very field, together with the philosophy of science, has been increasingly used as a chief vote against values and notions absolutely and universally valid. According to most cultivators of those two fields, science is to be understood in terms of its sociology, or a meticulous registering of the ever shifting consensus of scientists. In looking for the rise of this or that consensus the "deepest" that is offered is a psychoanalytical post-mortem, if not vivisection, of the scientists themselves. Few historians and philosophers of science feel compunction over the fact that in that dubious process the image of science has ceased to offer anything worthwhile, unless the worth is measured in purely pragmatic success.[17]

This "academic" dismantling of individuals and society provides the icing to the dismal cake of a cultural disintegration through the skyrocketing of crime and a possible biological demise through licentiousness. One may therefore be wise not to treat with ready contempt either Hélène's or her father's uncompromising insistence on absolute values, whetever their naiveté in seeing those values secured by questionable political movements, such as the Action Française.

At one point, however, the academics — physicists no less than historians of science — remain very much on the defensive with respect to Hélène's crusade on behalf of her father's memory. They have failed over two generations to steal the march on Hélène. Unlike her, they did not show readiness to be counted. It was in the pages of Hélène's book that for the first time Marcelin Berthelot (and his accomplice, the Nobel-laureate physicist, Lippmann) were identified by name as guilty of a crime against science and against a prominent scientist. Until then, that is for almost exactly fifty years, nothing appeared in print about those two as being responsible for the shameful rejection by the Sorbonne, in 1885, of a brilliant doctoral thesis on the thermodynamic potential, which now forms a part of the Microfilm Landmarks of Science. The crime could be covered up for two reasons. Legion was the number of those scientists and academic administrators who owed their position and advancement to Berthelot, perhaps the foremost academic powerbroker in the late 19th century. Many others were fearful lest they suffer recriminations through references to the crime committed against Duhem, relegated for the rest of his life to the provinces.

Berthelot's ukase, "this young man shall never teach in Paris," is recalled three times in Hélène's book.[18] In a negative sense those references form the crux of her narrative. To blunt their force or to deflect it, the time-proven method of silence could seem the most effective means. Moreover, silence on the real issue could be made unnoticeable by a few, carefully evasive words. Such was the gist of the review which George Sarton, a chief figure and power-broker in the historiography of science, published in his influential quarterly, *Isis*, on Hélène's book less than a year after its publication:

> This is the second biography of the late P. Duhem (1861-1916) in a few years. The one by Pierre Humbert appeared in 1932 (*Isis* 21, 399). This, written by the only child of Duhem, is better than the former and contains some excellent pieces, such as the witness of André Chevrillon (pp. 55-78) and the admirable letter which Duhem wrote to the Père Bulliot (pp. 158-59). Unfortunately, this is still not a real biography, but rather a panegyrics. The author often talks of Christian charity, but on occasion forgets to practice it, and her book contains too much rancor and shows too much bitterness to be altogether amiable. This is a pity because Duhem deserves better than that; a true critical biography. Duhem's reflections on science and industry appear to me a bit narrow (p. 228). It would be necessary to correct them by comparing them with those of Henri le Châtelier (1850-1936) in his last work: *De la méthode dans les sciences expérimentales* of which we shall talk again later. G. S.[19]

Every statement of this short review was part of a tactic aimed at securing a very specific purpose, namely, the damning of Duhem with faint praise.[20] The very last phrase was a plain red herring, rather odorous. Sarton invoked a French physical chemist, Henri le Châtelier, whose deep-seated dislike of Duhem was never based on scientific arguments. Sarton could not be ignorant of this, nor could he be unfamiliar with the dislike which Le Châtelier fomented in his many students against Duhem, a dislike that long survived Le Châtelier's very long life. Only with this in mind could a reader of Sarton's review guess something of his motivations in seizing on a detail which was minute in Hélène's book (a mere page according to

Sarton's admission) and was a very small part of Duhem's vast publications.

No more reputable was Sarton's expressed desire for a "truly critical biography" of Duhem. As the editor of *Isis* he had just accepted for publication a most uncritical criticism of Duhem, in which Duhem was charged with nothing less than plain manipulation of texts and facts.[21] That Sarton himself could not easily take criticism lay behind his criticism of Hélène as one who does not practice at times Christian charity while constantly preaching it. Why did Sarton not find important to hint, however briefly, at the flagrant injustice committed against Duhem's genius and life? Were those guilty of that injustice not to be deplored because the injustice was committed against a devout Christian? Or perhaps no mention was to be made of that injustice because too many academics — physicists, physical chemists, philosophers and historians of science, and editors, to boot — have become co-conspirators in the technique of damning Duhem with faint praise.[22]

Such a technique is always the fruit of bad faith which blares forth in Sarton's reference to Duhem's admirable letter to Bulliot, though audible only by those familiar with that letter. Could Sarton, a notoriously enthusiastic Freemason and a Jew, whose religion was mere humanism, really admire that letter? He must have realized that the letter amounted to the clearest clarion call ever sounded in defense of Christian religion, culture, and education. The letter calls for a frontal resistance against the principal claim of the anti-Christianity of the French Enlightenment, namely, that science could not arise until Christianity, and especially the Catholic Church, had been discredited. The letter unmasked those who urged all mankind to swear by science alone and forswear anything which scientism declares incompatible with a science taken not for rational investigation but for substitute religion.

Sarton could but feel uneasy with this new biography of Duhem in which a poignant page or two recalled Duhem's early awareness of his works being plagiarized. Sarton was skirting around the moral abyss of plagiarism as he set himself up, in an article carried far and wide in the pages of the May 1919 issue of *Scribner's Magazine*, as *the* pioneering expert on Leonardo the scientist.[23] He would not have felt assured against being unmasked as a *parvenu*, if not a plain plagiarist, on the subject had he not felt that no one in the corridors of academic powers would raise a disclaimer. Indeed, as a principal figure in those corridors already at that time, he seemed to think that nobody would ever take him to task for stopping his reviews in *Isis* of Duhem's *Système du monde* with the second of its already five published volumes.[24]

Of course, there was no one even among the admirers of Duhem around 1937 who would have recalled such facts about Sarton as they saw his name next to Madame Paul Tannery's in the opening page of the 72nd issue of *Isis,* published in March 1937. In their "Appel pour l'achèvement du *Système du monde* de Duhem" the two stated that "if at least three hundred subscriptions would be forthcoming, the publication would be assured." The two hoped from "the bottom of their hearts that learned bodies, such as the Académie des Sciences, the Académie des inscriptions, and the Académie internationale d'histoire des sciences would unite with us to request that the publication of the *Système du monde* be achieved as quickly as possible."

A curious thing about the appeal, obviously drawn up by Sarton,[25] was the proviso that "to leave volumes VI to IX of Duhem's work unpublished is almost a scandal, if indeed they [the manuscripts] are in a publishable form." If anyone, Sarton could have easily learned about the by then almost two-decade-old conclusion of the committee of the Académie des Sciences: those manuscripts were indeed ready to be published, a point all too clear to the publisher for some time. Ten years later Sarton supplied the evidence that his heart was not really in that appeal.[26]

It would have been most difficult for Sarton to turn down Mme Tannery's initiative of the appeal. Her husband, the undisputed head of historians of science around 1900, was driven into his grave in 1905 by a signal injustice inflicted on him by those in the corridors of power in academia. Only Duhem dared to air this in print at that time.[27] Mme Tannery was not only a chief force behind the publication, in twelve volumes, of the collected essays of her husband,[28] but also a sober reminder to any and all in those very corridors.

The idea of the appeal came from Mme Tannery who, together with her husband, had very friendly ties with Hélène's father. Moreover the idea of that appeal came to Mme Tannery precisely because of the impact made on her by Hélène's book. She was not the only one to be impressed by it. Another was Mme Hélène Metzger-Bruhl, a leading historian of science at that time. Her letter, written to Hélène on September 19, 1936, from Houlvigue on the Atlantic shore, deserves to be quoted at length:

> Mademoiselle, I do not want to wait any longer to thank you very much for your very interesting book and for your amiable letter. I am also pleased to have the Notice on your father's life and work.[29] I plan to join it to that gripping biography you have written in order to be available to the readers of our library of history of science, in the center of Synthèse, 12 rue Colbert.
>
> From the family house in the country I went to the seashore and I took along your book for reading. I have come to know your father (I meant to say, his work) in a rather unexpected manner, because I have never heard speak of him when I was a student at the Faculty of Science as I was preparing for the diploma of higher studies in physical sciences which I obtained in 1912.
>
> Having problems with my eyes and unable to contin-ue studies with the microscope, I looked for a consolation for the interruption of my scientific studies. In 1913 I

married a professor of history from Lyon and my husband put his expertise at my disposal if I wanted to write a doctoral thesis (although I had neither the 'bachot' nor the licenciate) on the Faculty of Letters. . . . Unfortunately, as my husband was killed in the first battles of the war, I returned to Paris and decided to finish alone a work that was begun by two. I received the doctorate in December 1918, and during the oral exam several professors asked me why I did not quote Duhem who inspired me to write such and such pages. Taken aback I admitted my ignorance, and rushed to the writings of your father and immediately saw to what criticism I exposed myself by not knowing his works on history, science and scientific philosophy. I have just written to my publisher that he send you a copy of my *Les concepts scientifiques* where I rely almost to the point of indiscretion on what I have learned in his books. I have often asked myself what his opinion would be of what I have developed. I congratulated myself that he would have approved in a general manner, although he had drawn far better the consequences of some premises and gone farther than I did.

I am also pleased with the opportunity you have given me to render him homage. The only thing that disturbs me is that he had little sympathy for Jews like myself, and for certain ideas that are dear to me. But this may be a rather small matter, and it seems to me that I have exaggerated my scruples. It is not useful to revive old tensions in order to display all the admiration and gratitude which historians of science should nourish towards your father. I hope that the end of the *Système du monde* will soon appear in order to teach many things.

Four months later the two Hélènes met and in circumstances which for the author of *Un savant français* seemed to prove that her heroic efforts to write it were to pay off in the way she had hoped for.

A day of triumph

Though more than ready to fight for her father's memory, Hélène Duhem, as she wrote to Dufourcq on January 14, 1937, could not easily picture herself in the midst of representatives of the learned world. As the same letter reveals, she had to be persuaded by Hélène Metzger-Bruhl's "amiable letter" to come late that month to Paris and attend the annual meeting, on January 27, of the French group of the Académie Internationale d'Histoire des Sciences. It took further gentle pressure from Hélène Metzger-Bruhl to make her agree to deliver a brief speech at that meeting. On January 14 she was still telling Dufourcq: "Of course, I decline the honor of speaking, a risky honor for one who does not have the practice of speaking in public." As will be seen, she spoke as an accomplished speaker.

The first to speak was Maurice d'Ocagne of the Académie des Sciences. He certainly went to the heart of the matter as he singled out from among Duhem's many achievements the one whereby "he had definitively destroyed the legend, held for a long time by many authors for an article of faith, about the 'scientific night of the Middle Ages'."[30] His conclusion related to the imperative necessity of bringing to the public the unpublished parts of the *Système du monde*. He spared no words in extolling the value of the work: "Once available in its entirety, the work will have its place among the most beautiful acquisitions of the intellectual heritage of France in the contemporary period." Nor did d'Ocagne mince words about the magnitude of responsibility: "By not making the necessary effort on behalf of the publication of the remainder finished by Duhem, the powers of officialdom will fail in what they owe to the intellectual elite of the country, to its great renown in the world."[31]

The next to speak was Hélène Metzger-Bruhl as secretary of the group. She began by referring to the custom of the Académie to devote its annual general meetings to the work of a single scientist or historian of science, and recalled the suggestion made at last year's general meeeting of the President, Henri Berr, that a meeting be devoted to Pierre Duhem's work. That the meeting in question became the very next meeting, she connected with her reading of that past summer "a small book full of filial piety which Mlle Hélène Pierre-Duhem, who does us the great honor to assist at this meeting, devoted to the memory of her illustrious father." Almost immediately, Hélène Metzger-Bruhl turned to the topic of the unpublished status of half of the work that assured to its author universal recognition as a historian of science:

> In order to draw attention to this fact, I ask you not to leave this meeting before voting with unanimity the proposition which I now submit to you, with possible modifications, of course, as follows:
> The French group of historians of science associated with the Académie internationale d'histoire des sciences, goes on record with its wish that the unpublished work of Pierre Duhem, and in particular the concluding part of his admirable work, *Le système du monde de Platon à Copernic,* be speedily published because it will give the greatest service to all interested in the development of human thought.[32]

Then Mme Metzger-Bruhl read her paper, dealing mainly with those foundations of Duhem's philosophy of science that demand their elaboration through the analysis of its history. She began by recalling her discovery of Duhem, just as she had written about it a few months earlier to Hélène. Then she added: "The day after the exam I purchased a copy of his *Théorie physique* and (if I may say so) rapidly devoured his philosophical and historical works, together with the part of his scientific work which is within the comprehension of a former student of chemistry and crystallography."[33] Her lecture, which deserves to be rescued from the difficult-to-find issues of *Archeion*, came to a close with a reference to Duhem, the master of style: "At the same time Duhem is not only a scientist, a philosopher, and a historian, but also a great writer who knows all the secrets of persuasion. In reading him we become his allies and, instead of criticising his assertions, we wish to defend them against all criticism."[34]

The next to speak was Abel Rey who began with an homage to the author of *Un savant français*: "I bow in the name of all of you and of mine before Mlle Duhem, whose filial piety has just resuscitated in a beautiful book the man and the scientist her father was. I thank the friends of Duhem for taking part in this commemorative meeting. Thanks to Mlle Duhem and to them, we gather before a living presence." Rey then recalled the unity of Duhem's work and person, whose crowning expression he found in the *Système du monde*. As to the source of that unity, Rey specified it in the gift of intuition, a gift especially possessed by Duhem. That gift made him a historian but only after it had enabled him to penetrate the nature and structure of physical theory in a manner not witnessed before. The same gift also made him see that the cure for the problems of modern physical theory lies in a remedy already discovered by the Greeks as they came to grips with the "system of the world." There Duhem found the very start of "the differential of the curve that follows the history of physics, a history which, on a superficial look, appears jostled and diverse, made of branches with no connection, but which is nevertheless one whole in its essence just as the human spirit that created it."[35]

Rey's reconstruction, in considerable detail, of that documentation had nothing less for its supreme lesson than the claim that Duhem performed "a Copernican revolution in the historiography of science." Tellingly, this statement of Rey followed his reference to Duhem's discovery of the theory of impetus taught in 14th-century Sorbonne. Whatever one may think, Rey continued, of Duhem's philosophical views which he tried to support with his historical researches, his presentation of that differential is but "the rendering, through detailed and painstaking documentation, of the incontestable witness of history."[36]

Rey's concluding words related to Duhem's "magnificent work interrupted by a premature death, caused perhaps by immense work . . . which he did not cease to pursue for a single day, a work threefold and one." As to the unpublished part of that work, Rey said precisely what Hélène had above all at heart, the emphasis on Duhem's contribution to French culture:

> France which he served and honored, the great scientific bodies of which he was a part, all those who profited and still profit from his labors, cannot any longer let so many admirable pages fall into oblivion. The disputes of schools and persons must fall silent and bow before a tomb and a glory. To Duhem who had most unjustly suffered some enmities of high echelon, to Duhem who was forgotten all too often while still alive, to Duhem to whom we are so far from having done justice, to him we owe this reparation: to bring to light all that remains of his thought.[37]

Following Rey's discourse, members of the group approved by acclamation the resolution presented on behalf of the publication of the *Système du monde*. Then Henri Berr, Director of the Centre International de Synthèse, took the floor. After voicing his great pleasure having initiated, with Mme Metzger-Bruhl, the meeting, he offered a statement, precious in its brevity:

> I have known Pierre Duhem as a schoolmate in the Ecole Normale and I was delighted by the contact we maintained for some years through letters which I carefully kept. He graduated at the head of the class and in evoking him — of medium height, energetic, with a look full of

intelligence — I also see a series of remarkable scientists in his wake, such as Lucien Poincaré and Jacques Hadamard.

When I undertook the publication of the *Revue de synthèse* around 1900 — an undertaking not without originality at that time — I wanted to make considerable room there for the history of science. I turned to Pierre Duhem who approved of my enterprise and promised his collaboration which his enormous amount of work made impossible. I am glad that, by rendering him homage publicly, I add a new link to those old memories. It now remains for us to see to it that he be restored to the place which he deserves in the intellectual history of our times.

The next speaker to take the floor was the great mathematician, Hadamard, who once more testified to the enormous intellectual debt he owed to Duhem and to the depth of their friendship. He referred to the few years they had spent together on the Faculty of Science of Bordeaux as he said:

> Duhem was my educator in mathematics and physics; he opened for me new vistas in thermodynamics and shared with me his very mind; those were unforgettably beautiful years, but circumstances separated us when I was given a chair in Paris.[38]

Professor Laignel-Lavastine, president of the meeting, then asked Mlle Hélène Pierre-Duhem to speak of her father. She rose to the occasion:

> Ladies and Gentlemen:
> It is not without very great emotion — which you will kindly excuse — that I address you today. My emotion is all the greater as I am carried in thought twenty-five or thirty years back to the time when my father worked in solitude in Bordeaux. I think of his teaching at the Faculty of Science where, in some years, he had only one student. I think of his works in the history of science that sparked

but little interest, and, on their publication, no echo, at least in the French press. Did he not rejoice over that extraordinary event when his colleague and friend, Albert Dufourcq, called the attention of the readers of the *Revue des Deux Mondes* to the discoveries of the master from Bordeaux?[39]

What a road has been traversed since those distant years! I have no better proof of this than today's commemorative meeting. Allow the daughter of Pierre Duhem to express to you her deepest gratitude. That gratitude is aimed at all those who have honored by their presence the homage rendered to her father's work. That gratitude is addressed above all to the speakers who have shown to you the various aspects and, at the same time, the unity of that work, or recalled memories they have kept about its author.

Let me first thank those among the speakers who initiated and organized this meeting: Mr. Berr who first thought of it a year ago and, assisted by Mme Metzger-Bruhl, did everything to carry it to a happy conclusion. I also thank Professor Laignel-Lavastine who accepted to preside at this meeting; Mr. d'Ocagne whose expressions of esteem of my father's work can hardly be counted; and Mr. Abel Rey whose magisterial study showed the unity of that work. I cannot but recall that Pierre Duhem himself recognized the measure of sympathy and, indeed, of comprehension, with which he penetrated his thought and gave a perfect portrayal of it.

I should voice special thanks to Mr. Abel Rey and Mme Metzger-Bruhl for the motion, for which they both took the initiative and which opportunely recalls that a very important part of the work you celebrate remains unknown. Those unpublished parts, that comprise four volumes of the continuation of the *Système du monde*, deal with the epoch of particular interest for Pierre Duhem, the virgin territory he had deciphered, that 14th century where French science shone with brilliance, the times of those two geniuses, Jean Buridan and Nicole Oresme, exhumed by my father.

The last volumes will show, alas, what the author calls the "desolation of the University of Paris." The torch will pass to the universities of the Roman Empire. He makes the reader sense the coming of the Italian glory of the Renaissance. But the spark of that light shall find its source in the teaching of the Parisian masters of the 14th century. Have you not thought of this by deciding to honor their historian in this very city of Paris that was his own native soil?[40]

It was then the turn of Aldo Mieli, perpetual secretary of the Académie internationale d'histoire des sciences, to speak. After recalling that Duhem greatly approved of the foundation of the Académie and that, except for his premature death, he would have become one of its founding members, he said he would limit his remarks to his personal debts to Duhem. One of those debts derived from the encouragement he received from reading the *Théorie physique* at the very moment when he most needed it, or the moment when he wanted to know the conceptual foundations of what he practiced as a physical chemist. About the same time Mieli also discovered Mach's work: "I felt so much more attached to these two savants as they attacked, not as a method but as an explication of reality, that atomistic theory which I was no more disposed to accept in that latter sense. And I believe that in the not too distant future, when the hyperatomistic infatuation of contemporary scientists has passed its crisis, the views of Duhem and Mach will receive renewed admiration and approval."[41]

Mieli also felt impelled to credit Duhem for the much needed reassurance about taking up the study of the history of science as his vocation. Duhem did that service to Mieli through a letter following the receipt of Mieli's first major work in the history of science, a study of the scientific thought of the pre-Socratics and of the Ionians in particular. On reading that letter, Mieli, to quote his words, "felt largely compensated for the attacks of one or two presumptuous historians and for the benevolent scepticism of a few true historians who did not want to admit that there could be a general history of science." Mieli then read the letter itself:

Bordeaux, Dec. 12, 1915

My dear colleague,

    I have received your lovely card and your first volume on thinkers that preceded Aristotle. While waiting for the time to study it at leisure, I have rushed through it, with an interest that you can easily imagine. I was seized with admiration and, may I also say, with fright on seeing the prodigious erudition which your book presupposes and with which you regale your readers. Your work will certainly be among the most useful works and I will be pleased to study it thoroughly. At this moment I cannot do as well as I would like to. Several periodicals I collaborate with have suspended publication until the end of the war. At least I shall ask to be put in charge of reviewing your work in the *Bulletin des sciences mathématiques*.[42]

Mieli's concluding words could but give great satisfaction to Hélène who in writing her book aimed at retracing her father's portrait in such a way as to do justice to his sincerity and frankness. "Unfortunately I can no longer profit by the advice and encouragement of Pierre Duhem who, as confirmed by Mlle Hélène Duhem in her beautiful book on her father, never parted with his frankness, at times brutal but always admirable, in the manifestation of his ideas and opinions. A few months after he had written that letter, he left us forever, depriving France of her greatest historian of science at that time."[43]

After three other speeches, of less interest here, Professor Laignel-Lavastine, brought the meeting to an end with words addressed to Hélène herself about her father: "He served you,

Mademoiselle, as father and mother. We regret the premature death of the great man he was; and we appreciate that, though having the same sadness as we do, you keep evoking the noble person whom you have so much appreciated and loved."

Hélène could not hope for more as she saw herself surrounded by eminent savants, all eager to help her in the last great effort to make the unpublished part of her father's masterwork available to the world of learning. One can see her immersed in the outpouring of sympathy, good will, and offers of competent help. She must have been particularly happy at meeting Abel Rey for the first time. As will be seen shortly, he had most effectively helped her for the past year or so in her second campaign to secure the publication in full of the *Système du monde*. She was, of course, disappointed that, because the meeting was on a Wednesday, Dufourcq could not come from Bordeaux. To be sure she hoped that after the meeting she could still meet Dufourcq who regularly returned to Paris for the weekend.

She hardly missed Freymann whose name was conspicuously absent from the printed list of those attending the meeting. As will be clear from the next chapter, in early January 1937 Hélène hoped that Freymann would have no more to do with the *Système du monde*. "The good intentions of the Mexican leave me wholly unmoved. He can no longer dupe either me, or Mr. Rey, or you. Mme Metzger, who had less to do with him, is still ready to entertain illusions," she wrote to Dufourcq on January 14. She drew, thereby, as in a flash, a devastating portrait about a prominent publisher. That she did so for weighty reasons is the point to be dealt with in the next chapter.

6

Portrait of a Publisher

A valuable ally

A feature, curious in itself but ominous in retrospect, of Hélène's great day in Paris was the absence of the name of Freymann on the list of those who attended the meeting.[1] He might have found it impossible to be present at a gathering that was to resound with calls for a prompt publication of the *Système du monde*. To face in person a number of prominent intellectuals, and Hélène herself supported by them, would have demanded more than a thick skin. Of course, he must have received an invitation sometime in late November 1936, a time of some grave puzzlement for him. On the one hand he could but feel certain that the full publication of the *Système du monde*, if it ever were to take place, would follow a course charted by him. On the other hand he could not help having occasional misgivings for two reasons. One was that he had for some time given emphasis to monetary matters, including the subvention from the Ministry. What if the money were to be suddenly forthcoming? The second reason was more subtly troublesome. For a year or so now an independent third party had entered into his dealings with Dufourcq and Hélène. He had therefore to reckon with the possibility that those two might have already obtained inside clues about his true portrait as the publisher of the *Système du monde*. Thus, he had to face the possibility that were he to appear at that meeting, his insistence on his resolve to publish the *Système* with all possible speed would sound hollow in the ears of at least two people, Hélène and Dufourcq.

In gathering those clues the starting point was Hélène's inquiry, made in obvious desperation, as to how much subvention Freymann would need in order to begin the publication of volume VI. By mid-1935 it became clear to Hélène that only money could break the impasse, especially after Freymann referred in late February 1935 to the "original conditions" of the contract. By speaking of "conditions" instead of "contract" Freymann could but think of the subvention by the Ministry and possibly also of the help, far less substantial, from the Académie des Sciences. But at that time neither the Ministry nor the Académie seemed to be ready or able to help.

Nothing specific was, however, said until July 11, when Freymann felt impelled to state that Hélène's insistance on her financial rights perhaps made her insensitive to the "danger that exists for us in immediately publishing . . . a work of such importance at a moment when libraries, which used to buy a work of that importance and remain its chief clients, no longer have sufficient funds available and reduce their orders more and more." This defense did not dispose of the question of why Duhem's work had to be left out of important works still published, and by Hermann et Cie itself. At any rate, Freymann once more protested his own personal interest in the publication and thought that it would be a good thing if Hélène could come to Paris and discuss matters in person.

Added to the same letter was a statement of sales during 1934 which showed that a total of 17 volumes were sold of the *Système du monde* during that year and that 70, 85, 8, 8, and 7 copies remained in stock of volumes I to V respectively. During that year 186 copies were sold of *La chimie est-elle une science française?*, a good performance for a book already twenty years old. Including sales of Duhem's *Leçons de mécanique chimique,* and *Thermodynamique et chimie,* a total of almost 4,000 francs were due to Hélène as royalties. The sum was equivalent to a typical school-teacher's five month's salary. Meager as the sum was, Hélène could not dispense with it.

At any rate, in mid-August 1935 Dufourcq read in the *Journal des Débats* a report about a book, *Thales,* edited by a certain Abel Rey, director of a new Institut d'Histoire des Sciences.[2] Dufourcq immediately thought that if things were not going well with Freymann, Abel Rey might perhaps intervene. Since he could not recall that Duhem had any correspondence with Rey, he asked Hélène for information. In the same letter Dufourcq voiced his hope that the new law allowing the government to rule by decrees might improve conditions and lead to a speedy publication of the *Système du monde.*

This was the point which Hélène took up first in her letter of September 2 to Dufourcq. She felt that the new law might still leave "a work of long stretch in paralysis." Not that she had abandoned the *Système du monde.* "Two months ago I have posed to Mr. Freymann an altogether specific question about his formal and immediate intentions, letting him understand that in spite of all my desire to have him as publisher, I would go elsewhere if necessary, because I would never abandon the publication of that work." In view of the frustration she had already experienced, her resolve must have been very commendable. She also informed Dufourcq about her unwillingness to go to Paris and have direct talks with Freymann. Her reason was very much to the point: "The Mexican cannot be pinned down and never wants to give a clear answer." Hélène also knew that she had an important thing in her favor "of which I carefully avoided talking to him. In spite of the crisis you see that the *Système du monde* still sells and volumes III, IV and V are virtually out of print." She was resolved "not to authorize a new printing and reserve a second edition of the first volumes to the publisher who will complete the work."

She then turned to Dufourcq's question whether her father had any correspondence with Abel Rey. "I don't know but I don't think so," was her answer. She thought she could not at the moment "search through all of Papa's letters that would certainly contain letters from Abel Rey had he received any." At any rate she knew well the origin of her father's essay, placed at the end of the second edition of his *Théorie physique,* and assured Dufourcq that once the tranquil days returned she would look in her father's correspondence. The next major point of the letter, already seen, dealt with her plans to explore Plon as a possible publisher of her biography.

After telling Dufourcq, on September 19, that she could not find a letter from Rey, Hélène asked him: "Is not Mr. Abel Rey a bit sectarian? Is my memory wrong on this point? Would he help the publication of a work devoted entirely to the glory of Christian thought and equally to the support of the ideas of Duhem which as anyone knows, have no right to be cited in the official scientific world?" There was nothing new to report in that letter of September 19 about Freymann. At any rate, she was as grateful as ever for Dufourcq's "most valuable interest in the *Système du monde.*"

On September 30, Freymann expressed his regrets that misunderstandings continued between Hélène and himself. Things stayed where they had been for some time. On October 22, Dufourcq informed her that he had just written to Abel Rey without referring to her. "If he responds kindly . . . there will be enough time to know him well." Dufourcq had high hopes that as director of the Institut d'histoire des sciences Rey could effectively promote the publication of volume VI. Rey's reply came within three days and contained the astonishing news that since 1919 he had been thinking about ways of publishing the remainder of the *Système du monde!* Dufourcq therefore thought it best to inform Rey about the fact that the work was practically out of print and ask him to explore the size of the financial support Freymann would require. Dufourcq did not seem to know that Rey was also the director of the section on history of science in Hermann's vastly growing series of *Actualités scientifiques et industrielles*[3] and therefore the ideal man for the task.

On reading Rey's letter to Dufourcq, which the latter sent on to her, Hélène felt a surge of hope. She thought she would write to Rey, but she felt very differently about Freymann whose latest letter simply ignored the *Système du monde!* "I shall not write at all to Freymann again," she unburdened herself to Dufourcq on October 27. Once more she took the view that if Freymann were really interested in coming to an agreement with her, this could be done in letters just as well as by a visit from her to Paris. Two days later Dufourcq advised her that "this is the moment for us to be silent. Abel Rey said he would act: let us allow him to act. If by next January or February I see nothing happening I will take charge myself. Don't hesitate to nudge me again if perchance I were to forget about it."

Here was the prospect of another three or four months to be lost, a pattern too familiar to Hélène. In her letter of November 25 to Dufourcq, a letter largely taken up with the publication of her biography, one reads the lines: "I wait with disquietude for news about the results of Mr. Abel Rey's interventions. Our troubled times are not at all favorable and the coffers of the State are empty, so it seems; it will be more convenient to finance the next elections than to publish a work like that!" On the 29th Dufourcq had to admit: "From Abel Rey I have nothing and I have no right to be astonished."

No sooner had Rey's letter arrived on December 11, than Dufourcq sent it on to Hélène. Dufourcq felt inclined to recommend to her Rey's negotiations with Freymann. Their essence was that the remaining parts of the *Système du monde* would be first published in the form of fascicles, the very form of Hermann's *Actualités scientifiques et industrielles*. The publisher was willing to assume half of the cost of publication and recover the other half from sales. Production of the first fascicle would begin immediately.

In this change for the better Dufourcq saw two drawbacks: The publisher did not seem ready to undertake immediately the production of volume VI (presumably consisting of four fascicles). Further, the project meant the abandoning of the original contract. Still Dufourcq thought it was a plan worth trying, "because, if you stick to the original contract, you will be with it to the end of time, without having done anything, without having anything printed. The thing is to have things done." Dufourcq suggested that Hélène ask Freymann to assume 75% of the cost of production. With production under way, it would also be possible, so Dufourcq thought, to gather subscriptions and ask for a contribution from the Institute in the form of a prize. "The good will of Rey is evident," Dufourcq wrote and asked her to write a note of thanks to be forwarded by him to Rey, as quickly as possible "in order not to lose time." Both knew that three full years had already gone by in fruitless and intense negotiations. Neither of them suspected the number of additional fruitless years still ahead of them. Dufourcq certainly did not suspect that the card he sent to Hélène on the last day of the year would look very ironical in retrospect. There he spoke of the New Year as one to witness the publication of volume VI.

To be sure, in early February Dufourcq felt convinced, upon receiving a letter from Rey, that Freymann was ready to start publication "immediately." But this meant only that he was ready to consider a draft of a new contract on the basis of the points specified in Rey's communication now two months old. His letter of February 2, 1936, contained the ominous foreboding: "I may be wrong. Perhaps there is still some trap laid for us. I must, however, say that I do not see any." He, however, felt it to be a good idea to ask Freymann for a specification of the delay between the production of four fascicles and their being gathered together in one volume.

A week later Dufourcq thought it wise to save the contract under consideration from an impact of the threatening devaluation of the franc, once the elections were over. As it turned out Hélène was to be saved from evident contradictions in the draft of the contract submitted by Freymann.[4] Worse, Freymann included a clause about possible delays of three to four years, a clause which Dufourcq urged Hélène "not to accept at any price." On April 22 she learned that during all 1934 the sales of the *Système du monde* amounted to very little: two copies of volume I and one copy of each of the remaining four volumes. Towards the end of April, and after two letters from Rey, the draft submitted by Freymann seemed to Dufourcq "a means to disarm you," he wrote to Hélène in asking her to verify his view, a view very pessimistic indeed: "If my judgment is correct it is obvious that we must abandon the hope always dear to me, that is, to come to an understanding with Hermann about the completion of the *Système du monde*! A grave decision, but today it seems inevitable to me." Then he volunteered to ask Mr. Bourdel, an old friend of his at the publisher Bloud, who once helped him with legal advice, "to take the whole matter in his hands, and ask him to [make it possible for Bloud to] print the volumes still in manuscript, for I think we shall succeed in the end." It was an end that had to be hastened: "We have to succeed by all means, because we shall soon be, without any doubt, in a total revolution."

A publisher unmasked

At the end of May, Dufourcq could only rejoice in the publication of Hélène's biography of her father. He congratulated her for her "obstinacy." He obviously meant a particularly strong mettle. If she needed to prove it with the production of her biography, even more was she in need of it with respect to the *Système du monde* because Rey's letter of May

30th to her brought very disconcerting news. The letter was in reply to his having received a copy of Hélène's book: "I thank you from the depth of my heart for the magnificent homage you have rendered to the memory of your father, the great scientist and the great historian of science. I would like very much for his capital work to be fully published, an outcome that would indebt to him everybody interested in the history of science and especially those who work in that field." Then came lines full of revelation:

> Since the main points of the printing of the four volumes had been laid down by Hermann, to yourself and to Mr. Dufourcq, about the publication of the four volumes, I have telephoned the publisher more than fifty times. I have obtained more than ten meetings where the principal party gave me nothing tangible. I have been given, I do not how many times, promises relative to a draft of the contract. Twelve days ago I had, however, a conversation with Mr. Freymann, the principal wheel in Hermann et Fils and the husband of one of Mr. Hermann's daughters. He promised me that the contract would be submitted to you and that he would notify me about it. I am still waiting. I am tenacious and I will continue to wait.

According to Rey the publisher blamed the delay on Mr Dufourcq's request for a guarantee against the devaluation of the franc and he suggested that it might be a good idea to draw up the contract in terms of a "realigned" franc. Still, Rey had to admit that in spite of his urging the publisher to draw up a new contract in that sense, which he took also for "good sense," he could register only one result: "Nothing." A week or so later, on the Feast of Pentecost, Dufourcq informed Hélène that Rey "begged" him to take note of his letter sent to her. That letter, coupled with the "revolutionary" conditions in France, bode ill for the future of the *Système du monde*. "One must remain obstinate, nevertheless, this is the duty — by asking the Holy Spirit to give us light — and to save France."

In replying on June 10 to Rey, Hélène began with the expression of her profound gratitude for his interventions on behalf of the publication of the *Système du monde*. "Nothing in the world," she continued, "is so dear to me as that publication. I cannot think without anxiety that, for one reason or another, those precious manuscripts just might fall prey to fire. That would destroy, once and for all, the discoveries they contain." She pointed out that all her steps had been met by Hermann with "an inexplicable inertia," and with references to the "economic difficulties." But, she continued, "since the war, though there have been periods of crisis, there were also normal times of which the publisher should have taken advantage. I find it all the more difficult to explain that inertia as the published volumes are out of print or almost, in spite of their highly increased price." She repeated her absolute opposition to the photographic reproduction of any of the volumes "because the *Système du monde* forms a whole" and expressed her readiness to look for another publisher if Hermann continued in its reluctance to publish the complete work.

Four days later, she pointed out in her letter to Dufourcq that it was now clear that Rey too was "at the mercy of Hermann's inertia." The latter she described as the strategy of following up "beautiful promises with vagueness when it comes to giving firm commitment." She hoped that on reading the copy of her letter to Rey, Dufourcq would see clearly what was at the bottom of her thinking: "If nothing can be obtained from Hermann, why procrastinate with him forever instead of contacting another publisher?" Finally, she noted that she could not understand the advantage of Rey's suggestion that the signing of the contract be postponed until the fixing of the franc's new value: "It seems to me that royalties are always in terms of percentages of the sale price and become inflated if the latter is inflated." At any rate, what really concerned her was "to see published these previous volumes whose manuscripts might be destroyed, as I said to Mr. Rey, by a fortuitous accident."

Vagueness certainly characterized the first full page of Freymann's letter of June 24 to Rey in which the former complained that "half of the work would have been done, had Mlle Duhem not followed the advice of certain persons," whom he identified only with generic references to his previous communications. In the second page of his letter, thickly typed, Freymann began with the proposal that at a future fixed date, which he did not care to specify, the status of volumes still in stock, would be settled and the original edition be declared terminated. He then proposed that all the first five volumes be reissued and in fascicles at that, so as to make them available to a larger readership. There would be new title pages, a general prospectus of the whole plan, and a new partition in sheets of 16 pages so as to permit a proper start for each fascicle. While all this should have struck all the interested as a totally new plan, they could only be dumbfounded by Freymann's total silence about the production of fascicles that were to comprise volume VI. Moreover he left undefined the rate at which he would be ready to proceed with that new edition. Did he want to postpone the publication of volume VI and the rest forever?

Rey must have been perplexed because Freymann hastened to assure him that the new proposals would leave the original contract valid. Freymann, he thought, could however invoke the uncertainty of times against committing himself to a specific rate of publication. Rey might have seen things differently, had he known the original contract. He left therefore the closer examination of Freymann's proposals to Hélène. She guessed some deeper reasons behind this new and baffling maneuver of Freyman and she specified them on August 23 to Dufourcq, the only one to whom she could talk in confidence and with candor:

I must tell you my feeling: I can see but disadvantage in signing the contract as proposed by Freymann and this is why. The situation is clear, I have the contract that stipulates that Hermann must publish the *Système du monde* one volume per year. Since 1918 the publisher has refused to carry out this clause. I think, and I would like to have certainty on this point, that this gives me the right to consider the contract null and void, leaving me free to bring my volumes [and manuscripts] to another publisher. What makes things easy for me is that the work is practically out of print. Hermann suspects this, because I forbade him any new edition as long as the remaining volumes had not been published. Now with this new contract Hermann precisely wants to tie down this freedom of mine to proceed with a new edition, at the same time when concerning the publication of the remaining volumes, that alone are of interest to me, he limits himself to a vague promise, because the "conditions" are a pure excuse or a pretext not to undertake anything. Since 1918 the "events" have been a reason not to carry out a formal clause of the contract; what else would it be since no delay has been considered?

Then she came to what she guessed was the heart of the matter and, as subsequent evidence will suggest, was very much on target:

I cannot help asking myself to what length would the House of Hermann not go in order to prevent the publication of the *Système du monde*. This may seem incredible, but there is the "Jew" beneath. The old Hermann became a convert, but he did not lead all his family to the baptismal font. The volumes to be published will be crushing for anticlericalism. They will show at great length the role of Buridan and Oresme. It would be said that all this must not be allowed to appear in print.

The only blemish in this diagnosis was Hélène's use of the term Jew. She should not even have spoken of anticlericalism. She should have rather referred to the secularism generated by the Enlightenment which took science for the true savior. Implied in that tenet was the view that the Savior and the religion He inaugurated had to be first discredited in the minds of men so that the new "savior" might rise like a Phoenix after having been buried for a thousand years in the darkness of the Middle Ages. Such distinctions could not be expected from Hélène when learned and zealous Catholics remained inexplicably blind to the liberating vistas provided by Duhem. His researches, more than anything else, provided that new outlook on Western intellectual history in which the birth of science is not presented as that of Minerva's — fully armed, fully grown, and almost in a single instant, true to the scenario of a genuine myth.

Perplexities and persistence

At any rate, in mulling over the dark vistas of publication Hélène could not even consider her only escape, a legal procedure against Hermann, for which, as she put it, "I have neither the taste nor the money." Nor could she envisage a real support to come from the widespread astonishment over the "scandal of the last volumes of the *Système du monde*" as exposed in her recently published book. "What pains me," she wrote to Dufourcq, is that "*La vie catholique* did not breathe a word" about her book. "I have sent," she continued, "an inscribed copy to Jean Guiraud who was Papa's classmate [at Stanislas] and who, following Papa's death, wrote a nice article on him in 1917.[5] This time it is the silence of *La Croix*. Still it could have recalled [from the book] Papa's letter to the Père Bulliot. How many ecclesiastics would have been happy to see that presentation of the relation between science and faith by one who could talk about science with authority! But that man was not a 'democrat' and they dare even to say it! This is what

Hélène at about twenty-two
(snapshot thrice enlarged)

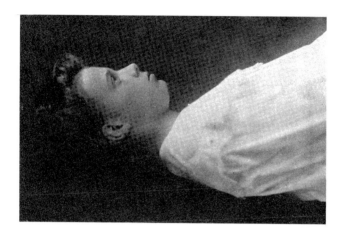

Hélène at about eleven

Hélène, about six, with her grandmother

Hélène at about eight,
with her father and grandmother

Hélène (third from left)

with Cécile Brandt, Mme A. Defauw, N. de Defauw, and Albert Defauw (c. 1922 — manual exchange re-keyed)

Le système du monde, vol. X, pp. 412-14
with corresponding ms pages.
The latter are given with a 25% reduction,
with exception of the second page,
which is enlarged by 5%

Slashes in the facsimile of the printed
text indicate the end of a ms page

LE MOUVEMENT ET LE TEMPS

En discutant les âpres problèmes qui ont trait au mouvement, Nicoletti ne se montrera, non plus, ni métaphysicien pénétrant, ni logicien rigoureux.

Ce ne sera pas faute d'érudition ; il ne se sera pas contenté de méditer les leçons d'Aristote et de son Commentateur ; des auteurs modernes, il aura lu les plus célèbres ; nous ne l'entendrons pas seulement citer Gilles de Rome et Walter Burley, dont les noms reviennent si souvent sous sa plume ; nous l'entendrons critiquer les opinions de Guillaume d'Ockam [1] et de Grégoire de Rimini [2], voire de John Wicleff [3] ; ce ne sera pas,

---

1. PAULI VENETI Exposilio super libros physicorum, lib. III, tract. I, cap. III, dubium secundum, fol. sign. p, col. b.
2. PAUL DE VENISE, ibid.
3. PAULI VENETI Op. laud., cap. cit., dubium secundum, fol. sign., p, col. c.

bien entendu, pour admettre les opinions de ces auteurs ;
plus que jamais, il restera ou prétendra, dans son *Expositio,*
rester fidèlement attaché à la doctrine du Philosophe.

Il examinera, par exemple, ce doute[1] : « Le mouvement
local diffère-t-il du mobile et de l'espace parcouru ? » —
« Remarquez, dira-t-il, que ce doute a été introduit ici à cause
de l'opinion d'Ockam, au gré de laquelle le mouvement local
ne se distingue pas du mobile, et de l'opinion de Grégoire
de Rimini, au gré de laquelle le mouvement local ne se distingue
pas de l'espace ou du lieu.

» Argumentons contre ces opinions[2], particulièrement contre
celle d'Ockam, et, tout d'abord, de la façon suivante :

» Supposons que Dieu anéantisse toutes choses, sauf la sphère
ultime, et que celle-ci continue de se mouvoir comme elle se
meut maintenant ; à chaque instant, cette sphère se comporterait, d'une manière intrinsèque, autrement qu'elle ne se comportait auparavant ; il faudrait que, d'instant en instant, elle
acquît quelque changement ; mais ce qu'elle acquiert de nouveau, ce n'est point elle-même ni quelque partie d'elle-même ;
elle acquiert donc quelque mouvement, qui est distinct d'elle-
même, et en vertu duquel l'on dit qu'elle se comporte maintenant autrement qu'elle se comportait auparavant, autrement
qu'elle se comportera tout à l'heure ; mais elle se mouvrait
alors exactement comme elle se meut à présent ; c'est donc
qu'elle acquiert déjà un mouvement local distinct d'elle-
même. »

Jean Buridan pouvait, contre la doctrine de Guillaume
d'Ockam, user d'un tel raisonnement, car il avait rompu avec
le Péripatétisme ; mais peut-il l'invoquer, celui qui prétend
soutenir les opinions du Philosophe et de son Commentateur ?
Ceux-ci ne tiendraient-ils pas pour chimérique ce Dieu qui
peut anéantir toutes choses, sauf la sphère ultime ? Et d'une
telle sphère, privée de tout lieu immobile auquel son mouvement pourrait être rapporté, diraient-ils qu'elle se meut ?

Et que dire du second argument par lequel Paul de Venise
prétend confirmer le premier ? Traduisons-le : « Dieu pourrait
anéantir toutes choses, excepté la matière première en mouvement et la sphère ultime ; il pourrait mouvoir la matière

---

1. PAULI VENETI *Op. laud.,* cap. cit., dubium secundum, fol. sign. p, col. b et c.
2. Cette argumentation est reprise, presque dans les mêmes termes, mais un
peu plus sommairement, dans *Summa philosophiæ,* pars sexta, cap. XXVII.

IV.

De mouvement et le temps.

En discutant les âpres problèmes qui ont
trait au mouvement, ~~et au temps~~, Nicoletti ne se
montrera, non plus, ni métaphysicien pénétrant
ni logicien rigoureux.

Ce ne sera pas faute d'érudition ; il ne se
sera pas contenté de ~~les~~ méditer les leçons d'Aristote et de son Commentateur ; des auteurs moder-
-nes, il aura lu les plus célèbres ; nous ne l'enten-
-drons pas seulement citer Gilles de Rome et
Walter Burley, dont les noms reviennent si sou-
-vent sous sa plume ; nous l'entendrons critiquer
les opinions de Guillaume d'Ockam [1] et de Gré. t

[1] Pauli Veneti Expositio super libros physicorum, lib. III,
tract. I, cap. III, ~~dubium secundum~~ fol. sign. p, col. c. ┤

-gorie de Rimini, Jean Buridan, voir (John Wi-

(1) a

-claff (2); ça ne sera pas, bien entendu, pour admet-

-tre les opinions de ces auteurs; plus que jamais,

il votera ou prétendra, dans son Expositio, rester

fidèlement attaché à la doctrine du Philosophe.

≡ (3)

Je examinera, par exemple, ce doute : "Le

mouvement local différa-t-il du mobile et celles-

pace parcourus?" - (Remarquez, dira-t-il, que ce

ce doute a été introduit ici à cause ces opinions

..., ... du gⁱa de laquelle le mvt.

- vement local ne se distingue pas du mobile, et

à l'opinion de Grégoire de Rimini, au qⁱ de

laquelle le mouvement local ne se distingue pas
du

(3) Pauli Veneti Op. laud., cap. cit., dubium secundum

fol. sign. p, vel. 6 et c.

(1) Saul de Venise, ibid.

(2) ~~Pauli Veneti .... op.cit.,..............................~~
~~signʳ.........................~~

(2) Pauli Veneti Op. laud., cap. cit., dubium secundum, fol. sign.
p, et c.

de l'espace ou du lieu.

(1)

» Argumentons contre ces opinions, particu-lièrement contre celle d'Ockam, et, tout d'abord, de la façon suivante :

» Supposons que Dieu anéantisse toutes choses, sauf la sphère ultime, et que celle-ci continue de se mouvoir comme elle se meut maintenant ; à chaque instant, cette sphère se comporterait, d'une manière intrinsèque, autrement qu'elle ne se com--portait auparavant ; il faudrait que, d'instant en instant, elle acquît quelque changement ; mais ce qu'elle acquiert de nouveau, ce n'est point elle-même ni quelque partie d'elle-même ; elle acquiert donc quelque ~~chose de nouveau~~ mouvement, qui est distinct d'elle-même, et en vertu ~~duquel~~ on dit qu'elle se comporte maintenant autrement qu'elle se comportait auparavant, autrement qu'elle se comportera tout à l'heure ; mais elle se mouvrait

alors exactement comme elle se meut à présent ;
c'est donc qu'elle acquiert déjà un mouvement lo
-cal distinct d'elle-même. »

Jean Buridan pouvait, contre la doctri-
-ne de Guillaume d'Ockam, user d'un tel raison-
-nement, car il avait rompu avec le Péripatétisme ;
mais peut-il l'invoquer, celui qui prétend soutenir
les opinions du Philosophe et de son Commentateur ?
Ceux-ci ne tiendraient-ils pas pour chimérique
ce Dieu qui peut anéantir toutes choses, sauf
la sphère ultime ! Et d'une telle sphère, privée de
tout lieu immobile auquel son mouvement
pourrait être rapporté, diraient-ils qu'elle se
meut ?

Et que dire du second argument par lequel
Saul de Venise prétend confirmer le premier ? Rep.
Traduisons-le : « Dieu pourrait anéantir toutes

choses, excepté la matière première en mouvement et la sphère ultime ; il pourrait mouvoir la matière première vers la sphère ultime ; ce mouvement est un acte, selon la définition du Philosophe ; partant, si ce mouvement était la matière première, la matière première serait un acte, contrairement à ce que le Philosophe et le Commentateur enseignent au premier livre des Physiques. »

Imagine-t-on le Philosophe et le Commentateur attribuant à Dieu le pouvoir de faire subsister une matière première dépouillée de toute forme et de mettre en mouvement cette matière nue ? Vraiment, pour soutenir les principes du Péripatétisme, Saul fait appel à des suppositions qui en sont la négation formelle.

Il fait appel aussi à de multiples textes d'Aristote qui, tous, distinguent nettement le mou-

première vers la sphère ultime ; ce mouvement est un acte, selon la définition du Philosophe ; partant, si ce mouvement était la matière première, la matière première serait un acte, contrairement à ce que le Philosophe et le Commentateur enseignent au premier livre des *Physiques*. »

Imagine-t-on le Philosophe et le Commentateur attribuant à Dieu le pouvoir de faire subsister une matière première dépouillée de toute forme et de mettre en mouvement cette matière nue ? Vraiment, pour soutenir les principes du Péripatétisme, Paul fait appel à des suppositions qui en sont la négation formelle.

Il fait appel aussi à de multiples textes d'Aristote qui, tous, distinguent nettement le mouvement du mobile et de l'espace

*je suis bien heureuse de
vous voir bientôt et vous
embrasse tendrement*

Hélène

Conclusion of Hélène's letter of June 8, 1911
to her father

Duhem's signature on his letter of June 7, 1991
to Hélène

Hélène's signature on her letter of March 5, 1937
to Albert Dufourcq

Hélène (third from left)
in the procession to Duhem's grave, following the dedication, in 1952, of a plaque placed on the house in Cabrespine

Pierre Duhem at about fifty-three

closes the columns of *La vie catholique* and of *La Croix*. People there are sectarian: religion and country count for them only in relation to politics."

Hélène then touched on the Spanish Civil War. The side she took can readily be guessed. She concluded by once more giving vent to her anxiety about the future fate of the *Système du monde*: "I am trembling with fear that the precious manuscript might be at the mercy of a fire, always possible, in these troubled times." The postcript of the letter was a brief report about a visit, in July, of two professors (Roy and Duffour) of the Faculté des Sciences of Toulouse: "They came in pilgrimage to the grave and house of Papa."

Hélène's next letter, of August 30, to Dufourcq began with a reference to the postcard he had sent from Ainhoa. It reminded her of her Papa "who loved to paint that charming village."[6] Then she excused her failure in not responding to an article in the *Alliance française* which Dufourcq had sent to her. "At this time, in addition to the customary work, I do the work of gardener; my days begin very early and in order to find time to read a bit I have to prolong the days until about 11 in the evening. But by then I am so much overcome by fatigue that when I want to write, I fall asleep over my paper." What a precious glimpse into her far from easy life, especially for a task such as hers! Dufourcq's good news related to Bourdel who wanted to see the table of contents of the rest of the *Système du monde*. The implicit thought that perhaps Bourdel would succeed in finding another publisher led her back to Freymann: "His game plan is clear. He will not publish the new volumes because that would have called for expenditure, but first he will do the photographic reprinting [of the first five volumes] which will keep giving him benefits without the cost of typesetting. He had already done that, without my authorization, with the first two volumes and this why he still has 68 and 84 copies of them respectively, when he should have none."

Apparently, Freymann hinted somewhere about a luxurious production of the remaining volumes because Hélène now asked: "Why such a deluxe edition? The composition is very costly because of the frequent footnotes, although texts in Greek ought to be rare in what remains to be published." Then she recalled that Doublet "who had already helped Papa" and Manville, "a former assistant of Papa who wrote to me touching letters about his old master,"[7] were ready to help her with the proofreading. She was willing to go along with any plan that assured the publication of the *Système du monde*. As to the two places, the Institute and Hermann, that let her down, the latter was far more to blame in her eyes: "Hermann gives so little evidence of being serious. It seems to me that a consciencious publisher who really wanted to publish, who would give dates and exact sums, who kept firm agreements, would perhaps obtain subvention from the Académie des Sciences. . . . It is, however, rather dangerous to count on any favor: Papa was never one to have been helped in any manner."

She then told Dufourcq about a letter she had just received from a Portuguese scholar eager to obtain a copy of the *Système du monde*. "Everywhere he is given the reply that it is out of print." It seemed to her that "the publisher wanted to let the work fall into oblivion. Yet the various articles I am receiving show that Papa is famous and the unpublished volumes are certainly the ones that are of the greatest interest, the most original part of the entire work." On reading this one cannot help wondering why the professionally trained historians of science of those years, and most of them of more recent years, let someone with no professional training whatever keep voicing, as if in a wilderness, the word about this all-important fact. Perhaps because they suspected it to be of overwhelming importance destined to overwhelm their most cherished perspectives.

Ten days later she asked Dufourcq for a few more days of reflection before writing to Rey. "Today I am receiving Mme

Doubourg who is in the area and comes here as a pilgrim in memory of the friendship which her husband had enjoyed with my father. Monday it will be twenty years ago that he left us. . . . I hope that through God's mercy he is in Heaven and from there he helps those who labor — first of all you, Monsieur — to make known his work." She was indeed so much short of professional information as to muse at the end of the same letter: "I have received this note from *Archeion* of which I hear for the first time. Could it perhaps help us?" Four months later she thought that *Archeion* would make the difference. She was right but in a sense that, fortunately for her, she could not foresee. Humans are built to endure the future only if much of it remains hidden from them.

Another publisher?

Hélène's next letter to Dufourcq, written on September 13, most likely in the evening, was marked by her thoughts about the twentieth anniversary of her Papa's death. Her feelings were worthy of the tenacious fighter her Papa was. They could take on the intensity of a steely resolve and daring at the slightest spark. The latter came, as if a sign from Heaven on the eve of that special day, from a letter of Bourdel who made a pointed reference to money available in state funds for scientific research. She thought it would be best to ask squarely about the exact sum Plon would demand for the publication of the *Système du monde* and then knock on the right door. She was ready to try anything.

Bourdel also referred to the opposition of the official University circles to her father's work. She thought that it could be countered through the rising popularity of her father: "I want no other proof than the success (rather unexpected) of my little book. When I say 'success' I do not think of sales, I don't know whether it sells well, I never dared to demand this from Plon. But I think of the great number of articles which it prompted. I do not want to boast and I do not attribute this to the book itself. It merely helped. The truth is that Papa's glory was hidden beneath ashes and that only a little puff was needed to make it come to light."

She saw that light shine again in the fact that "his discoveries in the history of science now reach the public. I have seen articles in various journals on the discoveries of Nicole Oresme, Buridan, and Albert of Saxony. In numerous journals (yesterday in the *Revue générale des sciences*[8]) strong requests were made to scientific Societies and civic powers for subsidies necessary for the publication of the part still in manuscript, the most important part of the work." She thought that officialdom itself would be unmasked by its refusal when there is money available for other things. "This would be an evident proof of a formal resolve to snuff out the truth contained in those manuscripts. I think that if that formal opposition would manifest itself in a refusal there would now be a public reaction and I would be eager to provoke it in some newspapers of the Right. But I think that if there is money, if one knocks on the right door, it will be difficult to say no."

Hélène must have felt a sacred fire taking hold of her as she began to exploit another remark in Bourdel's letter. "Certain publishing houses," she read, "would retreat in front of the official opposition of the Sorbonne." Is not hidden in this, she asked Dufourcq, "the very reason for which Hermann has, since 1917, never resumed the publication of the work, not even when the economic situation was prosperous, not even when the copies in stock were diminishing, and not even when — I have been reassured about this — the Ministry was ready to maintain the subvention and readjust it to the current value of the franc?"

Such were worthy reflections, though not to be wasted on unworthy academics. She recalled that her Papa "used to say that Hermann was the meeting place of all scientists from the Sorbonne. The old Hermann liked Papa very much and had the independence of publishing his works. The stopping of the publication of the *Système du monde* coincided with the passing of the firm from Mr. Hermann to his son. The Ministry never withdrew its subvention. Would not this be a justification for knocking on the door again?" Her last remark was the question whether, in view of what Mr. Bourdel wrote, would it not be better to get rid of Hermann and look for money afterwards?

Three days later, she begged Dufourcq's pardon if he thought her obstinate in thinking that parting with Hermann was the first step toward the eventual publication of the *Système du monde*. Judging the situation from a great distance she could easily persuade herself about the merit of her question: "How could a few thousand francs be refused if they are needed for the publication of a work which such an elite acclaims in France and abroad?" She was to be disappointed in thinking that a sum equivalent to the yearly earning of two or three laborers would be easily forthcoming.

She was in for further painful disappointments. Her letter of September 17 to Plon provoked an immediate negative reply. As Dufourcq wrote to her two days later, "that door was now closed." Further, it remained true what Dufourcq had pointed out to her on September 1, namely, that "no publishing house would better serve the glory of your father's work than Hermann would." As shown by Hélène's letter of September 17 to Dufourcq, she was perplexed indeed, partly because she knew that Rey was still eager to give his services. The question she posed to Dufourcq was whether Rey should be made privy to her tentative plans to break with Hermann. She trusted Rey partly because of Rey's readiness to speak of Freymann's bad faith.

Her letter of October 30 to Dufourcq was prompted by her reading the latest volume of his *Avenir du Christianisme*, a volume dealing with the Church in the 17th century. She thought of that century as having special appeal in France to many who, like herself, could trace their family roots that far. She possibly thought her own predicament reflected in the

upheavals witnessed by that century as she commented to
Dufourcq: "To every age its sadness and struggles." She sent to
him another packet of articles and reviews written about her
father under the impact of her own book. They further
strengthened her dream which, although intensely pursued by
then for almost three years, had not come an inch closer to
reality. She had, as has been seen, very specific ideas about the
true cause of a delay that would have caused almost anyone else
to despair. In the letter which Rey wrote to her on November
10 she found an authentic confirmation of those ideas.

Old hostilities and new hope

"I had a conversation," Rey began, "with Freymann who is the
true head of Hermann Publishers. The conversation was rather
stormy. Finally he promised me to write to you and set forth
clearly his project. I confess that I am rather reluctant to believe
it." The essence of the project was that since the remainder of
the *Système du monde* was to appear first in fascicles, the first five
volumes had to be cut up into fascicles with a new pagination
in order to assure a proper start for each fascicle. "I admit,"
Rey continued, "that I do not understand the need for such a
procedure. Nothing would be simpler than to reprint all the
five volumes as they are and cut them into fascicles, in common
accord between you and him. This would preserve the proper
sequence of pages and would permit the immediate production
of volume VI first in fascicles and then as a whole."

About Freymann's insistance that he could not start except
by producing volumes I - V in fascicles, Rey could only think
that it was due to some "personal considerations" on Freymann's part. "It is difficult to report here all his reasons which,
I believe, are mainly financial. . . ." Rey did not seem to notice
that three lines later he began to provide the evidence to the
contrary. "To my great astonishment, I have found him reticent
when the matter of subventions came up. He told me that Mr.
Cavallier (who is now, through a subtle maneuver, at least for

this year, director [of the Centre Nationale de la Recherche Scientifique])[9] was not in favor, nor was Perrin for reasons as much scientific as political. I see that basically Freymann is afraid that subventions would obligate him to publish and, in my opinion, he would rather not have them. He would not, however, admit this. . . ."

Rarely were three dots more expressive both of being in full view of an unconscionable tactic and of the sadness felt over it. "I am therefore," Rey continued, "pessimistic, for the moment, because he does not want to begin the publication of the manuscript parts — or he cannot do it financially." The latter reason, as will be seen shortly, should have appeared unconvincing to Rey precisely because of his connection with Hermann as the editor of the history of science section of its very prosperous series, *Actualités scientifiques et industrielles*. He was, however, certain that it was best to look for another publisher. In proof of his confidence in Hélène and of his own probity, Rey continued: "I am telling you all this very confidentially because my relations with Hermann et Cie prevent me from pursuing that course. But, in good conscience, I am unable to tell you anything about this plainly." Rey's own feelings found expression even in the formal conclusion of his letter: "Allow me, Mademoiselle, to convey to you, with the expression of my sadness, my very respectful regards."

Hélène's sadness, which could easily be imagined, did not diminish her resolve. In reporting to Dufourcq on November 12, she kept her calm while deploring the news about Cavallier, who, so she recalled, had a year or two earlier assured her of his support. "This is discouraging! . . . as everything, in this moment, is discouraging — but this is not a sentiment to nourish. It is better to continue the struggle!"

Dufourcq's long reply of November 14 began with an affectionate note: "Be sparing with your apologies about your importuning me. See in me the old uncle who had for the father you miss so much as much affection as admiration and

who sees in young Hélène one of his innumerable achievements." That he considered her a member of the family came
through his way of reporting about the latest, fifth, child of his
eldest daughter, Henriette, "who as Mimi amused your father
so much."

As to the struggle, Dufourcq tried to put the best light on
a patently hopeless situation. More to the point was his
comment on Rey's words on Cavallier and Perrin. He reported
that Cavallier, whom he described as one "ready to resort to
admirable legal acrobatics," was "wholly contemptuous of your
father's work." Regarding Perrin, he knew that he belonged to
the group around Langevin "about whom I know what he
thought of your Papa. Undoubtedly these fellows will not
ignore the matter. And today they are the rulers. This is certain." Dufourcq should have added that Langevin was the
director of the theoretical physics section of the *Actualités
scientifiques et industrielles* while Perrin directed its section on
atomic physics. As such they often met Freymann from whom
they certainly learned about Hélène's efforts to secure the
publication of the *Système du monde*. It is difficult to imagine
that Freymann had not been strongly influenced by their
hostility toward Duhem and his ideas. In fact, as early as 1904
Langevin had mounted a virulent attack against Duhem's
alleged efforts to "medievalize" the study of physics.[10] It is just
as unlikely that the same group had not been alert to the most
dangerously "medieval" contents of the volumes of the *Système
du monde* still to be printed.

Dufourcq thought that the advice of Rey, in whom he
expressed full confidence, about turning to another publisher
was worth considering. He also saw in him, together with
Madame Metzger-Bruhl, the best and only avenues "towards
the scientific world, non-Catholic and Catholic, international
and national." As to the publisher to contact, Dufourcq thought
of Vrin, certainly a Catholic, and the publisher (under the
directorship of the Père Théry, a Dominican, and Gilson,

professor at the Collège de France) of the collection, *Histoire de la philosophie du Moyen Age*. Vrin, Dufourcq thought, might even consider a co-publication with Alcan, which, not being a Catholic publishing house, had ties with officialdom. "A confidential contact with Vrin seems to me the most opportune move at this moment."

In her reply of November 23, Hélène expressed her surprise over "the hostility of Cavallier" and "Perrin's omnipotence." These two factors brought her to believe that behind Freymann's "equivocal attitude" there lay something more serious: "Hermann was given the task of sabotaging the publication at any price. Berthelot has his troops in the successors." She informed Dufourcq about her having sent three copies of volume III of the *Système du monde* to Vrin. "Vrin was ready to pay for them, which I accepted. I can certainly use that money." She hardly ever let Dufourcq know anything specific about her daily financial struggles. The suggestion about Alcan seemed to her a good one, all the more so as Alcan was the publisher of Mme Hélène Metzger-Bruhl's books. She thought that perhaps Emile Borel, a classmate of her Papa in the Ecole Normale Supérieure, might be a good contact with officialdom to obtain subventions. Borel had just read her book and sent a gracious letter, with pleasant reminiscences about his former classmate. Finally, she assured Dufourcq about her readiness to follow his advice which was inspired by his having "the cause of the publication of Papa's work so much at heart."[11] As to herself, "I make it my task to forget that I am his daughter, in order to see the matter only from the scientific and French viewpoint. This is enough to make me revolt!"

The end of November seemed to bring final deliverance. "I believe, this is it," began Dufourcq's letter of November 28. It informed Hélène about his meeting, the day before, with Vrin. The latter was informed in full about the story with Hermann and the fact that no official subvention could be expected. "Vrin is with your Papa's work. He perceives its

greatness, and I think I am not adventurous in stating to you
that he has the sincere desire to bring that work to completion.
I have sensed that very desire in him. He even thinks it is
possible to begin with volume VI." Still, Vrin had to wait for
the return of Gilson, at the beginning of January, from America. "But Gilson will surely be favorable," Dufourcq went on,
probably on the basis of what he had heard from Vrin. "Gilson
seems to have had the intention about a dozen years ago of
considering the project." Vrin himself thought of publishing
one volume every two years, perhaps one a year. He was also
given assurance that Dufourcq himself and Manville would take
care of the proofreading. After all this, the postscript would
appear like a silver lining in silvery clouds: "Vrin told me in his
very words: the chances are 99% against 100% that we come to
an agreement." Rarely was an appraisal, realistic in all appearance, so much in error in spite of the fact that Vrin's only
concern was about a possible legal battle with Hermann. Vrin
was in fact so eager as to ask Dufourcq to transmit to Hélène
the money due for the three copies of volume III. Dufourcq in
turn was eager to urge Hélène to send a formal notice to
Freymann about the legal obligation of Hermann et Cie to
resume publication one volume per year.

Most welcome as was all this news, Hélène did not reply
immediately. By December 1 a reply from her could have been
in the hands of Dufourcq who might have started wondering
a few days later about not having received anything. The fact
was that the latest issue of the *Revue universelle* contained an
article about a new author's law which gave many second
thoughts to Hélène. Only if the new law was not retroactive
did she have any chance of wresting from Hermann the manuscripts. Even then she could face a costly legal battle: "I live
from day to day and a litigation of this kind would put me on
the street." She thought that perhaps Hermann would be
satisfied with the first five volumes and let go of the remaining
volumes still in manuscript. In that case, however, a new title

would have to be found for the second part and "would have thereby cut in two a work whose composition is of such beautiful unity. But is not this damage less serious than to let that work be buried and fall into oblivion?"

Hélène thought that Gilson's absence was a blessing in disguise as it gave her time for reflection. She recalled that Mr. Jordan had spoken to her, years earlier, of Gilson's intention to publish the manuscripts. "But at present Mr. Jordan does not want to forgive me for having said that my father was not a democrat and that he was anti-dreyfusard!" The fact was that at the moment, as before and after, Hélène, the valiant fighter, failed to understand that in order to win a war it was not necessary to win all the battles and even less important to correct one's very allies on any and all detail. Her impetuousness failed to discover most genuinely "democratic" aspects in her Papa's comportment and thinking. Unfortunately, then as now, certain labels did not easily lend themselves to a balanced interpretation.

"Dear Mademoiselle and Friend, have no doubt. I shall do everything so that you will have no expenditure whatever, not even any threat of [court] costs," Dufourcq hastened to reassure her on December 11. "Your old 'uncle' sends you his heartfelt good wishes for Christmas." Hélène must have approached Christmas in a very cheerful mood. The meeting which the French Group of the Association Internationale d'Histoire des Sciences was to devote to her Papa's memory was only a month away. Whatever her uneasiness about her presence there, she knew it was to be her great day. She perhaps thought that on that day she might even announce the publication by Vrin of at least the remainder of her Papa's great work.

As the day of that meeting approached, she felt a groundswell of good will rising towards her. Tangible evidences of it were the topic of her last letter to Dufourcq in 1936. Her own book sparked wonderful results. "This morning," she wrote, "I have received a most lovely letter, a letter also most laudatory of my Papa's work, from someone totally unknown to me, Georges Lecomte, to whom Plon had a sent a copy of my book." She also wrote to Dufourcq about the freshly published book, *L'Eglise et la science,* by Louis de Launey, a geologist member of the Académie des Science, which contained a good popularization of her father's findings in the history of science.[12] Yet, she put de Launey in the Catholic "Front populaire," that is, among Catholics ready to collaborate with the government. That her father's work will have to be published with the help of that "Front" may make "my dear Papa, and his dear masters of the 14th century, laugh in heaven. But I hope that they will obtain for us God's blessing on our efforts so that we may succeed."

Apart from Hadamard, always ready to help, she listed a recent article in *Action française* by its editor, Gonzague Truc, on her father's work together with an appeal for the publication of the rest of the *Système du monde.*[13] It would now have been Hadamard's turn to smile forgivingly for having been put in that virulently anti-Semitic company. Even more forgiving would have been the smile of Mme Metzger-Bruhl, the last major subject of Hélène's letter to Dufourcq: "Finally you will see all the interventions which that amiable Jewish woman, with whom I happened to enter into correspondence, plans to take for the diffusion of Papa's ideas. Her small book, *Les concepts scientifiques,* of which she sent me a copy and which I have read, is most interesting and shows her to be a disciple of my father. Who would have thought that such support would come from distant relations of Alfred Dreyfus! . . . How unforeseeable is life and what contrasts does it offer! Add to all this, in order to complete the story, the beautiful article by Jean Guiraud in *La Croix!*"[14] She must have now realized that she had criticized that paper a bit prematurely.

Her thoughts returned to Mme Metzger-Bruhl: "Mme Paul Tannery has written to me the finest accolade about her: 'though an Israelite, hers is a correct and pure soul.' This can be felt in her letters and I feel great sympathy for her, without knowing her." She failed to realize the patronizing touch of her remarks and, more importantly, the injustice lurking in Mme Tannery's concession. Her concluding words were about the winter. She hoped that the Dufourcqs, including the "machurés," would weather it in comfort. Although snow covered the surrounding mountains, she basked in the glow of the coming meeting in Paris, where she hoped not to encounter Freymann. She felt she had at last seen through him as one who had no more chance of duping her again, and not even such seasoned academics as Abel Rey and Dufourcq. Hers was the practical certainty that the *Système du monde* had at long last a new and trustworthy publisher.

7

Victory Snatched by War

An Avertissement typeset

Almost immediately after that great day was over, it became clear that Vrin would not publish the work. Gilson's advice to Vrin, if asked and offered, would have most likely matched the diffidence about Duhem's apparently positivist philosophy he had just voiced in a prominent though not French context.[1] But even if Gilson had been favorable, there would have remained the question of whether it was possible, without a major legal battle, to wrest the rights from Hermann & Cie. Also, words about the success of the January 17 meeting must have convinced Freymann that considerations of public relations alone demanded a concrete start with the production of volume VI. Only in such a way could he put an end to speculations about his absence at that meeting.

Things seemed to move suddenly in high gear. In fact, around the weekend of January 21, Hélène and Freymann had several conversations. Most likely, Abel Rey and Hélène Metzger made Freymann understand his duty to suggest a meeting. This may be the background for an undated letter by Rey, a reply to Hélène's words of appreciation for his good services. Rey was self-effacing: "I have rendered but a small part of what is owed to the memory of Pierre Duhem by all who work in the field which he had so marvelously deciphered, and, in a more general sense, by all whose work touches on philosophy and on the physical and mathematical sciences. I beg you to accept the expression of my respect and admiration." The last words may have referred to the speech Hélène delivered at that meeting.

At any rate, Hélène had hardly arrived in Cabrespine when she received a letter, dated February 2, from Freymann. It began with a reference to the "various conversations we had concerning the publication of the *Système du monde.*" Curiously, Freymann did not mention royalties as he turned to the original contract of June 21, 1913, although he spoke of it as a document "which in our view retains all its validity." He promised a full account of all sales of the first five volumes as of December 31, 1936. He then promised a reprinting of the first five volumes, both as single volumes (each in 700 copies) and as 27 fascicles in the series, *Actualités scientifiques,* under three subdivisions.[2] Then followed art. 5 in which Freymann, in direct departure from the original contract, offered 10 percent royalties both for the new printings (in volumes and in fascicles) of the first five volumes and also for copies of the original edition of the first five volumes still in stock. The same royalties were to be paid for volumes and fascicles of the still unpublished part.

Freymann promised to produce the unpublished part, "whose manuscripts are at the Institute," at the rate of "at least one volume per year." Hélène was to assume responsibility for proofreading. "As soon as these proposals are accepted by you," Freymann continued, "we shall proceed to the reprinting of the first five volumes in a second edition and to the typesetting of the sixth volume, so that the 27 fascicles may appear at the same time as the 28th fascicle, the first of the still unpublished part." Then Freymann expressed his confidence that these details "faithfully reproduced the substance of our conversations."

Hélène immediately sent Freymann's letter to Dufourcq who heavily penciled it. His remarks indicated that he was not present at the conversations between the two. He urged Hélène to request an inventory with payment by March 1. Most importantly, he took issue with art. 5. "You reject art. 5 which modifies your father's original contract. By referring to the late Mr. Hermann's loyalty to your father, you should demand that Freymann pay you 40 percent royalties for all copies of the first five volumes published. You can agree to 10 percent royalties for volumes VI and those to follow."

Hélène must have been surprised to receive on February 6 the full account of all copies sold of the first five volumes during 1936. The total was 10 copies (two copies of each volume) and, as each sold for 210 francs, her royalties of 40 percent were properly calculated as 840 francs. The statement also contained the information that 66, 82, 5, 5, and 4 copies of volumes I to V respectively, or a total of 162 copies, were still in stock of the first edition. Hélène did not have to be a mathematician to realize that the eventual sale of 162 copies would guarantee her almost fourteen thousand francs, or the annual salary of a university professor at that time.

Two days later she sent by registered mail her long reply to Freymann. She first insisted that the fascicles could only appear under a general title exactly conforming to the main title on all the five volumes already published. This meant that no fascicle was to carry the name of another scientist as a general editor of the series. After specifying minor details about the price of each fascicle and their time of printing, Hélène turned to art. 5 which, as she began, "has modified, to my sole disadvantage, the contract to which we, you and I, have declared ourselves to remain in conformity." Your proposition, Hélène continued,

would deprive me of three-fourths of the 40% royalties due to me on the copies still in stock. This 40% for the last 100 copies of the first printing of each volume was the sole recompense [my father demanded] as the first 400 volumes were sold by you to your sole benefit. I would be most pleased to donate to you that difference of 30% on all volumes [copies] still in stock , but I regret I am not in a situation to do so. Therefore I fully count on your sense of justice to recompense me in conformity with the spirit of the contract of June 21, 1913. As to the fascicles and the other volumes of the second edition and to the first edition of the fascicles and volumes VI and following, you will give me 10% of the sales. I would be much obliged if you were to express your agreement on these different points to which I have called your attention by specifying them and at the same time I expect, from your perfect sense of justice and from your courtesy, an acceptable solution to art. 5 on which we are in disagreement. As soon as I receive your reply, I shall let [the Institut] transfer to you the manuscript of volume VI.

In the postscript Hélène reminded Freymann of his promise to give her, prior to her departure from Paris, the sum due for the sales of copies during 1936. She was willing to excuse Freymann for his failure to do so with a reference to the brevity of her stay. It took another ten days before Hélène received that sum.

Although Hélène failed to receive a quick reply from Freymann, she might have given authorization to Dufourcq to take the manuscript of volume VI to Freymann. She must have learned from Dufourcq that the manuscript had been handed over to Freymann, otherwise she would not have referred to this as a fact in her letter of February 15 to Freymann. In the same letter she voiced her hope that the typesetting would start promptly. She expected galleys so expeditiously as to ask for three sets of proofs. The third was to be kept by O. Manville, professor of physics at the University of Bordeaux and a former student of Duhem, who had volunteered to read the proofs

once they had been corrected by Hélène.[3] She then noted that
of her father's two photographs she had sent in her letter of
February 8, "there could be no question about the importance
of the first where all those who saw my father in his customary
posture of paging through a book, would easily recognize
him."[4] As to his signature, she went on, "you have it at the
bottom of all his letters. It always has a remarkable neatness, and
therefore it is unnecessary that I send you a sample."

From Dufourcq she had also learned that Freymann
thought of asking a prominent scientist to write a preface to the
new edition and to volume VI. "I am informing Mr. Dufourcq
by the same mail," she wrote to Freymann,

> that I am formally opposed. No one, either in France or
> abroad, has the qualification to present the *Système du
> monde* of Pierre Duhem. A preface of that kind would
> represent a real impropriety which would repeat the rather
> unpardonable one connected with the [re-issuing of
> Duhem's] *Thermodynamique et chimie* where Mr. Boutaric
> thought it natural to give his own name as if he had been
> its author. Therefore, on that point my opposition is
> categorical. The new edition shall appear in a form identi-
> cal with the first, save for the *avertissement* the text of which
> I have already sent to you. In the same way the publication
> of fascicles should appear under the general title of *Système
> du monde* . . . etc, by Pierre Duhem, and not in a series that
> would carry the name of its director.

As late as February 23, there was yet no reply from
Freymann. Hélène sent a registered letter, in which she
requested from Freymann a formal report on the immediate
start of the work of production: "As I have always written to
you, the new edition which you plan of the first five volumes
will not have my approval except in conjunction with the
publication of the subsequent volumes, still unpublished. The
first fascicle of the second edition must therefore have a short

avertissement announcing that publication. This, so you have told me, is absolutely also your intention."

Freymann sent his reply on the 26th. Concerning art. 5 he did not budge an inch. He promised payment of 10% royalties within four months after the end of each calendar year and added: "As you know from the inventory [sent on Feburary 2] the number of copies still in stock is not large at all. For the loss which you think you will suffer, you will be largely compensated by the new edition and by the publication of the volumes to follow." What this meant was that either Hélène agreed or publication would be postponed indefinitely.

Hélène had no choice but to make a full handwritten copy of Freymann's letter and send it to Dufourcq. In her covering letter she told Dufourcq about her readiness to accept Freymann's terms. She took the view that since most of the 66 and 82 copies of volumes I and II respectively came from a second printing (done around 1926) she should demand 40% royalties only for copies, a total of 14, from the original printing. She calculated the 30% difference to be 882 francs which she hoped to obtain from Freymann. But she did not make this a condition. "I shall therefore send my approval to Freymann and I would ask, as indemnification, this sum of 882 francs which should not be enormous for him while it is no small amount for me. What do you think?"

She thanked Dufourcq in advance for going to the Institut and carrying the manuscripts of all the remaining volumes to Freymann. "I tell you once more about my gratitude for the trouble you are going to take, but I know that you will not re-read these pages, written by your friend, without emotion." Most importantly, she thanked God that "in these times of crisis, threat, and uncertain future, the publisher is so certain of success that he will bring out the work of my dear Papa. Now one of the principal tasks of my life will be realized." Attached to that letter was her formal authorization of the Institute to remit in Dufourcq's hands all the manuscripts of the *Système de monde* so that he may hand them over to Hermann et Cie.

The next day she sent to Dufourcq the text of her introduction to the new edition, asking for suggestions to modify it here and there. "You may be surprised that I thank the publisher, but this appeared to me the only way of making clear that no subvention whatever came forth for the publication of the *Système du monde*, and that the publisher can act businesslike, but [as for] the Institute! . . ."

The only thing that came from the Institute was Picard's typewritten letter, dated March 9, 1937, stating the reception by Dufourcq of the manuscript of volume VI. Apparently even in this respect there had been a misunderstanding, of which many more were to come. Still, in the long run it had to appear a blessing that only the manuscript of volume VI had been handed over to the publisher.

For the moment everything seemed to go ahead at great speed. On March 10 Freymann informed Hélène that he had just received from the printers the proofs of her introduction or *avertissement* and that earlier that day he had been visited by Dufourcq who brought the manuscript. Freymann fully agreed about which of the two photos to use and promised quick work on Duhem's signature. As to the final small detail of differences about royalties, he again was evasive. He merely noted that the volumes in question had not been sold yet and that their actual price would have to be co-ordinated with the price of the new volumes.

Hélène was not convinced, but for the moment her thoughts were dominated by having under her very eyes the *avertissement* typeset:

> The first edition of this work appeared in 1913. In the foreword that opened volume I, Pierre Duhem had written: "The work whose publication we undertake today, will have vast proportions, *provided God gives us the strength*

to complete it." This hope of his was not granted. God decided otherwise, because Pierre Duhem died and the work he had undertaken was not completed. However, the proportions that already frightened him in 1913, had been exceeded. While he thought to present the history of cosmological doctrines from Plato to Copernicus in eight volumes, he had completed the tenth volume when death surprised him. Still he had not reached the goal he had fixed for himself.

Of these ten volumes only five have appeared so far. They now form this second edition. The postwar economic difficulties did not allow the publisher to continue with the publication and the manuscripts of five volumes were deposited, at our initiative, into the keeping of the Académie des Sciences, until the time when they would finally be published.

We are grateful to Hermann et Cie that, in spite of the difficulties still present, they responded to the wish of French and foreign historians of science and undertook today, at the same time when the first five volumes are republished, the publication of the sequel given them by Pierre Duhem.

Cabrespine, March 10, 1937   Hélène Pierre-Duhem

On March 15 she wrote to Freymann and made firm claims on that sum of 882 francs. Three days later came Freymann's reply. He began by pointing out that he and Dufourcq did not have in mind a preface by a prominent scientist but a collection of favorable views on the *Système de monde.* Then after complaining about Hélène's "categorical tone," he protested his good will and sincerity: "I register with pain that I have not succeded, in spite of all my efforts, to convince you of my good will and the admiration I have for your father. I assert categorically that I would not be capable of doing anything that would in the slightest do harm to the name of Mr. Duhem." He then stated his readiness to disburse the sum of 882 francs. Finally, he assured her that all the covers of

the fascicles and volumes he would send to her for proofreading
would conform in full to the specifications set by her.

In her reply of March 19 Hélène apologized for her tone,
referred to her tight financial situation, and expressed hope that
"nothing could now delay the reprinting of the first five
volumes and the typesetting of the sixth, as our agreement is
now complete." If she now thought that after her two-year-
long dealings, stretching over 1935 and 1936, she had made a
rash judgment in her letter of January 17 to Dufourcq that,
neither she, nor he, nor Abel Rey would again be "duped" by
Freymann, she was indeed very wrong.

A year goes by

Two months later, on May 25, to be specific, Freymann
informed Hélène that "in a few days" she would receive the
galleys of the first fascicle (corresponding to little more than 100
pages) of the sixth volume of the *Système du monde*, together
with proofs of the covers of the five fascicles of volume I. In
another ten days, she would have the proofs of "all the
elements that would give a clear picture about the entire new
edition." She was also assured that concerning anything not to
her liking, he "would do all to give her satisfaction."

The following day came half a dozen prints of the photograph of Duhem standing in front of his bookcase, with a book
in his hand. Added was the information that the printer,
Barnéoud, promised to send "shortly" the first galleys of
Volume VI. On June 10 there followed the improved version
of the photos and six days later Freymann hastened to forward
Barnéoud's letter with a reference there to the galleys to be sent
very shortly.

Meanwhile a letter came from Louis Blanc, the old parish
priest in Cabrespine, now recovering from a long sickness in Le
Castans, who began by apologizing for being late in sending
word to the author of *Un savant français*. What struck the abbé
Blanc most in the book concerned details about Duhem's care

for the lowly, and his letter to the Père Bulliot "where he presents irrefutable arguments against an alleged antagonism between science and religion, and with a firm mastery of the subject he proposes a plan, suggests ideas about a rational triumph of Catholicism." He then volunteered a detail about the Huc affair: "Many people wondered how a father, so high in the Republican ranks, could suggest to his son to push the dust in the libraries when all the able-bodied men of his generation chose the trenches for domicile." After noting a printing error in the book, the good abbé continued: "I cannot help comparing Duhem to the great figure of the Old Testament, to that Moses, who died before he could enter the Promised Land. . . . Since the war and its dangers led to a lessening of sectarianism, Duhem would have, had he lived, been rehabilitated and given a chair in the Capital where he could have unfolded all his valor."[5]

About the same time a strange shadow seemed to fall on the promised land which Hélène hoped to reach soon. The promised galleys were delivered by Barnéoud to Freymann but with a note that owing to the reorganization of the printing shop, the rate at which the rest of the galleys were supposed to come was no longer feasible. At any rate, the first small installments of the galleys came and this was enough for Hélène to be filled with joy. She sat down, for the first time in her life, to proofread a highly academic work. She noticed misprints of Greek words and even some Gallicisms, no longer customary. Late that month she sent all the corrected galleys with the manuscript to Dufourcq with queries concerning those points.

On June 26 Dufourcq hastened to assure her that she was on the right track with her observations. The next day Dufourcq wrote: "It is today that for the first time [in many years] I have looked at the exquisite handwriting of your Papa. With what emotion, you can imagine! With all my heart I give thanks to God!" He asked for Manville's address in Bordeaux and told Hélène that he would keep the manuscripts until the final proofreading had been done.

Duhem's handwriting was indeed exquisite and free of corrections to an astonishing degree throughout the manuscript. Its pages reproduced in this book should convey the fact that neither the copy-editor, who marked up the manuscript for the printer, nor the printer could have had an easier job. On that basis alone it was reasonable to expect all the proofs of volume VI to be on hand by the end of the summer, at the latest. Hélène indeed felt so sure as to publish a notice about the project in the *Express du Midi* in Carcassonne.[6] On receiving a clipping of the article from Hélène, Dufourcq commented, on July 3, by tying together the expertise shown by Hélène in proofreading and the broader significance of the project itself as set forth by her in that article.

Obviously, she used an old letterhead of her Papa, because Dufourcq began:

> What a surprise, what a moving surprise, dear and excellent friend! And what a source of emotion is that letterhead from the Faculté des Sciences de Bordeaux, with 'Physique théorique' printed on it. And what a joy is mine as I keep reading the article in the *Express du Midi!* I would note, à propos the words you send me concerning the galleys, how much your handwriting recalls that of your father! But there is more to all this than mere calligraphy. By the luminous clarity with which you handle the points you touch upon, by the concise comment with which you bring to a close each paragraph, by the striking expressions aimed at retaining the reader's attention, by the art with which you are able to refer to the actual crisis of the country where you live, by the history [of a publication] you want to present to the reader, one can very well see that the author of the article knows of whom and through whom she speaks.

Dufourcq seemed to be more pleased by that article than by the galleys themselves (which is to say a great deal) as he concluded: "May the good Lord send more 'Pierre' and more daughters of such father!"

On August 12 Freymann notified Hélène that Barnéoud had finished five more installments of the typesetting of volume VI and promised her to speed up the work as much as possible. Meanwhile Hélène informed Hélène Metzger about the progress and received from her in early September a reply which began with a praise of Freymann as one "who had set aside the funds necessary for the work." After noting the need to have as many scientific publications as possible speak of the project, she added: "We have almost achieved our aim; let us see to it that it is effectively accomplished in order to rejoice fully." She thanked Hélène for sending her a copy of the third edition of La théorie physique together with a batch of offprints of Duhem's articles. In return she instructed the publishing house Alcan to send various books of hers to Cabrespine. It was clearly her friendly feelings for Duhem's daughter that made her ask: "Do you think that it is possible to do research in Cabrespine?" And, thinking of the need to have periodicals and sourcebooks on hand, she asked again: "Or do you already have a large library of your own?"

On reading this Hélène could not simply smile as she did when, in writing the biography of her Papa, she recalled an American publication where he had been identified as "Professor at the University of Cabrespine."[7] Now she must have thought that perhaps it was not the best idea to have given most of her Papa's books to the Library of the University of Bordeaux. Her regret might have been even greater had she known that there the priceless collection was not kept together and, if one may add, not even a list is available today of the titles in question. And she must have shuddered on thinking about her learned friend's reaction were she to find only one bookcase in the entire house, to say nothing of her very simple, almost primitive, living conditions. In 1937 electricity was still the exception, not the rule in that little village, which no automobile could reach before the early 1920s.

It was in those conditions and in a place far removed from the world of the learned, that Hélène kept correcting the galleys of volume VI and the covers of all the fascicles into which the first five volumes were to be divided in addition to being printed also as single volumes. On October 9 Freymann sent word that could easily make her think that perhaps towards the end of the year, or very early in 1938, the first five volumes of the *Système du monde* would appear in second edition and also as twenty some fascicles, together with volume VI:

> I have the pleasure to tell you that we have finished the reprinting of the first five volumes which now await at the binder the items which you have in your hands. In a few days you will receive the covers of the volume which Barnéoud is typesetting and who reproduced exactly the text of the older volumes.

As it turned out, ten full years later the sheets of those five volumes were not yet entirely printed and were still to be sewn together. Freymann's letter of October 30 provided further evidence of great progress: "Under separate cover I am sending you further galleys of volume VI which I beg you to correct." That set of galleys she may have corrected prior to her departure to Mas de Marin for a visit with uncles, aunts, and cousins on her mother's side.

Hélène returned to Cabrespine on November 17 and ten days later she wrote to Dufourcq that "for seven days another big package of galleys has been waiting on my desk to be proofread." She had her hands full. She had to give catechism lessons and attend in Carcassonne a lecture by a catechist from Paris on the art of bringing the catechism to the level of very young children. In addition "I was named vice-president of the Royalist Young Ladies of Aude and I have indeed much to do." She could not do much politicking even if she wanted to: "The Société des Amis des Sciences reduced my yearly pension and I have therefore to enhance my efforts to bring more out of my little property and increase the number of rabbits I raise, which I did so far only for our domestic use. In addition I have promised to write several articles."

In the rest of her long letter she spoke of her efforts to put together her father's correspondence concerning the publication of the *Système du monde*. The project, as will be seen shortly, originated with Dufourcq, who in a conversation with Freymann thought that volume VI might be properly introduced in such a way. Putting together that correspondence may have been her first systematic probing into her father's vast scientific correspondence,[8] but she was very much to the point in writing to Dufourcq that the steps leading to the publication involved correspondence only with Hermann, the Père Bulliot, Darboux, and Bayet. Going through those letters she found that the Père Bulliot appointed as his literary executor his cousin, the abbé Mulsant, superior of the Institution Sainte-Marie in St Chamond (Loire): "But since that abbé Mulsant may himself be dead, where could the correspondence of the Père Bulliot be found?"[9]

This question contained more than meets the eye. It raised the specter of an unforgivable neglect on the part of the intellectual world, and especially of Catholic French intellectuals, to set up a committee in charge of collecting Duhem's letters. Hélène too should have felt some remorse of conscience. Hers was a unique opportunity while at Sainte-Agnès during much of the 1920s to contact friends of her father because some of them would have certainly helped if prompted by her. Now she was faced with the nearly impossible. At any rate, the correspondence she had put together, and reproduced here as an Appendix, witnessed to her born abilities as a researcher and writer.

And so did the list she had composed of persons, institutions, and periodicals that were to be recipients of the 50 complimentary copies of each volume to be printed. In fact Freymann himself asked her to work on that list, an all too clear sign that he too expected a publication in the spring of 1938 at the latest. In fact, after having met with Freymann on November 18, Dufourcq wrote to Hélène: "I have given him the galleys (up to 40) with permission to break them into pages. And we have talked at length and in very friendly fashion. It seems to me wise and just to thank him for the vigor with which he follows up the printing of volume VI." It was during that conversation that Dufourcq asked Freymann whether it would not be a good idea to ask Hélène to put together her father's correspondence about the publication of the *Système du monde* and found Freymann most receptive.

The postscript of the letter carried an item even more important in retrospect. There Dufourcq reported that "Freymann spoke of the persistence of hostility which your father had to face." This could only indicate that not a few of the prominent scientists and philosopher-historians of science, of whom many turned up every month in Freymann's offices, expressed their displeasure on hearing from him that Duhem's great work would be published in full at long last. Freymann's range of gathering information was in fact so wide as to be able to tell Dufourcq that one of the very few who had great admiration for Duhem was F. Enriques, of the University of Rome, although, as Dufourcq noted to Hélène, Enriques was anti-Christian. In fact, Enriques was very anti-Duhem.[10]

Two more years go by

That the dossiers of Dufourcq, who in all appearance carefully kept all communications from Hélène, do not contain anything from her for the month of December is easily explained by her letter of January 5, 1938. All during December she had been hard at work on the epistolary history of the steps that led to the original publication of the *Système du monde*. She left it to Dufourcq's discretion to leave her own brief introduction to it as she felt that she might have put "the dots too strongly on the i's or perhaps the feet into the platter." On re-reading those letters she found the long delay in the publication "particularly scandalous." The correspondence showed, in her view, that by deciding on a luxury edition, the publisher took advantage of her father's trust in leaving all details in his hands. She called Dufourcq's attention to the passage in a letter by the Père Bulliot who reported to her father Picard's words: "The Academies have funds they don't often know what to do with." The rest of the letter, which began with a reference to the bitterly cold winter in Cabrespine, was about the problems of finding some more letters about the original publication:

> I could find but one letter by Papa. It is a copy of a letter to Mr. Darboux. Only the very beginning deals with the *Système du monde*; the rest deals with his candidacy to the Académie. I did not have the courage to leave out that part because it is so beautiful, simple, and typical of Papa's character. Also towards its end one finds his thought returning to the *Système du monde* which he is afraid not to have the time to complete. Just as with my preface, I leave you, Monsieur, entirely free to omit the rest of that letter. Have you had a reply from the relatives of the Père Bulliot? It would be so useful to have the letters Papa had written to that worthy religious. I have written to the abbé Joannés Wehrlé[11] who was Papa's classmate in the Ecole Normale and was in possession of most of Delbos' letters.[12] He answered very kindly saying he did not have a single letter from Papa. He suggested that I write to Maurice Blondel[13] which I plan to do. This shows that if I wanted to publish Papa's correspondence, I would, without doubt, be up against insurmountable difficulties.

Hélène was soon to suspect that she was to face difficulties far more insurmountable and almost unbearable as well. She expected all the remaining galleys of Volume VI to arrive but was to learn from the letter which Dufourcq wrote to her from Paris on January 16, 1938, that he had no new galleys. As one familiar with the standard excuses, he wrote: "What to do? It seems that we must not budge by waiting for a contribution from the Ministry, and not even by letting the month of January go by, when one begins to talk about the problems to be brought with the Spring." It was not so much the problems typical of that season, as the political crisis on the horizon that Dufourcq had in mind. The situation, "which keeps worsening with every day would, I am afraid, create new difficulties for the publisher." He advised Hélène not to worry for the moment about her Papa's corrspondence. The letter contained, however, a far more important detail. There Dufourcq spoke only of volumes I and VI because, according to his best knowledge, the other volumes needed only a new title page and a new cover to be reprinted. As a prolific author he could competently speak of the speed with which books already in proofread galleys could be broken into pages and printed. Ideological sensitivity was, however, needed on his part to make the most significant remark:

> As to volumes I and VI you could perhaps write an urgent letter to Freymann. Volume VI seems to me to be complete in galleys. Only to break them into pages and sewing them together remains to be done and this usually goes quickly. Undoubtedly the same is true of volume I. I am afraid that the general situation and the hostility of some official circles make Freymann slow down . . . .

Prophetic words that must have raised more and more nagging doubts in the minds of Hélène as well as of Dufourcq as increasingly lean weeks and months began to go by. April came and the only good news to cheer about was the publication of the issue of *Archeion* that carried the text of speeches delivered at the meeting in Paris. Dufourcq was elated. On

April 20, three days after Easter, he wrote to Hélène: "I have just finished reading the copy of *Archeion* with joyful emotions. It is the triumph of your Papa announced over the tomb of enemies petrified by stupidity and ill-will. May the good Lord be blessed and you be thanked for having sent me this precious issue!"

Dufourcq also thought that the fall of the government of Blum and of the Front Populaire was perhaps the sign if not of real change at least of some respite: "Don't you think," he asked Hélène, "that the moment has arrived to intervene immediately with Freymann? It is necessary that he should resume the printing right away and that he immediately produce volume VI. It is ready." Perhaps Dufourcq should have said that volume VI must by now be certainly ready. It was not to be really ready even ten full years later.

Another recipient of that issue, inscribed by Hélène, was Abel Rey. He replied: "I am very touched by your dedicating a copy to me. I did what I could, and I wish but one thing, namely, that I have not hurt through my inadequacy the great memory we celebrated."

In the dossiers kept by Dufourcq[14] the next item is a postcard, written almost five months later, on September 17 to be exact. Months were indeed going by at an exasperating rate. The postcard began: "Dear friend, I wanted to write to you, I want to write to you . . . without speaking of volume VI . . . but I have hardly have the courage. Let me tell you at least of the joy which your long letter to my wife has brought to me. I was afraid that you had been overcome by frustration." He thanked her for sending him *France réelle*,[15] a book unknown to him. "I applaud your valor. May the good Lord bless you, intrepid daughter of an intrepid genius, and protect you!"

Courage and resolve she needed because she was deprived even of the joy of receiving in time for Christmas Freymann's letter, dated December 24. Or perhaps Providence saved her from noticing already on Christmas eve an ominous sign that only a careful reading could detect. First, Freymann informed her that within a week the correction of the page-proofs of the first six signatures of volume VI and therefore its first fascicle, would be completed. This was good news and bad news as well. Those six signatures meant only the first 96 pages of a volume to comprise well over seven hundred pages. Such was a progress that could make any snail envious. Most likely it did not occur to Hélène to think of the several decades, and not of several years, that on such a basis the production of the entire work would demand. No human with any hope, let alone with the hope of Christmas, could have been willing to conjure up the future so bleakly and so realistically as well.   The other four points, relating to the covers of the various fascicles, were insignificant. Perhaps less hurting would have been this incredible delay, if Freymann had not concluded the letter with the words:

> I take this opportunity to thank you for your patience and for your willingness to wait so that the times in which we live may allow me to fulfill the promise I have made to you with great joy, and to tell you about the emotion which I feel on seeing the [first installment] of the final page-proofs of the sixth volume which soon will appear. This would fulfill the desire which I had for many years to collaborate, to the extent of my means, in the realization of the literary monument conceived by your Father and I infinitely regret that God did not let him see it being brought to conclusion.

This paragraph might not today appear a patently severe indictment of Freymann's protestations of good will, had he not included the phrase, "to the extent of my means." At that time anyone doing regular "window-shopping" on Place de la Sorbonne could have readily sworn that in the 1930s Hermann et Cie kept producing about two scores of new books every year. Today, the evidence is still available to anyone willing to

page through the corresponding issues of *Livre Français*.[16] Freymann simply took an all too transparent cover when he
suggested a serious constraint on his "means" which were very
substantial indeed. Furthermore, any other publisher who had
already paid for the paper needed for the reprinting of five large
volumes, with 700 copies of each, and had already paid for the
typesetting of a manuscript amounting to another very large
volume, would have hastened the day of the first returns for his
expenses through sales.

Dufourcq tried to send cheerful words to Hélène, whenever opportunity arose. On January 13, 1939, as he visited in
Lisieux, he wrote a postcard, showing the interior of the
Cathedral which once had Oresme as its bishop: "In the Cathedral of Lisieux we have prayed for the one who had discovered.
Nicole Oresme, for his daughter, and for the speedy completion
of the *Système du monde.*" The strength which only prayer can
give was very much in order. The true color of Freymann
began to emerge in vivid hues. On January 23 Dufourcq went
to his offices with the finally approved page-proofs of fascicle
II of volume VI (corresponding to its pages 113-237), about
which he noted that they had been received by the printer on
August 17, that is, a six full months earlier. Dufourcq continued: "I hoped not to meet Freymann. Naturally, I did not
succeed, and could not avoid shaking hands with him. 'Now
that we resume work,' he said 'all will go very fast.' 'Ah,' I answered and left. This man is disgusting. What a humiliation to
be laughed at! . . . The only question to ask is about the extent
to which the father is mocked as his daughter is being laughed
at."

Curiously, Abel Rey, a man with full familiarity of the
large number of books Hermann et Cie was producing, some
of them very expensive to typeset because of the many mathematical formulas in them, failed to diagnose Freymann correctly, at least for the moment. His letter of February 21, 1939, to
Hélène has this postscript: "I have repeatedly spoken with

Freymann about the reprinting and printing of the *Système du monde*. I am distressed by his delays. I think things would not go better with other publishers. I shall resume action. It is certain that it is not his intention to go so slowly. I think he has to face great difficulties. But this is one more reason to press him all the more. I will do my best."

That Rey failed to reach the proper conclusion about Freymann received an unexpected confirmation three months later in a letter which J. Pelseneer, secretary of the Comité Belge d'Histoire des Sciences wrote to Hélène on May 11. He started with a reference to Mme Tannery who provided him with Hélène's address. He presented his letter as "the manifestation of the very keen interest which some persons, among many others, take in the magnificent work of Pierre Duhem." One of them was "a colleague and friend" of Pelseneer, identified at this point only as a professor at the University of Uppsala, "who thinks he can dispose of a very considerable sum set aside for the support of works on the history of science. Now, among the works announced recently, the continuation of the *Système du monde* should occupy the first rank."

Then came the subtle revelation. Pelseneer, certainly well informed of what publications in his field were to appear, believed to have learned from Hermann's prospectus that only the first five volumes were to be reprinted as Fascicles 664-690 of the *Actualités scientifiques*. "Is the publication of the rest assured?" he asked Hélène. "This is what we do not know, and, in case the answer is negative (which would be infinitely deplorable), my Swedish friends would like to know precisely this (please do not see any indiscretion in their request): what would be the sum needed for the publication of the remaining four(?) volumes. What is the sum which the publisher demands as guarantee per volume, in order to undertake the publication?"

That Pelseneer spoke of four volumes reflected the occasional references, available in print, that when Duhem died, he left behind manuscripts of another four volumes. It also reflected on Freymann's reluctance to make advance publicity for the republication of the remaining five volumes or at least of the impending publication of volume VI. At any rate, on learning from Hélène's letter of June 25 that she had not yet received any communication from Sweden, Pelseneer assured her, on June 29, that he would write again to that colleague and friend of his, whom he now identified as Professor Nordström.[17] But, Pelseneer added, Nordström "is overworked and takes three to four months to reply. But I want to assure you of his admirable devotion to all that relates to the history of science." Pelseneer might have added that in July and August it is particularly impossible to expect any committee in Sweden to deal with such matters. Yet those two summer months were crucial. September 1, 1939, was approaching.

Encouraged by this letter, Hélène again must have broached to Freymann the question of financial help. She also brought up the question of royalties due to her for sales of *Thermodynamique et chimie, La chimie est-elle une science française?*, and *Leçons de mécanique chimique.* "In these conditions," he wrote on July 7 with obvious reference to the increasingly menacing international situation (although many quarters were ready to enjoy the summer lull), "we are unable to take an inventory and give you satisfaction." Then he informed her that although 20,000 copies had been mailed out of the prospectus announcing the latest issues in the *Actualités scientifiques*, only ten or so orders had come in for the Duhem titles. Then he stated that the first five volumes had been printed, and that their covers, together with the covers of the corresponding fascicles, would be sent to her immediately. Then came the last two paragraphs that should be given in full:

> I do not dare to tell you again that I do my best. But in spite of myself I have to keep in mind the financial situation. Business is deplorable, we are forced to slow

down more and more. Still I state to you that, before the
return from vacation [September 1], the five first volumes
and the entirety of the sixth as well as the fascicles, will be
on sale.

As to the financial facilities of which you speak, I
know only of those Mr. Dufourcq had mentioned to me,
but the very organization of our firm makes a recourse to
outside help difficult and all the more so as this offer comes
when the thing is almost finished and, presonally, I want to
be the sole beneficiary of having accomplished this work
with my own means, a consideration that would become
void if a sum, however small, were to be given to me at
the last moment.

In mid-August Hélène saw her hopes dashed that before
the end of the month she would have in her hands the volumes
for which she had already been waiting with growing intensity
for at least three years. Mme Tannery ordered fascicle N° 672,
entitled, "La théorie des marées," only to be told by Freymann
that "the entire Duhem work is with the binder and that no
part of it will be available before the end of September." This
reply of Freymann, dated August 8, Mme Tannery forwarded
to Hélène with a query whether she had the material of that
fascicle in the form of galleys. "Nothing goes well at this
moment, one has to admit."

Together with these remarks came a long letter from Mme
Tannery whom Hélène had informed about Pelseneer's letters.
After having talked with other historians of science, Mme
Tannery could offer only wise words of advice about strategy:
"The opinion [of the gathering] was unanimous that you should
not let things become dormant. Freymann must carry out the
terms of the contract. If he claims financial problems, possibly
real, he should be all the readier to accept the offer made to
him. He can himself specify guarantees concerning that offer.
But since that offer allows him to carry out a contract about
which he is defaulting, he must accept it. We, your friends, we

shall write all about this to Freymann." One wonders whether Hélène could find any comfort in Mme Tannery's own plight with her publisher: "I am always in loud quarrel with Beauchesne." Mme Tannery thought that to keep working was the best medicine. Her long letter offered to Hélène only one useful item. She would waste her energy were she to turn to the other Hélène: "I think it is best not to count on Mme Metzger. She is a charming woman but, being very tied to Freymann on account of her little volumes, she would not be able to take your side unequivocally."

Then as September got under way, the shadows of the greatest threat yet to the free world, and first of all to France, began to extend farther and farther. Contrary to expectations, no bullet was fired at France through all September. By October it was almost certain that the attack on France would not come for months. Hélène hoped against hope until mid-November. Then she penned a letter of which only one paragraph survived. Freymann quoted it as he replied almost a month later. Freymann began:

The way you have written your letter embarrasses me. You pose questions, and you accurately foresee the answers I can give. You know more than anyone how painful it is for me that you would wrongly interpret what I am going to write, but I am forced to do so because you have written: "You, Mr. Freymann, you would certainly invoke the actual circumstances. Still the fact remains that when the thing was possible, you did not act, in spite of your formal promise given to me, and in spite of your written commitment which is now shown to be a lie."

Freymann continued:

This could not have been said better, nor with greater force, but I expected something else because since I have given you my word I have already spent more than 90,000 francs on the first five volumes that are not yet completely done. It is evident that I am the only one to deceive you. But I would like to know what you think of others who, for reasons of friendship, family relations or camaraderie, have done less than I did, although I am merely a distant though fervent admirer of your father.

Throughout the entire letter there was not a single reference to the strict obligation of Hermann et Cie to publish in full the *Système du monde*, nor of the vastly overdue nature of that obligation. Nor did Freymann face up to the problem of why three full years had not been enough for one of the foremost scientific publishers in Europe, if not in the whole world, to typeset and print a seven-hundred-page volume from a gemlike manuscript. He again cited the meager response to the 20,000 catalogues announcing the first five volumes and volume VI.

It should not be difficult to imagine what Hélène thought on reading Freymann declare once more his resolve to do his very best. Worse, that declaration of good will ended with the phrase: "I cannot give you an exact date [of publication] lest I should fail once more to keep my given word." Had she conjectured that even after twice seven years no exact date would be forthcoming from Freymann, she might have wondered whether she would live that long at all. Apart from the fact that she was approaching fifty, she knew that at that moment only the notoriously carefree failed to be seized by ominous forebodings. Her deepest concern was not, however, for her own life, but for the ultimate fate of the priceless manuscripts. For the next six years she had to live on the meager assurance given to her by Freymann in the same letter: "Barnéoud must continue the typesetting of volume VI. He has the part of the manuscript still to be typeset and you can be assured that he will take all the necessary precautions to safeguard it, including the case of bombardments which you naturally foresee."

Seven terribly lean years

After the long and cold evenings of winter had passed, came a spring with no sign of hope. Before it was over, Hélène's beloved France seemed to lose forever her chances to be victorious again. As everyone else, she too was suffering great losses. She certainly lost a valiant ally when Abel Rey passed away in 1940 at the age of sixty-six. As the war years went by, Hélène could feel time and again that her own victory, once almost within reach, was snatched from her once and for all. It was very difficult to appraise correctly the strength of resistance fighters one of whose centers was in the Montagne Noire, just a dozen miles up the road from Cabrespine. The area was familiar to her from the time when as a young girl she began to accompany her father on his outings during summer vacations. Her sense of frustration could only increase when she received, in late November 1943, an inquiry from Louis de Broglie, perpetual secretary of the Académie des Sciences, whether she would agree that Edmond Faral, administrator of the Collège de France, might study the copy of a medieval manuscript which the Père Bulliot had obtained for Duhem. For, as if in an afterthought, de Broglie added: "Let me recall, on this occasion, that, at your request, the manuscript of volume 6 had been handed over to Mr. Albert Dufourcq, professor at the Faculty of Science of Bordeaux, who had assumed the task of publication." Why, Hélène could muse, did de Broglie fail to refer to the publisher?

It was not until May 6, 1944, that Hélène heard again from the one, Freymann, legally in charge of that task, a task all-important from her viewpoint. He wanted her to know that he was still in Paris and that he intended to send her, upon receiving her reply, copies of the first two fascicles of volume VI, although "they are not yet on sale for various reasons difficult to explain to you." He also stated his intention to send her the proofs of the third fascicle of which he had the galleys. In all evidence he referred to the final proofs. "As you see, in spite of the difficulties we face, I try to do my best to accomplish what I promised you in order to render homage to the memory of your father."

Here was a faint glint of hope that a cruel war had not perhaps irretrievably snatched victory from her hands. Her hopes must have risen high on hearing in late August about the liberation of Paris. But for another two years no word came from Paris. All those years, seven exceedingly lean years, must have been a time of daily agony for Hélène whom one can easily picture walking deep in thought almost daily to her father's grave. In the house everything reminded her of him. On the desk in the room where he died, there was still the blotting paper showing his last signature. She woke up every morning at the sound of his exquisite alarm clock. On occasion she paged through the letters he had written to her every day over much of his last seven years. The large table in the study was covered with his manuscripts, notes, and correspondence — and the galleys and page-proofs of the still unpublished volume VI of the *Système du monde*. Would it and the remaining four volumes ever be published? Could all her efforts, frustrations, and agonies stretching now over ten years have been in vain?

8

Victory at Long Last

Towards a dead end

The letter Hélène wrote on September 22, 1946, to Freymann
was the first he acknowledged as having received from her since
1940. He was equally astonished, as he put it in his reply of
October 17, 1946, that none of the four letters he had written
to her during the war years had reached her in Cabrespine. The
last of those four letters, dated May 16, 1944, was now quoted
in full by Freymann. In that letter he had informed her that he
would send her copies of the first two fascicles of volume VI
were he to receive a reply from her. Those two fascicles were
not, however, to be put on sale until all the fascicles of volume
VI were ready. He therefore looked forward to her reply in
order to send to her for correction proofs of more of those
fascicles "and move forward with the work of production in
spite of the difficulties we are having." Freymann had to be
certain of her whereabouts because of his fear that some
"manuscript pages may be lost." Since manuscript pages were
sent with the first proofs, Freymann obviously meant to send
the material representing fascicles 3 and 4 of volume VI. Only
by the wildest stretch of imagination could all this be called a
forward movement.

Equally unconvincing did Freymann sound in stating that since he had Hélène's letter of September 22 in his hands, "we can now initiate a new period of activity and, I hope, we can complete without interruption the publication of the *Système du monde.*" Then Freymann gave specifics about the status of production. He was ready to send the page proofs of fascicles 4-6 of volume VI for final approval, which meant that most of that volume was ready to be printed. It also became clear, however, that contrary to his statement of August 1939, the sheets of none of the first five volumes had been sewn. In fact all volumes still needed the title page, and this was also true of the fascicles corresponding to them. All the material, he wrote, "was kept in a warehouse where we had to hide all our books of which the Germans demanded all copies when written by authors (considered as hostile to Germany) and your father had the honor of being placed in that category."

Freymann knew how to play on Hélène's patriotic feelings when he added that he "had to create the appearance during German occupation of not possessing any copy of any book written by your father." Still he was able to sell copies to people about whom, as he put it, "he was certain that they would keep the secret." He in fact volunteered the information that the royalties due from those sales amounted to 1,932 francs and 80 centimes. But once more he turned to making much of the difficulties: "Paper is still extremely difficult to find, the printers work part-time, and the last works I have produced with Barnéoud had to be typeset in half-space in order to make room for other orders." And to show that he was really in a hurry, Freymann spoke of the printer's impatience with the delay who "made me pay interest for not being able to free his typefonts for other work."

In the very first days of 1947, Dufourcq could write to Hélène that he had in his hands volume V and the first two fascicles of volume VI. He was happy to hear from her that progress had been made with that volume. He asked her to send him without delay the remaining fascicles she was correcting. She was advised to remind Freymann about the depreciation of the money but was not to cross swords with him about the contract. Dufourcq also reported that his son Norbert, "who works now with Larousse as a sort of general manager,"[1] was very much abreast of all that was going on in the publishing world: "He is most certain that all is frighteningly difficult: lack of paper, rise of wages, decrease of revenues, etc." Dufourcq certainly thought of "big Norbert" when he said in conclusion: "Don't ever lose faith in your old friends, and never hesitate to lean on them whenever you think you are having difficulties."

That those "old friends" particularly included Norbert was made clear in Dufourcq's next letter, written on February 9. It contained a little note, with data furnished by Norbert, about the rise of book prices since 1938. The rise was modest between 1938 and 1942, strong in 1943, and "vertiginous from 1944 to 1947. A book that was selling for 25 francs is selling at 110 francs in 1947." Dufourcq hoped that these data would help Hélène "see clearly." Both were concerned about Freymann's long silence. Only on February 28 did Freymann acknowledge the receipt of the final page proofs of chapters iv to vi of volume VI (or pp. 239-510) and the first page proofs of ch. vii (pp. 511-576). "I wait for the galleys of what is still missing in order to make the pages, and print the four fascicles (30-34) of volume VI which, together with the first two fascicles, will allow us to issue the entire series [of fascicles]."

But ch. viii on Ockham and ch. ix on the Parisian eclecticism, a total of 150 pages, were not mentioned by Freymann. He rather resumed talking about economics: "I still have much difficulty in obtaining paper, and Barnéoud is overwhelmed with work because of the many restrictions on working hours. Most printers work four days a week and this reduces in catastrophic proportions the rate of production."

Dufourcq's next letter, written at the end of March, brought somber premonitions. It was saddening enough to have no news from Freymann. His silence was ominous. On trying to visit him on Saturday, March 29, Dufourcq found his offices closed. Worse, Dufourcq, already seventy-five, had to speak to Hélène of his advancing years: "Because my strength is rapidly decreasing and because one should not be caught by surprise, I convey to you news that may be important. If I happen to die before the full publication of the *Système du monde*, here is something you may find useful, in want of something better." The item related to the formation of a new group of Catholic scientists with a bureau at 61 Rue Madame. Hélène was to get in touch with them if the Institute continued ignoring the work of Duhem. "If only Abel Rey were still alive!" Dufourcq added.

On April 16 Dufourcq was able to visit Freymann and did his best to keep a friendly tone of conversation. "I have decided to avoid all dispute and to create an atmosphere of cordiality in order to increase our prospects of seeing the publication of the *Système du monde* resumed. It seems to me that the goal has been achieved." But it also became very clear to Dufourcq that since January 16, or over three full months, nothing was done with the proofs. Further, nobody seemed to know the whereabouts of the manuscript pages relating to those last two chapters. At first, Dufourcq thought that they might be in his house in the Pyrenees where he could not return before mid-June. The only tangible item in his hands was a note, dated March 12, 1937, an acknowledgment from Freymann of the receipt of the manuscripts of volume VI.

Clearly, things were heading towards a dead end instead of a happy ending. As so often in the past, once more Freymann took refuge in doing nothing as he knew that Dufourcq and Hélène had no means of taking matters before a tribunal and that he could safely ignore suggestions about possible subventions. But Freyman could also overplay his hands. Dufourcq did not, however, let him know that he had failed to dupe him. This happened when on April 16 Freymann gave to Dufourcq the very same proofs which the latter had already given back to him fully proofread three months earlier. A month later Dufourcq wrote to Hélène: "Should I begin by telling you that I am as discouraged as you are? You know that I forced myself to close my eyes in order to be able to continue talking and keep the contact. And now, without trying, I caught him, our Mexican, in a flagrant act of . . . a comedy."

But if Freymann could not be trusted any longer, to whom could they turn? Dufourcq thought that perhaps Hélène should call the attention of the Académie des Sciences to an already more than impossible story concerning the monumental work of one of its late members. What Hélène may have thought of this suggestion can only be guessed. Perhaps after feeling utterly hopeless and powerless for a week or two, she began to rally. Quite possibly she suggested during the summer to Dufourcq that she would move into the capital for a while at least to take things in hand. Dufourcq then learned to his great relief that she had given up the idea of "quitting L'Oustal." He could not have agreed more wholeheartedly as shown by his letter of September 25: "All is so complicated today and so expensive. . . . Let us hope that better days will come, at least for you!"

The turning point

Those better days were indeed ahead in the future, though still a very distant future. Hélène could not even suspect that she hit upon the move toward a turning point as she suggested to Dufourcq a couple of persons, among them Elie Cartan, the venerable and famed mathematician,[2] as people worth contacting. Undoubtedly Hélène thought of him as the one who, when her father died, obtained a yearly pension for her from the Société des Amis des Sciences. She urged Dufourcq to see Cartan upon his return to Paris. Dufourcq was ready to do anything, although at that point he thought the whole matter hopeless, humanly speaking. Moreover, he could not find the manuscript in question in his summer house in Chilho. He found there only such manuscripts that belonged to the first chapters of volume VI, chapters in final page proofs for almost ten years, in fact already printed as fascicles. On October 4, broken hearted, he mailed those manuscripts back to Hélène: "You understand that small fissure I feel in my heart, the pain that I did not succeed better in helping you and getting the *Système du monde* published. May God's will be done! He knows what He is doing!"

Almost a month and a half later, on November 14, Dufourcq met the venerable mathematician and had a "two-hour-long conversation with him." Cartan must have heard more than an earful from Dufourcq. Without any delay Cartan contacted two colleagues of his at the Académie des Sciences: its perpetual secretary, Louis de Broglie and Joseph Pérès, a specialist in mechanics and also the vice director of the Centre National de la Recherche Scientifique.[3] Two days later Cartan informed Dufourcq that both of them were ready to throw their full support behind the publication of the *Système du monde*. In particular Pérès was convinced that the Centre would provide the necessary subvention. On November 21 Cartan made an unannounced visit to Dufourcq who immediately realized its portent. Hélène was to submit with all possible speed a request to the Director of the Centre and give all the necessary details.[4] In the long letter of Dufourcq, written on November 22, there was only one paragraph that sounded more comical than dramatic. His was an almost complete unfamiliarity with the main topics covered in the manuscript that was to constitute the remaining volumes and the chronological end of the work.

On December 6, Cartan informed Hélène about the receipt of her letter of November 22 and also told her that he had to wait for the return of Pérès from Rome. He assured her that Pérès would promptly transmit her letter to the Director of the Center and that "Pérès is very firm about making the matter succeed, including the publication of the remaining volumes as well." He thinks, Cartan continued,

> that your father's work is so important that he would not neglect its publication at the earliest possible date. Here is therefore a serious hope which I am very pleased to communicate to you. May Almighty God let it become a reality. If it becomes necessary, we shall let Mr. Louis de Broglie intervene.

Invoking God's help was no mere formality with Cartan. Nor was that help to be taken lightly in a case that dragged on for still another seven years. Here too, only by not knowing the future could one relish the sweet moment bringing the foretaste of a victory however remote.

Victory loomed near in Dufourcq's eyes as he reported to Hélène, on December 4, about his latest talk with Cartan. As a new ally Cartan appeared more important with every new contact with him. Cartan was also a most valuable source of contact with others. Cartan seems to have suggested that Hélène write to Sarton, which she did on January 15, 1948. A month later Sarton sent to her, in French, the following reply:

> Your kind letter of January 15 arrives at a critical moment for me as I am getting ready to be absent from Cambridge for about seven months. I will be in Paris in May because I promised to give there four lectures (the Faculty of Letters, the Faculty of Science, Collège de France, Centre International de Synthèse). There I shall meet almost all French scholars who are either working in the history of science or are more or less interested in it. I will, therefore, have many occasions to insist on the importance of completing the publication of the *Système du monde* and I will not fail to do so. Please, Mademoiselle, accept the expression of my great respect. George Sarton

As Hélène was to find out from Dufourcq three months later, Sarton was far from being sincere in voicing serious interest in the publication of the *Système du monde*.

Meanwhile she had learned from Dufourcq two important facts. One was Cartan's international stature as a man of science. In December he went to London as the one whom James B. Conant, President of Harvard University, suggested to the Royal Society of London as his replacement at its commemorative meeting on Rutherford. The other also showed Cartan as a man of science, that is, one most appreciative of facts. He began to have doubts about Freymann's honesty no sooner had he reflected on the data in Hélène's letter. Matters now reached an irrevocable turning point, even though that point remained yet at a great distance. Hélène and Dufourcq, who seemed to be hopelessly trapped, could now begin their great move of encirclement. The move was great also in that it took much more time to complete than they dared to think. In Freymann they now found an antagonist most unwilling to admit defeat.

Hélène wisely thought that by mid-January 1948 Freymann would have received a request from the Centre National de la Recherche Scientifique to present details about the subvention he would think necessary. She could not, of course, suspect the strength of Freymann's resolve (amply revealed in his negative reaction in August 1939 to a possible subvention from Sweden) not to share his eventual profits with anyone else. Hélène's letter of January 18, 1948, to Freymann began with registering the fact that she had not received any communication from him for a full year. She found this especially strange in view of Freymann's repeated references to the printer's eagerness to have the fonts freed for other works: "I am astonished at not having received the page proofs of galleys 68 -73 and that a full year had to pass without the work having been advanced by a single line. Yet, in terms of our contract you have obligated yourself to publish one volume per year!" She finished the letter with a request for another long-overdue royalty statement.

On February 20th Hélène began her letter to Freymann by registering his failure to reply to her letter of January 18th. On February 23 Freymann replied by stating that "certainly this year volume VI will be published." Then he turned to the matter of subvention: "Frankly, I prefer not to count on it too much, because the sums I have already used for the reprinting of the first five volumes and for the production of the sixth, already exceed one and a half million francs, and the Centre has never given us a comparable sum, and certainly not in the actual circumstances of restrictions and economizing." Freymann simply inflated the original figure of about one hundred thousand francs by the suddenly runaway inflationary rate. Again, three and a half years after the end of the German occupation, he should not have referred to it as the reason for not putting on sale Duhem's *La science allemande* which he had to hide during that period. He, however, had to admit that all the first five volumes of the *Système du monde* were still in sheets, waiting to be sewn together into volumes.

Clearly, Hélène had to muster determination to outlast her antagonist. She could but derive a similar conclusion on reading Pelseneer's reply of March 10, 1948, to her letter of February 20. As one now attached to the science section of UNESCO, Pelseneer had many opportunities to speak about the *Système du monde* with historians of science. They gladly offered the inexpensive rhetoric of "waiting impatiently for its publication" but did not move as much as a finger to make it a reality. Nor did Freymann hasten with production. At the end of March volume VI had its ch. vii in final page proofs (pp. 511-572), with still one hundred and sixty pages to be done.

On Easter vigil, March 27, Dufourcq prayed that the Risen Christ might reinvigorate Hélène's charity, hope, and faith. She was urged to correspond with Freymann only through Cartan or Louis de Broglie whenever possible. Dufourcq saw rays of

hope in the political situtation: "The Marshall Plan begins in
June or July; the Prague affair will strengthen the unity of
Western Europe with America, of England with France and
even of Italy with us . . . . It is not in vain to hope that a
barbarized and atheistic Russia would turn the world against it
and we shall see, through God's grace, better days. Read the
Exultet . . . and may the joy of Easter illumine, strengthen, and
transfigure your soul!"

In early April Dufourcq obtained the information through
the bookstore and publisher Gallimard that its request for a
copy of volumes I and V of the *Système du monde* was refused
by Freymann on the ground that no copies were any longer
available. Dufourcq cautioned against dragging Freymann to
court on the basis of that information. The slightest such move
"costs very much," Dufourcq wrote to Hélène on April 3.

A telltale lecture

Hélène was, of course, more than entitled to "be impatient."
Still, if the war was to be won, lack of patience could not be
allowed to engage one in unnecessary skirmishes and battles.
"Should I tell you," Dufourcq wrote on May 20, as he
acknoweldged her letters of April 8, 16 and May 16, "that I
understand your impatience? I fully share it." In that letter
Dufourcq spoke of the return of Cartan's son from Harvard and
of Cartan's plan to see Sarton who was scheduled to give a talk
at the Institut Poincaré on May 24. Then Dufourcq quoted
Cartan that Sarton's lecture, organized by the Académie
Internationale d'Histoire des Sciences, "will be on Stevin and
Viète. Perhaps he will go to see Hélène Duhem."

Did Cartan hope that Sarton might go to see Hélène in
Cabrespine? In fact, even if Hélène would have been much
closer to Paris, Sarton would not have taken the trouble to see
in person the daughter of by far the most eminent historian of
science until then and even until today. The reason for this was
simple. Sarton's lectures and his conversation with Dufourcq

showed that Duhem's stature clearly bothered him. This became all too evident to Cartan and Pérès as they attended with Dufourcq another lecture of Sarton, given in the Collège de France, on May 26, on "La Science et la Tradition." The idea of going there was Cartan's who also arranged for an after-lecture meeting with Sarton. The rest should be given verbatim from the letter which Dufourcq wrote on May 27 to Hélène:

> I was therefore there, and I must say that this was for us — Cartan, Pérès, and myself — a deception. Sarton short-changed us. And, as in similar matters, I have to tell you everything, except the thoughts that come from the soul, you must, however, know what I have to insist on: Sarton is now publishing his work on science during the 14th century.[5] He spoke of it several times during his lecture (very interesting otherwise: tradition which is often opposed to science is its very soul) as he promoted his own publicity. He may be afraid that the publication of your father's work would undercut him and even prove him wrong here and there. So much so that he kept insisting that the manuscript of your father's work still to appear in print was, in its actual state, a pile of unpublishable notes . . . ! At this point I interrupted him: "I know the manuscript. Duhem generously let me use several chapters from it for my own work. I have always known his magnificent handwriting and the clarity of his mind." Still our friend [Sarton] insisted that this was not possible, because a manuscript is but a chaos of corrections. On hearing this I could not help thinking that he was not pleased at all to see Duhem's work to be published now, in addition to his . . . . I stopped insisting. The maneuver was too clear . . . . And we continued talking, very amicably. I suggested that he see Freymann. He answered that this would serve no purpose, but that after his return to Cambridge (Massachussetts) he would write and this perhaps would carry more weight. . . . Will he do it?

Sarton's attitude was tantamount to a refusal to look at the manuscripts in question. Unwittingly he followed the pattern of those, often deplored by him, who once declined to look through Galileo's telescope. Actually, Sarton did not want to look at Duhem's monumental figure. As he stated in the postscript of his letter, Dufourcq heard Sarton pronounce only once during his lecture Duhem's name and not once the title of his great work. Dufourcq may not have thought that in keeping silent about Duhem's monumental achievement in a lecture on the role of tradition in science Sarton did the equivalent of speaking of relativity without referring to Einstein. For it was Duhem, and no one else, who insisted, from *Les origines de la statique* on, that tradition was the very soul of science and that this is why it had a soul, or continuity. Sarton merely stole this idea from Duhem and he must have known this fully. Even today it would take a historian of science — not blindfolded by the deluge of references to paradigm shifts, mutations, revolutions, and other studiedly undefined devices — to be alive to the true measure of Sarton's devious performance. For much of his career he was setting himself up as the great pioneering expert in the history of science before Galileo, and especially on Leonardo and the Renaissance. No wonder that he had to keep silent on Duhem as far as this was possible without giving himself away too obviously.[6]

Sarton gave an all too clear account of himself in the eyes of Cartan, Pérès, and Dufourcq. The latter continued:

> When we were again alone, the three of us — Cartan, Pérès, and myself — all agreed we had been taken for a ride. Two questions were then uppermost in our minds: 1) how to speed up the publication of Volume VI. It is Pérès who would contact Freymann for that purpose and he will do his very best. The problem is that he himself is not on the best terms with Freymann either. It is up to us to pray that he succeeds. 2) Does the contract signed by your father with Hermann obligate him — and therefore you —

to stay with Hermann for the printing of the remainder of the work? Cartan, Pérès, and myself, we have the very keen desire to part with Hermann and to have volumes VII, VIII, and IX published by the Centre National de la Recherche Scientifique. Is this legally possible? What does the contract say? This is the big question.

Dufourcq hoped to get some information on these points from Hélène whom he informed that "Cartan begged me to thank you very much in his name for your letter and to reply to you on his behalf."

Meanwhile she received from Freymann, between May 20 and 25, the galleys of the first 252 pages of the manuscript of the chapter on Ockham, or about two thirds of the entire chapter. Freymann's covering letter of May 20 included the phrase: "I have the pleasure of telling you that all the finally approved page proofs [of the preceding chapters] have been printed and as soon as the entire volume VI is ready, what I hope will happen in a very short time, we will publish the volume and the fascicles as well as the reprinting of the first five volumes of which only a very few pages are still to be done."

A very short time

Thus, in Freymann's very own words, only "a very short time," perhaps a month, would have been necessary to typeset the remaining manuscripts (amounting in print to about a hundred pages) of volume VI. In another month, and not later than mid-August, all six volumes could have been put on sale. And all the more so, because Freymann could, from June 16 on, see himself freed from any further financial burden to complete the enterprise. On that day he had in his hands a formal contract offer, dated June 15, 1948, from the Centre National de la Recherche Scientifique for the publication of volume VI. Article I identified the persons and firms involved. Article II stipulated that 1,500 copies be printed. Article III assured

Hermann et Cie of three hundred thousand francs to be paid by the Centre immediately upon publication. It was a loan, which, as Article IV had it, Hermann et Cie had to pay back by taking out 20% of their yearly revenues accrued from the sales of those volume. No time limit was set for the total repayment. Article V however assured the Centre of being given access to a full account of all sales.

Between June 14 and June 18 Freymann asked Hélène three times to be as quick with the proofreading as possible. He made, however, no reference to the contract offer of which a copy was obviously sent also to Hélène. On June 22, Dufourcq could inform her that, owing to the intervention of Cartan and Louis de Broglie, the Société des Amis de la Science decided, at its meeting of June 9, to augment her yearly pension by five thousand francs. On July 26 Dufourcq felt encouraged to write to her: "With you I begin to believe that without much delay we shall see the publication of volume VI. . . . What a joy that day will be for me, wherever it finds me! And how well I did by contacting Cartan! And what a blessing is that friendship that ties him to Louis de Broglie! Where would we be without them?"

Dufourcq rejoiced too soon. At that point he, who in the same letter gave with happy abandon details about all his eight chldren and scores of grandchildren, could not suspect that *that* day was still six years away and would find him in Heaven. For the moment there was some progress. On the very first day of September pages 609 - 676 were ready for final proofreading. On October 1st the last chapter of volume VI, the one on Walter Burley and the Parisian eclecticism, was in page-proofs. Six days later Freymann asked Hélène about two small errors. Then silence fell. On November 25 Dufourcq wrote: "Freymann's silence makes me suffer all the more because in my sufferings and anguish I feel yours as well."

Dufourcq knew that all those waves of deep disappointments and deceptions, that had by then for over almost two

decades been splashing in Hélène's face, must have taken their
toll on her. He was eager to know about her health but in a
deeper sense:

> And now I want to come to you, to the sufferings and
> anxieties of your poor life. If you succeed in bringing to
> publication your beloved father's work, of what tortures
> the ensuing magnificent joy would liberate you! What a
> pain it is to think that your companion [Cécile], instead of
> being of help to you, is becoming a burden on you. And
> what to do to alleviate that burden? Why don't you tell us
> about your health? Is it strong enough for you to go on
> without too much exertion? Ever since that enigma [of
> Freymann's silence] has descended upon you, you can guess
> that my thoughts have been flying towards you in the
> measure in which I believed you were sinking into despair
> because of the interruption of the printer's work. You have
> been immersed into suffering, but for a reason. The good
> Lord supported you yesterday. He graciously will support
> you tomorrow. The trial passes, He will remain.

Dufourcq knew that Hélène would always be pleased by
news about the "machurés" and their children. He gave details
such as that Norbert's daughters were preparing for *licences* in
music: "Françoise playing the organ, Marie Claire the clavecin,
Colette the flute, Elizabeth the piano." He knew that Norbert
was particularly dear to Hélène. This is why she gave him in
1937, as a wedding gift, one of Duhem's priceless albums of
landscapes which he religiously kept.

But Dufourcq also knew that ultimately Hélène's thoughts
were invariably returning to things of ultimate importance,
especially the Church. For the Church, such were the last
words in that moving letter, "the situation has never been more
favorable. From all points of the world, even Gandhi with his
cows, everybody reckons with the fact that apart from Christ
and His church, there are only ruins, lies, bestiality, war, and

death. Let us pray and let us abandon ourselves into the hands of the Lord. Your old friend sends you his most affectionate friendship from the depth of his heart. Count on him always!"

Hélène had to read these moving words with mixed feelings. Of course, she owed immense gratitude to Dufourcq who had now for over twenty years displayed a fatherly love for her. But the more the years were added to her intangible debt toward him, the more anguishing it became. Now that another year had gone by, she could not help raise the question, which a Christian always does at the end of the year. The question is whether the end of the next year would find him or her still around. For Hélène this question was inseparable from the eventual fate of her father's great work. But she had to hope and push the cause no matter how distasteful another step, another letter, would be.

A strange dislike of money

There is no reference to the date of Hélène's letter to Freymann who replied on January 19, 1949, and excused himself with a reference to his sickness that kept him from his desk for three weeks. He informed her that Barnéoud had finished the final page-proofs of the entire volume VI and was working on the Index and Table of contents: "We hope to finish this work during the next month, but before that you will receive some proofs which Barnéoud is now working on." On reading this Hélène must have thought of various other occasions, one almost nine years earlier, when Freymann used the same expression, "during the next month."

February was that "next month" and on its tenth day Dufourcq felt that at long last something was really in the air. He hastened to pick up the pen and write to Hélène: "This morning I received a letter from good Cartan (he is always as good as his word) telling me that Freymann was now bound by a contract and that volume VI was to appear soon. For how many days now have I awaited, as you did, the famous volume!" Dufourcq immediately wrote to Cartan, telling him about his moments of despair. "He will, without doubt, go into action . . . . As soon as I learn something I will write." Things appeared indeed so hopeful at the Dufourcqs' that Madame Dufourcq added a few advance congratulatory words to her husband's letter.

Instead of volume VI, word came from Freymann on February 23 that volume VI seemed to be too thick and therefore he decided to break it into two volumes. This meant new covers, new title pages, new sewing, new binding — further unspecifiable delays in the publication of a volume that was already breaking all records in that respect in printing history. Freymann thought that the two volumes (Part I and Part II of volume VI) could be sold at a lower price and therefore more copies would be bought. Curiously, he did not reflect on why he, a seasoned publisher, did not think long before about the thickness of the volume although he should have known for years that it would run to more than 700 pages. He also mentioned, without going into details, that he had received a letter from the Centre National de la Recherche Scientifique. It was not the first, nor the last of such letters.

The true reason why Freymann suddenly found volume VI too thick may have an explanation in the letter which Cartan wrote on March 3 to Hélène. Cartan reported about his having learned from Pérèz that Freymann "unfortunately has a tendency to find insufficient the subvention offered by the Centre for the publication of the *Système du monde*." Still Cartan hoped for a quick publication. He was also pleased to inform Hélène that the Centre granted her an annual subvention. Cartan could not suspect the mixed emotions to be touched off in Hélène on reading his words: "I remain, as much as possible, in contact with my old schoolmate Dufourcq who is very much interested in the work of your father and who is always enchanted as he sees the work of publication advance bit by bit. Only because of him could I intervene with the Centre National de le

Recherche Scientifique. And our friendship has not suffered in spite of the many years during which we have been very far from one another." Dufourcq remained, of course, invaluable. But that "progress bit by bit," which would have made all snails envious, had to appear painfully ironical as the weeks and months kept going by as they had, time and again, for the previous sixteen years.

Dufourcq's letter of June 29 had the unique distinction of containing not a bit of reference to the *Système du monde.* Instead it dealt, in part, with Hélène's long-time companion and friend, Cécile Paradis who had serious troubles with her knees. She was becoming a burden physically on Hélène. The future seemed bleak. Hélène began thinking about the worst and suggested that she would leave the house, the old ancestral house, to Norbert Dufourcq. Or perhaps it could be sold and she would live on the income of the sum received. Suddenly the *Système du monde* appeared not to be a part of the world of the living.

A dead-letter contract

A month or so later, or early August, Dufourcq could say no more than that until October there was no point in resuming contact either with Freymann or with de Broglie. This meant that for another two months or more there was to be no progress whatsoever. Also, Hélène could not help thinking about the number of months she could still count on. The only cheerful, or rather, moving event in her life during those painfully slow summer months was a totally unexpected visit from a professor of history in the Ecole Normale of Montpellier, named Jules Duhem. On August 19 he wrote to convey his thanks for the moving reception. He began by excusing himself for coming with a friend who happened to have a car. However, it was he who, on arriving in the area, had "the sincere desire to go and see you. Together, we have been received by you, regaled with souvenirs, and we have seen with emotion the house where Pierre Duhem lived and the cemetery where he rests in the shade of the cross. For me this pilgrimage has been priceless."

Pierre Duhem would have greatly enjoyed that other Duhem's visit. He would have found in him a kindred soul and not merely a possibly very distant relative. Jules Duhem too was of Flemish roots on his father's side. He knew what he had lost when, through the influence of a relative of his, he was shifted from a school of the Assumptionist Fathers to "lay" education. He had his share in the agonies of World War I through the loss of his two brothers at the front. In an implicit but all too clear reference to the date of Duhem's death, he recalled September 14, 1916, as the day on which his wife's brother also died at the front. His wife was from Provence, daughter of an officer and of a teacher. Moreover, already in 1944, he had been proposed for a chair in the Collège de France. He was also attached to the Centre National de la Recherche Scientifique. One can easily imagine the conversation between him and Hélène who must have, as a result, been invigorated in her sense of mission.

As a historian Jules Duhem had earned renown as a specialist on Montgolfier and early aeronautics.[7] But he readily admitted to Hélène that although he had the first five volumes of the *Système du monde* and the third volume of the Leonardo studies, he had not seriously studied Duhem's thought. He was now ready to study Duhem in depth. Apart from his visit he felt very much moved by his reading of Hélène's biography of her father: "His life could be told only by you. I see him as if he were alive, the man of whom I have often thought, one who is so much above me and yet I find myself akin to him in soul and work. My name has indeed repeatedly suggested to many readers of my works that in addition to a spiritual kinship there was also a legal connection too [between me and your father]."

One paragraph in that letter must have particularly touched
Hélène. Not that Jules Duhem could really help, but he was
certainly ready to do his very best: "Your *ex-dono* [of your
father's works] touched me at my very heart. Not having copies
of any of my two major works on hand, I will ask my publisher
[Hermann] in Paris to send them to you. May my letter serve
until then as my *ex-dono*! You know what trials I go through,
and how weak my influence is. Still, if I can serve you in any
way, please feel free to make use of me. My contacts with
Hermann are now practically dead. A ministry is in charge of
the subvention which Hermann demands in order to publish in
a single volume my articles scattered in various periodicals."

Clearly, Hélène was not the only one who could not
deliver enough money to Hermann et Cie, or rather to its
director Freymann, who did not like money that, in his
estimate, was not sufficient. Moreover, it was not at all certain
that the Centre would provide more funds in spite of all of
Pérès' sympathies. Cartan was willing to contact him again, as
Dufourcq reported to Hélène towards the end of October.
From that letter there emerged for Hélène that very prospect,
the possible passing away of her best support, which must have
weighed heavily on her mind ever since Dufourcq had spoken
of it a year or so earlier. That Dufourcq found Cartan's
handwriting in his latest letter to him very uneven (indeed
almost illegible) bode ill, but even more so did Dufourcq's
decision to inform his son Norbert about the whole history of
the publication of the *Système du monde* in order "to enable him
to collaborate with you." That letter of Dufourcq is also the
sole source of information about a fire in Hélène's house and
her and her companion's lucky escape. Deadly danger lurked in
more than one sense and even things that otherwise would
have gone very fast had slowed down. It was only now that
Dufourcq found time to take up that "other Duhem's visit" in
Cabrespine.

Dufourcq's next letter, written for Christmas, offered no news except the old news that in spite of all, one had to go on hoping and trying as long as one had the strength to do so. The latter had to appear all the more important to Hélène because she was still recovering from the shock of a potentially disastrous fire. Furthermore Dufourcq gently advised her about the limited ability of Norbert to help: "You can count wholly on Norbert. But you should also think of the 'infernal' life he lives. In addition to teaching [organ] at the Conservatory of Paris, he runs his section [of music] at Larousse almost singlehandedly, and spends himself in giving marvelous (though exhausting) conferences everywhere on behalf of 'Jeunesses Musicales.' He will certainly see you when his apostolate takes him in your area. Not long ago he was in the Eastern Pyrenees." Another year had gone by and poor Hélène was nowhere with her great project. Was she to continue writing letters to de Broglie and to the Centre?

She wrote indeed on January 29, 1950, and three weeks later received a reply from de Broglie together with a copy of his letter to Freymann, a letter polite but firm. De Broglie promised to take up the matter with Pérès but no word from the latter came even as late as early April. It was now Holy Week and Dufourcq could but draw a parallel about the meaning of the *Tenebrae* and the apparent burial of Duhem's great work. He urged her to keep writing to Pérès at the Centre and to de Broglie. Unfortunately, she was not to explore the principal avenue still open: "De Broglie is such a great personage that he must not be importuned."

This was *all* the progress during the entire year of 1950. It could have easily broken the spirit of a strong man and all the more so the resilience of a frail woman, thinking and trying, alone and in far away isolation. There she had to cope with the hopeless ticking away of irretrievable time — hour after hour, day after day, week after week, month after month, year after year, and now decade after decade. It must have been a blessing for her not to know that three more fruitless years were still to pass . . . .

The first of those last three years of her apparently fruitless struggles from a total that was to be a full score of years, or one third of a lifetime, began with a letter, written on February 21, 1951, from G. Seigneur, an administrator at the Centre. He told her that Freymann was determined not to publish volume VI and the first five volumes unless he received assurance of a subvention for the remaining volumes VII - X as well. Seigneur found it somewhat strange that Freymann wanted a new project of subvention before publishing volume VI, a volume ready for more than two years. Freymann pleaded financial difficulties and assured Seigneur to submit a specific proposal by early March. Seigneur now asked Hélène to send her a copy of her contract with Freymann.

There followed on March 21 Seigneur's letter to Hélène: "I am distressed to register that volume VI had not yet been published in spite of all the steps I have taken with the publisher during these past years. I send you, under this cover, the copy of a registered letter to Mr. Freymann, which, I hope, will not remain without effect." Seigneur still had to learn a thing or two about Freymann.

And so had Mr Dupouy, the new director of the Centre,[8] whom a certain Lacour,[9] once a student of Duhem, volunteered to contact on behalf of Dufourcq. But, in his letter of May 22, Dufourcq cautioned her: "I will not be discouraged if the answer is embarrassingly dilatory." And again one had to count with the new elections: "We may have to restart, perhaps more energetically, if order returns in the country . . . ." On reading this she may have thought about her energies and about the many occasions when, for the previous twenty years, she had to resume her efforts again and again. She had much too often taken comfort from pieces of news such as the one in Dufourcq's letter: "What gives me great joy is the devotion of this excellent Lacour to the memory of his old teacher and to your very interests." And yet, illusory as this could appear, she had no choice but to hope against hope, just as her beloved father had done much of his life.

She had to muster hope because Dufourcq also informed her about the rapid decline of his and of his wife's strength: "I must tell you how much we have aged, my wife and I, and especially myself, during this past winter. Our physical strength leaves us, the firmness of legs disappears, and the noise becomes unbearable." Such was a sad follow-up to their joyful celebration of their golden wedding anniversary, three months earlier, on February 25th. Yet, Hélène once more had to see the admirable quality of Dufourcq's faith, the source of his never-failing hope. For, in addition to her, Lacour too was the recipient of a copy of a letter which Dupouy wrote to the two Perpetual Secretaries of the Académie des Sciences, one of them de Broglie, of course.

After reviewing the first contract between Duhem and Hermann, and the subsequent agreement between Hélène and Freymann, Dupouy went on with a one-line paragraph:

"This agreement remained a dead-letter."

Dupouy then recalled that Freymann had accepted the Centre's offer of three-hundred-thousand francs for the immediate publication of volume VI and signed a contract with the Centre to that effect on June 15, 1948. "Mr. Freyman promised at that moment to publish volume VI during the summer of 1948 and certainly before the end of that year." Three full years later Dupouy had to continue: "Now this volume, whose composition had been completed several years ago, still had not been published, because the publisher refuses to put it on sale until the printing of the first five volumes is done." In this connection Dupouy referred to the information he had gathered through his several conversations with Freymann during the previous two years. Unfortunately, he added, the Centre's contract with Freymann did not bind him in a way that could be pressed in court. Dupouy then added a paragraph that proved to be decisive in retrospect, but again only in the long run: "Mlle Duhem could, however, easily prove that the contracts signed in 1913 and 1937 have not been honored. But she finds herself in extremely precarious financial circumstances and it is, therefore, impossible for her to contribute, even partially, to the costs of court proceedings." Dupouy concluded with a reference to the keen interest which several members of the Académie des Sciences had expressed in Duhem's work, as a reason for his hope that he could count on the Académie which he assured of his readiness to intervene personally with the publisher.

On November 24, 1951, Mme Albert Dufourcq, née Madeleine Prot, passed away at the age of seventy three. It is easy to imagine the state of mind in which Hélène addressed herself, next day, to Dupouy. His reply, dated December 17, was short, but its firmness gave a new ray of hope which was what she needed most: "The publication of the works left behind by your father, Pierre Duhem, has not receded from the center of my attention. I have intervened with the publisher in a most energetic manner. Concerning the increase of the subvention, which has been accorded to you on the basis of 'Aide aux Savants,' I shall specifically call it to the attention of the Commission that will hold its session shortly. I shall keep you informed."

Alive in Cabrespine

The year 1952 brought only sad news from Paris to Hélène, or news that was of little if any use. The saddest news was the word about the death of Dufourcq on March 10, at the age of eighty. His son, Norbert, overwhelmed with ensuing problems, could not send his assurance to Hélène until April 10 regarding his readiness to assume his father's concern for the *Système du monde*. The only communication from Paris, during that year, was a perfect example of a largely rhetorical expression of concern. It came at the very end of December from the physicist Leprince-Ringuet, member of the Académie des Sciences and well known as a Catholic. Leprince-Ringuet spoke of the high esteem in which his generation of physicists held Duhem's work,[10] and, suggested to Hélène to contact the Centre National de la Recherche Scientifique and the Société des Amis de la Science. He did not seem to be aware of what had been going on for well over a decade. If this was not discouraging, he provided no encouragement for Hélène with his lack of readiness to contact those two places in person. Had he done so, he would have learned an earful. Clearly, there was something hollow in that esteem which Leprince-Ringuet claimed to exist. Forty years later French physicists, especially their Catholic kind, in Paris or elsewhere, still have to learn to esteem Duhem's work in its true value.

While the avenues in Paris seemed to be impassable, a small but precious avenue opened up in Hélène's own country-side and she quickly seized on that opening to let the world know that her father's memory was very much alive in Cabrespine. There and in the surrounding area, as far down as Carcassonne, there still lived people with fond reminiscences about her father's intellectual and human excellence. One of them was Dr. Girou, a physician in Carcassonne, who proposed to Hélène that a marble plaque be placed on the house where her father died. Dr. Girou also did the organizing with the result that people came from far away. Some wrote moving letters of excuse for their inability to attend. One of these came from Louis Roy, a great admirer and promoter of Duhem's ideas of electromagnetics,[11] who had just retired as professor at the University of Toulouse. But he still had to attend one last exam. Hélène knew that her father, so conscious of his duties as a teacher, would have fully approved of Roy's sense of duty and would have been fully satisfied with Roy's assurance that he would "certainly be present in mind."

The ceremony took place on Monday, October 27, 1952, at four o'clock, instead of at eleven in the morning as originally planned. The change was made at the last minute, so as to enable Mr. Laurent, inspector of the Académie des Sciences and its official representative, to arrive on time from Paris.

The ceremony, which was covered by *La Croix*, the big French Catholic weekly published in Paris,[12] began at the house where Mr. Greffier, mayor of Cabrespine, greeted the dignitaries and the large gathering which included each and every one of the village. "The people of Cabrespine still fondly remember the man who was Pierre Duhem and our children shall keep the memory of this magnificent day for a long time." From the house the entire gathering proceeded to the cemetery where Mr. Turc, mayor of nearby Castans, spoke as one who still remembered seeing Duhem hike with his daughter in the neighboring mountains, sketch "with beautiful precision and charm" the groves, the mountains, and valleys of our area, and, most importantly, take "a lively interest in the concerns and lives of their inhabitants."

The ceremony continued at the house. Hélène must have been taken back into the past by more than forty years as the abbé Gabaude revealed himself as the brother of that little tuberculous girl whom she and her father found on one of their hikes and suddenly felt that it was their duty to secure for her, at no matter what cost, the necessary cure.[13] Again, Hélène could but deeply resonate as Prof. Calas,[14] of the University of Bordeaux, sketched her father's scientific career with a competence that could only come from a specialist of physical chemistry, a branch of science which Duhem introduced in France. Most importantly, Prof. Calas noted in conclusion Duhem's resolve not to let "what he considered to be truth to be sacrificed either on the scientific level or in his personal life." It is to such men, Prof. Calas added, that "French universities owe that perfect independence which they enjoy today."

The speech delivered by Monseigneur Peuch, bishop of Carcassonne, sketched the unity of faith and science in Duhem. The bishop did so on the basis of Hélène's biography of her father. One can easily imagine her feelings as she heard the bishop quote in full from that biography a letter[15] which is one of the many rare such gems there, gems first made public by her. *La Croix* was now carrying to millions of Catholics in France and beyond, how a young woman teacher, recovering in the company of that little girl in one of the sanatoriums in Arcachon, had thanked Duhem for his mere example, in which the scientist and the believer were inseparably and harmoniously united, that had helped her recover her faith.

Finally, it was Hélène's turn who once more showed with her diction to be a genuine echo of her father's voice:

Monsieur le Préfet, Monseigneur, Mesdames et Messieurs,

I am truly incapable of expressing my feelings of gratitude for this magnificent homage of yours to the memory of my father.

On accepting the presidency of this ceremony, you, Monsieur le Préfet, evoked in a magisterial way, and in terms which fill me with a filial pride, the scientific work of my father.

Your Excellency, Monseigneur Peuch, has told us about the firmness of his religious convictions, the probity of his life, to illustrate that in his serene soul no incompatibility whatever existed between the Christian faith and a most rigorous and unfettered scientific thinking.

Then, you Professor Calas, you have brought here a most precious witness, the work of Pierre Duhem judged by his peers. This touched me to the bottom of my heart. With what emotion have I listened to you! You have evoked my father's activitiy at the University of Bordeaux, of my father who applauded the establishment of universities in the provinces and expected them to radiate in the manner of the Sorbonne. I relived these happy years in Bordeaux, years so full, so fruitful, during which my father spent his strength with the full ardor of his teaching. I thought of his care for his students and of the enthusiasm with which he conceived so many various works of pure science, of philosophy, of the history of science, but which all converged towards the same goal: the progress, the deepening of the route of theoretical physics across time.

Finally, I cannot thank enough Dr. Girou who first rendered homage in the newspapers to the work of the scientist. He was the organizer and initiator of this meeting, and he did so with vigilance and indefatigable devotion.

While alive Pierre Duhem avoided all honors. Those honors came to him, bit by bit, after his death, but never with such a great solemnity as today. I also would like to add, and with even greater emotion, that the entire population wanted to be united in bringing him homage. In addition to his scientific work, many think of him as a simple and good man, open to all as Mr. Turc and the abbé Gabaude have told us who both knew this from personal experience. This home, though the house of my family, was also a house for everybody. Who of the residents of Cabrespine has not entered this house, trusting and certain about the welcome or the help to be asked?

This memory, this tradition will now be forever engraved on the facade of the old house. For your readiness, Monsieur le Préfet, to accept the honor of presiding over the occasion, and for your graciousness, Your Excellency, to participate, please kindly accept the expression of my profound gratitude. And to all of you who wanted to be part of this ceremony, from the bottom of my heart I want to thank you.

She must have been particularly thankful to the Préfet for his presence, but especially for his impromptu suggestion that no gesture would more fittingly conclude the moving ceremony than the placing of a wreath on the memorial of those sons of Cabrespine who died in World War I and II. As the whole gathering walked silently to the memorial in the wall of the

Church she must have recalled the agonies her father suffered for those in the trenches, and his final excruciating agony, however brief, that put an end to his life. Her own agonies were meant to be less acute, but far more protracted. She now gathered much needed strength for more years of waiting and hard work still ahead of her.

The breakthrough

One can only guess Hélène's state of mind as she began her letter of January 8, 1953, to Freymann with the question: "Am I right in thinking that you are still concerned with the publication of the *Système du monde?*" She continued with a reference to her recent visit in Paris where she found that "several important people still think that the publication of the still unpublished volumes remain of the highest importance for the study of the history of science." Her old fighting spirit was fully alive, perhaps rekindled by the success of that October ceremony in Cabrespine. In Paris she must have visited above all Norbert Dufourcq and his oldest sister, Henriette, Mme Charles Gallet. Possibly she also contacted Jacques Hadamard. The reason for this conjecture will be given later. At any rate, she wanted to know Freymann's present intentions and their practical implementation. She then briefly recalled the data she had obtained from him years earlier about the completion of the first five volumes as well as of volume VI.

She received a reply, not unusual in itself, but which forecast some event which few if any could foresee at that moment. Of course, in a long drawn-out struggle, such as the one that saw her and Freymann at loggerheads now for almost twenty years, one thought could not help coming up on both sides: who will outlive the other? As it turned out, Hélène was to outlast Freymann by almost twenty years, but this would not by itself have added to the drama. Hélène herself could have hardly thought in such terms when she received, in mid-January, a note from Freymann's assistant: "We acknowledge your letter of the 8th of January, 1953, to our director Mr. Freymann, who is actually away from the office, owing to his wife's serious illness. We have transmitted to him your letter and he instructed us to let you know that he would answer your questions upon his return which we hope to be soon."

Most likely Freymann left Hélène's letter unanswered. He obviously thought that his delaying tactic would work, because it had certainly stood him in good stead whenever, during the previous twenty years, he had felt the need to take recourse to it. He was able to ward off Dupouy's insistance, in letters and in words, during 1952 and 1953, that the publication could no longer be delayed in view of the Centre's readiness to disburse the subvention at a moment's notice. He was able to continue with what in all evidence could but appear "sabotage" even when reminded by Dupouy that he had given, in Dupouy's very office in the Centre, his "word of honor" about resuming the business of publishing "right away." Freymann did not budge even in view of the fact that de Broglie was a co-recipient of most of Dupouy's communications to him.

Being privy to all this, at least in part, Hélène was able to restrain herself. Possibly she wrote to Freymann again in late Spring 1953, and certainly in the Fall of that year. Her letter of March 14, 1954, to Freymann pointedly recalled a letter she had written to him "several months earlier" with the remark that it had failed to be honored with a reply. She was not to be defeated. In mid-December 1953 she was once more in Paris "to visit several important personalities about the publication of the *Système du monde,*" as she put it in her letter of December 5 to Freymann. Most importantly she wanted to meet Freymann himself. It would have been their first meeting in seventeen years. She informed him that she went in the afternoon of December 21, a Monday, to the offices of Hermann et Cie at 6 Place de la Sorbonne, only to find the place closed! The same evening she had to take the train to Carcassonne, through Toulouse, a fourteen-hour journey. From

Carcassonne to Cabrespine it could be two to three hours more in a horse-drawn coach with the draft of winter winds freely moving across it. At Christmas, she could all the more feel united with those who had not been received at the inn . . . .

Her letter of March 14, 1954, was part of her mustering once more her resolve and courage. She may have been prompted partly by three letters she had received from an American scholar, who had just arrived in Bordeaux to spend a semester there in studying Duhem's work. Philip Wiener, the scholar in question, had already translated Duhem's *La théorie physique* into English, a work which heightened his interest in Duhem.[16] No sooner had he arrived in Bordeaux, with his wife and two daughters, than he had written to Hélène in Cabrespine, partly because of a misunderstanding between Rivière and Princeton University Press about her rights to royalties. Wiener asked whether he could visit her in Cabrespine, and whether she would meanwhile send him Duhem's manuscripts and correspondence which he was ready to microfilm at the University of Bordeaux at his own cost. Most important for Hélène was Wiener's reference to Chadbourne Gilpatrick, director of the Rockefeller Foundation, from whom Wiener, as a friend of his, was willing to ask for a subvention to speed up the publication of the *Système du monde*. A new ray of hope appeared on the horizon. Or would it be just another illusory flash?

More apparently promising flashes came with Wiener's letter of March 4. Dear memories must have come back to Hélène as Wiener spoke of Paul Saurel as his own teacher at City College in New York and one who never failed to extol the merits of Duhem. She was nine when she met Saurel, a doctoral student of her papa and from America at that! Wiener also thanked her for sending him a copy of *Un savant français*: "I have immediately started reading the impassioned pages full of details that I could not have found elsewhere. I feel I am being overwhelmed by treasures." Wiener also wrote to her that in walking to the Faculté, he went every day along Rue Pierre Duhem!

For a moment Hélène must have floated on cloud nine. She seemed to regain a much needed emotional momentum to make once more a major step. In her letter of March 14 to Freymann she again raised old questions about his intentions and planned procedures. This time she expected some reply because ten days earlier she had written to de Broglie. She recalled there the "unheard of obstacles" she had been facing with respect to Hermann et Cie and begged de Broglie to ask the Académie des Sciences to request formally that the Centre National de la Recherche Scientifique assume responsibility for the publication of the *Système du monde*. Hélène now made a request she could not easily make again. In a sense she played her last cards. In addition to the letters of Wiener, she found encouragement from Hadamard, a very important figure at the Académie and still a most devoted friend of her papa.

Most unexpectedly she received a quick reply, if not from Freymann, at least from Hermann et Cie, a reply also with a most unexpected content. The reply, signed on March 22, by a manager in the firm, informed her "about the decease of our Director, Mr. Freymann. Since the firm has not changed its structure, Mr. Louis Hermann, one of the managers, will assume its direction." It was therefore the new director who received the note, dated March 31, in which de Broglie, as perpetual secretary of the Académie des Sciences, had threatened the firm with a court action. Two weeks later, the new director stated in writing to de Broglie his intention to go ahead immediately with the publication of the *Système du monde*. She did not write in vain to de Broglie. It was with a light heart that Hélène read the letter which Hadamard wrote to her on April 14. There Hadamard, obviously unaware of that latest communication of Louis Hermann to de Broglie, still spoke of the "grave obstacle that had arisen through the death of Mr. Freymann." Hadamard thought that the principal difficulty still was the way of finding the complement to the contribution promised by the Centre and added: "How easy this would be if we were Polytechnicians!"

It is easy to guess what de Broglie's and Dupouy's thoughts were on reading Louis Hermann's letter to de Broglie. There Louis Hermann claimed nothing less than that, on studying Freymann's dossier on the subject, it was clear that according to Freymann himself "there was no need to wait for a subvention." For his part, Louis Hermann declined the plan of solliciting subscribers, because he could not guarantee a fixed price for the volumes still to be published. Nor did he see any reason to take up the suggestion of Philip Wiener to contact the Rockefeller Foundation about a subvention. Clearly, Freymann's spirit survived at Hermann et Cie. The profit forthcoming from the sales of the *Système du monde* was not to be shared by anyone else. Unfortunately, this policy almost succeeded in aborting the publication of a work to which in the same letter Louis Hermann referred to as "the source of great interest in the English speaking world."

This reference to "the English-speaking world" cut both ways for Wiener at least. On returning briefly to the United States for Easter, old copies of the first four volumes of the *Système du monde* were waiting for him. He was overwhelmed by Hélène's thoughtfulness. He now also began to see the mental drama behind Hélène's brief recount, in her letter of February 8 to him, of the sad story of her efforts to have the remaining volumes of the *Système du monde* published.

No sooner had Wiener arrived back in Paris, than he visited de Broglie, Dupouy, and Hermann himself. Here one detail should suffice from his three letters, written between April 14 and May 3, to Hélène. The one dated April 21 dealt mostly with his visit with Hermann and contained two references to the "increasingly scandalous delay" of the publication of the *Système du monde*. Clearly, Louis Hermann must have heard an earful about the biggest scandal in the modern history

of academic publications. To prevent that scandal from explod-
ing in his face, and in the face of the illustrious publishing firm
he was now heading, the best thing was to publish those
volumes with all possible speed and give Duhem and his valiant
daughter their long overdue victory. On June 30th Hadamard
informed Hélène that he felt most honored by her request to
present volume VI to the Académie des Sciences. Victory was
now smiling on her, although with a last-minute tease.

Compared with her struggle of twenty or more years to let
her father's masterwork see print in full, these next five or six
months before she had in hand the long awaited volume VI
seemed only a few minutes. Its last two lines carry the information that Barnéoud finished its printing in the 9th month of
1954 and that the publisher made a legal deposit of it in the
third trimester of the same year as #419 of books registered
during that period. It should not be difficult to guess her
feelings as she held the first copy of that volume in her hands.
The date of that moment may have come unduly late. As will
be seen in the next chapter, it was not until next April that the
publisher asked her for a list of those whom she considered to
be in the first place for a complimentary copy. At any rate,
word must have started spreading about the great breakthrough.
Here too, not only was it true that what is victory for some is
defeat for others, but that victory may reveal its meaning far
more effectively when seen from the losers' side.

The meaning of victory

The victory had far more to it than the appearance in print, at
long last, of the manuscript of a startlingly original scholarly
work. To see this additional aspect one should try to fathom
Freymann's true reasons for delaying so doggedly and bafflingly
the publication of the *Système du monde*. Whatever the regularly
recurring financially difficult times (which never cease in French
business parlance), mere financial reasons should have made it
imperative to put on sale the volumes in question as soon as

much of the typesetting and reprinting had been done. To do otherwise was to lose more and more of the returns of the capital invested in the venture. Again, financially it just did not make sense, certainly not from 1947 on when everything was ready, to decide against the acceptance of a subvention from the Centre lest the profit should be shared. The fact that there were few orders for the first five volumes and for the sixth volume, after they had been announced in 1939, called for putting the books on sale rather than holding them back. Reviews of the new volume, in fact the very availability of the first five volumes, could have reversed this situation. Actually, the new volume, when published, created a brisk market for the remaining volumes as well.

One must therefore take a close look at Freymann's repeated though brief remarks about his having heard hostile remarks toward Duhem in general and toward the *Système du monde* in particular. Could it be that he was intimidated by some prominent visitors in his office who expressed their displeasure with the plan of bringing Duhem once more to the fore, and especially an idea particularly dear to him and revolting to them? Anyone familiar with the already published volumes of the *Système du monde* and with the three volumes of Duhem's Leonardo studies, could easily guess what was to come, and on a grand scale at that, in volume VI and the following volumes. An indirect task of those volumes was to challenge some "sacred" dogmas of modern secularist civilization.

Not that Duhem mixed such reflections, however justified to any student keen on all the facts of Western intellectual history, into either of those massive works. But his massive documentation, which nobody could match, let alone challenge, of the existence of science during the Middle Ages, must have cut to the quick all believers in the principal message of the French Enlightenment and of the secularist civilization it bred and nurtured. According to that tenet science and "scientific" thinking were the only salvation for mankind.

The "truth" of this tenet largely depended on painting with the darkest colors those Middle Ages during which Christian salvation history became the matrix of Western civilization. While secularist Western civilization has gradually relented on its flat dismissal of the Middle Ages with respect to literature, architecture, and social organization, the same civilization still takes the idea of a medieval origin of modern science for a treacherous undermining of its entrenched positions. Today, almost a hundred years after Duhem, secularist historians of science, and secularist scientists ignorant of its true history, are far more aware of the bearing of Duhem's discovery of science during the Middle Ages than are those, Christians in general and Catholics in particular, who should look at him as their intellectual liberator.

Quite possibly, Freymann was not personally bothered by such considerations, but not a few of those who saw him fairly often in his office during the 1930s positively were. The names of those, whom Abel Rey reported to Hélène in 1936, included the name of Paul Langevin, always eager about the latest in physics but even more eager to promote a scientistic, materialistic, if not plainly Marxist ideology. Langevin was also the director of one of the subdivisions of the *Actualités scientifiques* and therefore regularly met with Freymann. Langevin repeatedly went on record with his contempt for Duhem.[17] Could not, in one of their meetings, arise the idea of first slowing down and then of postponing indefinitely the publication of the *Système du monde* and thereby save modern secularist culture from a major challenge? To dismiss such an explanation as a mixing of Christian ideology into scholarship is to forget the measure to which historical scholarship has been mixed up all too often with a very anti-Christian ideology.

At any rate, scholarship is based on an unconditional respect for facts and for their scholarly presentation. One of those ready to give Duhem's scholarship its due, without sharing Duhem's Christian convictions, was Wiener. He was eager to report to Hélène about Morris R. Cohen,[18] his teacher of philosophy at City College, as one who "used to speak with the greatest respect of your father's work. It is probable that in his conversations with his friend Cohen, Saurel often talked of the courses given by your father." But in 1899 and 1900, when Saurel did his doctoral work with Duhem, he could only see in Duhem the theoretical physicist. Duhem, the incisively sound and soundly incisive philosopher of science, was as yet hardly visible. Duhem the historian of science was still to emerge. Of course, Saurel later received all of Duhem's works on the history of science, but there is no evidence that he delved into them.[19] Whatever he told Cohen about Duhem the philosopher and historian of science must have consisted of generalities. These, for all their glow, could hardly spark a serious interest in Duhem, the historian-philosopher of science, which is something more than just speaking highly of him. Now that the full publication of his immortal work was finally under way, only the willfully blind could ignore its radiance. His daughter's remaining twenty years were bathed in its light and warmth.

9

A Long Sunset

Leonardo, sudden ally

On the first day of March 1955 the manuscript of volume VII was handed over to Louis Hermann at the office of Louis de Broglie, Perpetual Secretary of the Académie des Sciences. Once more a publisher was regaled not only with a manuscript of priceless contents but also in a peerless form. Otherwise, the publisher would not have been able to write to Hélène two days later that the manuscript had already been handed over to the printer. Duhem's manuscripts did not need so much as to be touched by a copy-editor. Hélène was asked whether she would do the proofreading, or would allow the publisher to choose one: "Have you not years ago entrusted that job to Mr Dufour [sic]?" In this question Hélène could rightly see an unintended slighting of her own vast efforts. Of course, by then sixteen years had gone by since she had finished proofreading volume VI. Dufourcq, her late great friend, certainly helped with technicalities of Latin and Greek, but the main task of proofreading was always hers. All this could be easily forgotten in the publisher's offices, especially with a major change in the policy there.

She must have been partly flattered, partly amused when a week later she received from the Perpetual Secretary of the Académie des Sciences a letter in which she was addressed as "Mademoiselle Pierre Duhem." This quaint *faux pas* could but confirm the sense of identity she had, by then for decades, intensely cultivated with the personality of her father. The letter informed her that the publisher was so "satisfied with the results of the publication of volume VI" as "to continue without delay" with the publication of the rest of the manuscripts.

The publication of volume VI created indeed a kind of sensation in scholarly circles. Suddenly Duhem's other works began to be looked for and were found to be out of print. Not surprisingly, the publication of volume VI drew special attention to Duhem's *Etudes sur Léonard de Vinci*. On March 6 the mail brought her a letter with the name Jean Langevin on the letterhead, followed by an apparently private address and telephone number.[1] A curious letter it was, to say the least, as it contained not a word about the publication of volume VI. Langevin began with the statement that "since your father's remarkable work on Leonardo da Vinci, although of interest to a certain number of scholars, had been out of print for a long time, I thought that it might be useful to make a very small reprint edition of it." Before going into details on partly financial points, "points rather delicate in view of three big volumes," Langevin wanted to know whether Hélène really owned the rights of publication.

Possibly Langevin thought that whatever rights Hélène had they might have expired as the last volume of the Leonardo had been published more than forty years earlier. At any rate, Langevin seemed so eager to go ahead with the work of reprinting as to ask Hélène about royalties she wanted for a reprint edition of a hundred copies of each volume. In her reply, Hélène specified a royalty of ten percent as customary with other books of her father. Her real concern related to the size of the new edition. She felt that the book deserved and justified a much larger printing. Last but not least she wondered aloud: "Excuse me, Monsieur, are you yourself a publisher, or to what publishing house do you plan to turn?" Privately, as will be seen shortly, she thought that Langevin might be the son or grandson of the physicist, Paul Langevin, hardly a friend of her father. So she must have been puzzled, or perhaps took this detail too for another evidence of "the change of the Lord's right hand."

On April 4, she received from Hermann a request to approve a slightly different typefont for the printing of volume VII which she found very similar to the type used for the printing of volume VI. She also noted in her reply that Albert Dufourcq died in 1952 and that she would be pleased if Hermann would find somebody to check Latin and Greek texts. She planned to write to Doublet, astronomer in Bordeaux, who in 1915 helped with the proofreading of volume V and in 1935 expressed readiness to help again. But would she find him still alive? She must have now realized that as the years went by she was left more and more alone. The world of her papa, a world in which she was still living in thought, was rapidly becoming a world of a distant past.

Two weeks later word came from the publishing house F. De Nobele, 35 Rue Bonaparte, that Langevin had been acting on its behalf. The publisher, De Nobele, was ready to offer the royalties requested by her and print 300 copies of each volume. She was asked to reply within a week, because the printer could not guarantee the price of production in view of the inflation. De Nobele had in fact set June 15 as the date of publication, and was ready to issue an appeal for advance orders in early May. The date of the contract, April 20, revealed the publisher's sense of urgency. Duhem suddenly became once more a sought-after author. All minor questions and requests of Hélène were given immediate and complete satisfaction. The contract assured her of full rights to the entire work, if another edition was to be called for.

The fact that three letters from the publisher addressed to her went astray, posed no complication. Hélène, whom Langevin informed about De Nobele's high standing as a publisher of books of art, received assurance that her royalties would be calculated according to the list price and not according to the price, 40% less, charged to booksellers. Still Langevin did not give Hélène any specifics about himself. Whatever role he played in the production of the reprinting of the *Etudes*, it showed efficiency. By May 23 the proofs of the title pages of the reprint edition were in Hélène's hands.

From the remoteness of Cabrespine, Hélène could at best guess the real role of Langevin in the publication of the *Etudes*. His name did not come up after Hermann read the announcement in the June 15 issue of the *Bibliographie de France*, about the publication of "*Etudes sur Léonard de Vinci* in 3 volumes." The news touched a nerve at Hermann et Cie where the work was originally published between 1909 and 1913. Hélène was asked whether she had given her consent to De Nobele. Hélène replied the next day, June 22, by pointing out that she was the sole owner of the rights to that work of her father. She also recalled that years earlier Freymann dropped the idea of republishing the *Etudes* as an enterprise with no monetary promise. Hélène could therefore write: "I was therefore very happy that a publishing house thinks of reissuing this very important work of my father." She hoped that the first 7 batches of the galleys of volume VII, corrected by her, had safely arrived in Paris. Her main concern related to the fact that she had received no word from any of those whom she had put on the list of recipients of complimentary copies of volume VI. She wanted to mail those copies herself.

Two days later she was informed that batches 8-15 of the galleys of volume VII, corresponding to pages 140 - 375 of the manuscript, had been posted to her. This meant that already one half of that volume had been typeset. If she thought that publication could come before the end of the year, she was to be rudely disappointed. At any rate, she received assurance that complimentary copies of volume VI had been sent to de Broglie, Hadamard, Dupouy, Pérès, Adrien Bruhl,[2] Norbert Dufourcq, and Max Black,[3] in addition to three others: Doublet, Dr. Girou of Carcassonne, and Jean Gabriel Lemoine, director of the Musée des Beaux Arts in Bordeaux.

The latter, who as a historian of Renaissance art had found a mine of information in Duhem's researches,[4] responded first and with reference to Hélène's foreword: "How well I understand your distress concerning the inertia of the publisher! I hope that he will realize the responsibility weighing on him! At any rate, were you to die, you have now lived up to your responsibility with respect to your father's work. What a relief this should be for you!" He promised to tell all that volume VI is a promise of even better things to follow and concluded: "I tell you all this in the name of all for whom Duhem's thought was a guide, a source of strength, and a revelation." On reading volume VI Dr. Girou found himself "stupefied by the immensity of information of its author on the history of science . . . who gives a passionate overview of the intellectual universe." A. Koyré, a leading historian of early modern science, would say the same, though with a revealing twist.[5]

Hélène rightly guessed that she would act in her father's spirit if she offered the manuscript of volume VI to the Library of the University of Bordeaux. J. Guinard, the librarian, replied on the 8th of July: "It will be an honor for the Library to keep the sheets that first contained the text of a work of capital importance for the history of science. Our gratitude is all the greater because the text is the work of one of the professors in whom the University of Bordeaux takes the greatest pride. You are not mistaken in thinking that the memory of your father has remained very much alive here. The presence of his manuscript in our collections will do much to make his memory even more vivid and to encourage young scholars to march in his footsteps."

Later that week, in mid-summer, the publication of the *Etudes* suddenly loomed large on the horizon as the seed of a potentially big storm. On July 11 Louis Hermann informed Hélène that he considered De Nobele's offprint reproduction of the *Etudes* a plain theft and grounds for legal action. While on reading this she could feel apprehensive, she could but smile on reading the next paragraph in which Hermann interpreted to her De Nobele's procedure as a maneuver of sheer profit taking. Once more the pot called the kettle black. In view of what had been going on since the 1930s, Hélène could hardly find convincing Hermann's argument that compared with the 2000 copies of volume VI, the few hundred copies of the *Etudes* did not constitute "a rescuing of her father's memory from oblivion." Finally, Hélène could but smile in disbelief on reading Hermann's claim that only the bad economic conditions prevented Freymann from reissuing the *Etudes*. Contrary to Hermann's claim, it was not Hélène who proposed around 1935 the reprinting of the *Etudes*. Freymann himself made that proposal. Last but not least, Hermann was just plain wrong in claiming that Freymann had dropped the idea because of economic difficulties and because at that time "the educated public was not oriented toward the history of science."

To Louis Hermann, who wanted to know the exact form of the authorization given by Hélène to De Nobele, she replied three days later. After giving the exact details of the contract she had signed with De Nobele, she referred to her complete lack of information about Mr. Jean Langevin whom she thought perhaps to be "the son or grandson of Mr. Paul Langevin." Concerning the difference of price between volume VI (2,900 francs) and the three volumes of the *Etudes* (15,000 francs),[6] she wrote: "I did not have the naiveté to think that De Nobele had anything more than his own interest in mind in reprinting my father's work. His own interest is his own business; mine was to be happy and proud to see this capital work of my father reissued." Finally she expressed her displeasure over De Nobele's less than fair attitude toward Hermann et Cie.

However, Hélène must have known that she may have mislead De Nobele by her insistance that she had all the proprietary rights over the *Etudes*. If necessary, her words to De Nobele could have been seized upon in a legal forum. But if this possibility had arisen in Hélène's mind, she could recall her frustration about the possibility of taking Freymann to court in the 1930s. The high cost of such an action would have now been defrayed by Hermann. Once more the roles had been reversed. This is why she could be peremptory in writing to De Nobele on the same day. She began with a reference to Hermann's astonishment on learning the news about the reprint edition. Then she continued: "I have told you that I am the sole owner of my father's rights to that work and on this point I am completely in agreement with Hermann et Cie. But I could not give you an authorization which my father himself could not have given . . . . You can hardly be unaware of the fact that this reprinting, done by leaving Hermann et Cie in the dark, can be taken for plagiarism. I would be very much obliged if you would repair this oversight as soon as possible, by obtaining the consent of Hermann et Cie." She concluded with a word of thanks for De Nobele's promise that the royalties for the brisk sales of the *Etudes* would be sent to her promptly.

In his reply of July 21 De Nobele insisted on the strict meaning of Hélène's assurance that she had "full ownership" over the rights concerning the *Etudes*. This meant that if there was any conflict of interest, it concerned Louis Hermann and Hélène. Hermann took up the matter only at the end of November and did so in a conciliatory tone. He felt that the annoyance caused to Hélène was more than enough reason to see the matter closed. Hermann could, of course, rightly complain that in view of the contents of its volume III, the reprinting of the *Etudes* might be prejudicial to the success of the eventual sales of volumes VII and VIII of the *Système du monde*.

On reading this, Hélène could have felt entitled to have her own complaint. At the end of September, only the first 64 pages of volume VII were in page proofs. If production continued at that rate, publication was not to come for another year. Nor were reviews of volume VI to come for another year, even in periodicals most sympathetic to Duhem's work. Such was the *Revue des questions scientifiques* whose editor wrote on August 4, 1955 to Hélène that he had just received volume VI from its publisher. Yet he received the three volumes of the *Etudes* at the same time!

The personal letters she began to receive about volume VI could, of course, but strengthen, if this was at all possible, her conviction about the unique value of the volumes still to be printed. One of those letters, dated July 7, 1955, came from M. Lacoin, a retired mechanical engineer, much interested in pre-Galilean science.[7] He wanted to know how soon would volume VII see print and whether he could obtain a table of contents of that volume and of the manuscripts still to be printed. He felt some urgency as he was preparing an article for the *Revue des questions scientifiques*: "Excuse me, Mademoiselle, for my indiscretion but the task to which I devote the final part of my life is, in a sense, a continuation of the work of Pierre Duhem."[8]

A month later came a letter from Dom Olphe-Galliard, head of the Benedictine Abbey of Sainte Marie in Paris. On August 5, within a few days of having received a complimentary copy of volume VI, he congratulated Hélène on her victory: "The memory of your father and his admirable work demanded this success as an obligation of probity on the part of French science. All those who knew Pierre Duhem, all those who attended his lectures and contracted thereby a debt of gratitude toward him, are now rejoicing over a result which adds, in the eyes of the world, a new ray to the glory of the scientist and the writer." Then the Abbot wondered how many of Duhem's students were still alive. "Ignorant as I am, I do not dare to call myself a student of Duhem. He was, however, for me an admirable model both as a man and a Christian, no less than a man of science. His moral physiognomy has profoundly influenced me. This is enough for me to resonate to everything related to his memory and his work that touch me to the depth of my heart."[9]

Loss and gain

A year later, in mid-summer of 1956, volume VII was still in the proof stage. Hélène could take some comfort in the fact that the publisher suddenly seemed to have been seized with a sense of urgency. Printing was completed in December. By then Hélène had for some months been trying to live a new life. The death of Cécile Paradis, her faithful companion for over twenty years, left her with more chores than she could have handled alone even if she had been much younger than sixty-five. In addition to a large house and garden to be kept in order, there were some animals — chicken, geese, rabbits, and goats — to be cared for. As one may expect, the ancestral home grew more and more untidy, outside as well as inside.

The same year also saw the forced going out of print of one of her father's works. On registering the lack of sales of the *Thermodynamique et Chimie* as re-edited by Boutaric, Hermann decided to send the remaining 76 copies to the papermill. While Hélène may not have felt too downcast by this, it was otherwise when word came from Gauthier-Villars that a similar fate was in store for two of her father's major works, the *Leçons sur l'électricité et le magnétisme* and the *Traité d'énergetique*. According to the inventory, 114, 69 and 124 copies of the three volumes of the *Leçons* were in stock at the end of 1955. The figures for the two volumes of the *Traité* were 258 and 264. On September 26 she was informed by the publisher that if no

word came from her within three months, all those copies
would be turned into pulp.

She, of course, sent word. The volumes were still intact
in April 1956, partly because of the intervention of a prominent
businessman in Paris whose wife was a childhood friend of
Hélène. Actually, there was far more to that connection. Mme
Henriette Gallet, the wife of Mr. Charles Gallet, owner of a
world-famous perfumery, felt that as the oldest child of Albert
Dufourcq she had to take on some of her father's concern for
Hélène. Henriette Gallet's good-will proved to be a chief gain
for Hélène for the rest of her life.

Hélène did her best to explain through Henriette to Mr.
Gallet the importance which the *Traité d'énergetique* had for her
father:

> I must give you some details about that work which is the
> crowning of all of my father's work in physics. I can talk
> of it only generally because this work of mathematical
> physics is totally beyond me. But I know that papa tried to
> interpret the laws that rule the physical phenomena and he
> thought that since the various systems of physics are
> ephemeral, the efforts of classifying them would give a
> more and more perfect picture of a true order in nature.
> The *Traité d'énergetique* is that effort of classification in
> which not only the actually observed phenomena can be
> located but also those to be observed in the future.

This nutshell summary of the *Traité* could have done credit
to a better-grade science writer. But the same letter of April 2,
1957, also revealed much of Hélène's penetratingly analytical
mind. First she pointed out that this "spiritualized concept of
physics" earned an unremitting hostility to her father already in
his student years. She suspected a plot:

> To what extent is that old hostility behind this plan to send
> his most important works to the papermill? I wonder . . .

because there are some unexplainable details in the letter of the publisher. How is it that if during the occupation the Germans wanted to send those works to the papermill, the publisher said nothing of this to me while at the same he continues sending me each year statements about the copies remaining in stock! And how can he ask me to authorize his sending those copies to the papermill if only 3 copies are left?

She wished Henriette a pleasant Easter holiday in Normandie: "Will the apple trees be blooming? Here the cherry trees turned my 'prairie' (*our* 'prairie') into a bouquet of flowers. The rain washed them away, the grass is covered with petals, one might say, of confetti, as if it were the day after carnival." And she thanked her in advance for her husband's help. The reason for her underlining the word *our* will be clear shortly.

In early May Mr. Gallet went in person to the offices of Gauthier-Villars and found it in chaos. In fact, the disorder was so great that yearly statements of volumes in stock had been sent out for the previous ten years without the stocks beings checked. The fact was that almost all copies of the *Traité* had to be destroyed, for fear of German reprisals, during the occupation. Only 3 copies were left of volume I and none of volume II, and, since the cause of destruction was a "force majeure," no damages could be claimed. Possibly Hélène took a slight patriotic pride in this outcome. Her father certainly would have looked upon it in that light. And he would have expressed confidence that the *Traité* would eventually be reprinted. This is in fact what happened but by then she had been dead for more than a dozen years.[10]

Hélène could take comfort in the fact that on March 8th Hermann asked for and received the manuscript of volume VIII of the *Système*. She learned of this from a communication from the Académie des Sciences, which also contained the list of chapters in that set of manuscripts. A letter of de Broglie also informed her that in taking charge of the mansucript, Hermann did not bring up the matter of subvention. In all evidence, the publication of the *Système* was proving itself very good business. This may have encouraged Hélène to press Hermann to re-publish another of her father's masterpiece, *La théorie physique*. On learning that she was ready to approach another publisher, Hermann asked for her patience until the completion of the *Système*. Work on the *Système* suddenly gathered speed.

Copies of volume VII were in the mail in early January 1958 and of volume VIII by early May of the same year. In fact, in early Fall 1958 Hélène approved for publication the page-proofs of volume IX and she did the same toward the end of the same year with the page proofs of volume X. Pierre Berès, the new director of Hermann et Cie, expressed on March 2, 1959, his hope that both volumes might appear within a month or so. The composition of the vast Index of Names for volumes VI-X was being done, a work about which Hélène had written on February 28 to Berès that she was pleased for not having been burdened with it.

Berès quickly turned her joy rather sour: "I think you find it just that the expenses for that work would be deducted from your royalties." On reading this she was seized by the memory of the injustices which Hermann et Cie had inflicted on her over many years. In her letter of March 9 she told Berès that he should have referred to the idea of a subject index which she had earlier mentioned and considered very important: "I do not see at all why I should reimburse a work I never refused to do. I find this all the more unjust because I have already suffered enough damages from your House. I know, Monsieur, that you have nothing to do with that and that you have wholly devoted yourself to the publication of the *Système du monde*, a work interrupted for thirty-eight years for which your publishing House is the sole cause. This interruption did great damage to my father's work."

She also felt it necessary to inform Berès about details of which he could hardly be aware: "You may not know that in

1938 Freymann demanded, in return for his promise that he
would bring out volume VI in the same year (!), that I re-
nounce my royalties of 40% for the copies that remained of the
first edition. I thereby foolishly parted with tens of thousands of
pre-War francs. I therefore find it absolutely unjust and mali-
cious that I have to infringe on my royalties for a work I had
not been asked to do." After excusing herself for having said all
this "in all frankness," she added that in comparison with an
Index of Subjects, the composition of the Index of Names was
not at all a major work. The latter could have been done by
any careful typist, and also at a leisurely pace as the page-proofs
of volumes IX and X had for some months been available.

Later that month she asked Henriette to ask her husband
to help settle her dispute with Berès. "In correspondence I risk
being harsh and I do not want to have a fight with him as he
promised that following the publication of volume X he would
publish two works of my papa which my dear papa esteemed
highly." The same letter of March 22 gives a glimpse into her
actual life in Cabrespine. First she expressed her appreciation for
Henriette's invitation to spend the Easter holidays with her
family in Paris:

> It would have been a great joy for me to accept as I would
> have found it a joy - not the capital, Paris; its noise and
> agitation do not attract me at all, as I am accustomed to the
> silence and recollection of my mountains - to spend a few
> days in your intimate company as we have so many
> thoughts in common and life here is very solitary. But I
> cannot be absent from here, as I have no one to replace me
> in all the work that constitutes my living in the country.

Hers was indeed a life of hard work, resembling the life in
many ways of a hard-working peasant woman.

It was also a life of the deep faith of such women. In the
same letter she expressed her regrets to Henriette that since she
could not go to see her, she would not be able to comfort her

in person in her distress: "I would like to unite with you in that communion of saints and in the merits accumulated by your holy parents, with whom may God unite you one day, for that soul whom they loved so much. I hope that you and Mr. Gallet are well and that you will be able to surmount your pain in thinking of your other children and of the joys they give you."

These words welled up from a strong contact with spiritual reality, the chief gain Hélène derived from her struggle of several decades on behalf of her father's work. A telling proof of this is the last paragraph of her last published writing, dated August 1959. Its text she kept in the form of a newspaper clipping, though without marking on it the name of the newspaper. She sketched in less than a thousand words the history of the more than a thousand-year-old church of Cabrespine that fell into ruins time and again. After recounting the last reconstruction in the late 1940s, a work that saw all the villagers rally to the sacred cause, Hélène concluded:

> Wanderer, as you go from Villeneuve to Pradelles and follow the zigzags of a rising road, stop on seeing this village where the houses seem to rise out of the river and lean upon one another as far up as the 'Tête épineuse.' You will see many of them in ruins, but go on and enter the beautiful church which, with her white walls, resembles a young bride, and then you will resume your journey with confidence in this small country and in France.

These words bespoke of her innermost thoughts. One can easily imagine her taking volume X of the *Système du monde* into that Church and placing it on the bench which one of the greatest French minds of recent times used to occupy. She must have done so in mid-May 1959. On the 18th of that month Louis de Broglie thanked her for asking him to present volumes IX and X on her behalf to the Académie des Sciences: "I hasten to inform you that Hermann et Cie had already sent me two copies of each volume, of which I have presented one set to the Académie on May 20. That set will be deposited in the Library of the Institute, whereas the second set will be bound in leather and placed in the collection we keep in one of the glass cabinets of the Secretariat of the Académie."

That the printing of volume X had been completed during the first trimester of 1959 served as further evidence that even the very last batches of the manuscripts Duhem left behind were in eminently printable condition. This, of course, may not impress latter-day scholars equipped with word-processors and laser-jet printers though not blessed with a moderately decipherable handwriting. The facsimile reproduction of two pages from the manuscript of volume X should dissipate once and for all the credibility of allegations typical of the ones Sarton made about the unprintable condition of Duhem's immortal work. Against the brilliant background of Duhem's peerless manuscripts, the true causes of an incredibly long delay show up rather darkly. The part of the French academic world as a whole in that dismal picture was not redeemed when on December 2, 1960, the Académie des Sciences awarded the Prix d'Amaule to "Hélène Pierre-Duhem for her contribution to the publication of her father's work."

The Prix d'Amaule brought her the modest sum of one thousand new francs. It was hardly enough to keep the house from collapsing over her head. If she thought of any reward for her heroic labors, she undoubtedly saw it as being the beneficiary of a most unusual affection. Friendships that last for a generation are better than usual. The fondness which the Dufourcqs had for Duhem and his memory was now being displayed by the third generation. That even some grandchildren of Albert and Madeleine Dufourcq looked upon Hélène as part of the family became all too clear when Charles and Henriette Gallet came to Cabrespine in June 1961. Hélène was to be taken to the cathedral of Toulouse for the ordination to the subdiaconate of the Gallets' youngest child, Jean-Pierre;

soon to be a missionary in Africa and, since 1989, auxiliary bishop of the new diocese of Kinkala, in the People's Republic of Congo.[11]

Hélène's meeting in June 1961 with her childhood friend, Henriette (Mme Gallet) was the first in several decades, and possibly her first meeting with Henriette's husband, Charles Gallet. The latter had by then purchased from Hélène her house in Cabrespine. She now had a safe yearly income from the sale of the house and relief from the cares of ownership. Hélène retained, of course, ownership over everything inside the house. She had a particular fondness for Marie-Madeleine, the eldest among Henriette's children, who, in addition to being at the ceremony in Toulouse, accompanied Hélène back to Cabrespine with her parents. Soon Marie-Madeleine began to spend part of her summers with Hélène and gain a glimpse of the books, piles of correspondence, manuscripts, albums, and memorabilia of the great French savant who, as well as his daughter, owed so much to her maternal grandfather, Albert Dufourcq.

Scholars awake

Compared with the glow of friendship and love that came to Hélène from the Dufourcqs (Gallets), small may seem the satisfaction she derived from the sudden awakening of scholars to the magnitude of her father's achievement. An already old pattern repeated itself in the fact that Duhem's own France once more lagged behind. That the manuscripts of volumes VII - X of the *Système* were ultimately deposited in the archives of the Académie des Sciences and did not follow, contrary to Hélène's original plan, the manuscripts of volume VI to the Library of the University of Bordeaux, is a case in point. It was a plan which had (as shown by de Broglie's letter of July 19, 1957, to her) the Académie's enthusiastic approval. That the manuscripts did not leave Paris can be seen as a blessing in disguise. The Library of the University of Bordeaux experienced a trauma in its move from the center of Bordeaux to the new campus in Talence in 1966. It now contains no list of the valuable set of Duhem's books on the history and philosophy of science which it received following his death. The new campus, although full of large lecture halls, does not have a replica of the "Amphithéatre Duhem," a chief pride of the Old University.

There is symbolism in this. The revival of interest in the history of science has followed very anti-Duhemian lines in France from the late 1950s on. It was then that the idea of "intellectual mutations" as advocated by G. Bachelard, and the idea of "scientific revolutions" as advocated by A. Koyré, began to be widely hailed as the chief explanatory devices in interpreting scientific history. In such a perspective the monumental work of Duhem could at best receive a condescending word or two. All too obvious was the slighting of Duhem in volumes I and II, dedicated to ancient, medieval and Renaissance science, in the four-volume *l'Histoire des sciences*, to which dozens of French historians contributed, under the editorship of René Taton, director of the Centre d'Histoire des Sciences in Paris.[12] The same pattern quickly established itself in the United States where Koyré's lectures were greeted by a younger generation of historians of science as having a "liberating influence" on them.[13] When most of the few Catholic scholars working in the field joined the bandwagon, they added the touch of prophetic truth to Duhem's complaint, in his letter of March 25, 1913 to Hélène about the neglect by Catholics of his works on the history of science.

Again, it was not in France that some younger scholars awakened to the research possibilites opened up after the publication of volume VI. Duhem would have been the last to be taken by surprise. It was his wont to take a long look at history. That his writings found a far greater response in the Anglo-Saxon world than in his own country, he had registered as a fact while alive. About the fact that this was to become a pattern, he would be entitled to muse today with a recall of the words: "A prophet is not without honor except in his own country."

This is not to suggest that Anglophone interest in Duhem's thought necessarily showed a genuine comprehension of it. On reading the letter which R. J. Seeger, Deputy Assistant Director of the National Foundation, wrote to her on June 10, 1958, Hélène must have wondered. Seeger began with stating that he had read Duhem's "The Views of a Believer" (he obviously meant "Physics of a Believer") and asked: "I would like to know if there is any other material which he has written on this subject or any additional information which others have written about his religious life. Perhaps you yourself could inform me about his theological views as well as his participation in organized religion."

Strange request indeed. Why could not the splendid profession of his Catholic faith, which Duhem made in that essay, be taken at face value? Was the difficulty to accept the genuinely Catholic in Duhem, a genius in physics and in its philosophy and history, a subtle reflection on a deep-running bias against Catholicism in Anglo-Saxon ambiance? It was to Hélène's advantage that, not being sufficiently familiar with English, she could not sense the unintended rudeness latent in the expression, "organized religion."[14]

The French had their own sort of invincible biases and bent on vulgarity. Hélène was no longer alive when a well-known French "Duhemist" asked Mlle Marie-Madeleine Gallet for permission to investigate the house in Cabrespine. His was the firm conviction that there he would find evidence about the "other woman" Duhem *must* have had. I myself heard it stated categorically and aloud, and in a gathering of American academics, that Duhem *must* have had a mistress![15] This cocksure confidence about facts on the basis of sheer though hardly pure imagination, can only generate the conviction that a Catholic priest specializing in the history of science *must* be hopelessly biased and therefore his books *must* lack intrinsic merit if he refuses to slight what was sacred to Duhem.

Hélène's reply to Seeger *must* indeed have contained a crystal clear statement on her father's firm Catholicism.[16] The latter was attested to in great detail in her biography of her father. Hélène could not, of course, be expected to write at that time an essay on her father's Catholicism. But she sent to Seeger a copy of volume VIII of the *Système*, a courtesy followed up a year later with copies of volumes IX and X — all gratefully acknowledged by Seeger. Hélène's generosity in replying to inquiries with reprints and books of her father, in addition to letters gracefully written, was, of course, in part motivated by her hope that a scholar at long last would really do a major work on her father. Promotion of his memory was her life-consuming ambition.

It is rather regrettable that C. Truesdell, who more than anyone could have mined the unsuspected riches of Duhem's often forbidding studies on theoretical mechanics, did not undertake such a study. Yet, he did not need word about the publication of the last five volumes of the *Système* to develop interest in Duhem. In his first letter to Hélène, written in French on August 30, 1962, Truesdell began with a reference to his essay, "A New Definition of a Fluid," published in 1950 in *Journal de mathématiques pures et appliquées*,[17] as one dedicated to Duhem's memory: "I have for long been a great admirer of the great scientist, your late father. In my essays I always insisted on the importance of his scientific work in hydrodynamics, elasticity, and thermodynamics." He then noted that the very first issue (which he sent to her under a separate cover) of the periodical edited by him on the history of mechanics was dedicated to Duhem.[18]

Hélène could derive special satisfaction from the last paragraph of Truesdell's letter: "I would like to obtain a portrait of Duhem in order to frame it and place it on the wall of my office, among the portraits of such *savants* as Gibbs and Cauchy, who are already there. I have a copy of 'L'oeuvre scientifique de Pierre Duhem,' but its frontispiece portrait is pale and has deteriorated. I would be very grateful if you informed me where I could purchase a good portrait, either a photograph, or a lithograph, or an engraving."

Truesdell duly received a fine photo of Duhem together with two books, one of them a re-edition of Duhem's *Recherches sur l'hydrodynamique*. The other was Hélène's biography of her father. "I began to read," Truesdell wrote on October 15, "with great interest the biography of which you are the author. I have framed the beautiful portrait and put it on the wall of my office next to those of Hadamard and Whittaker." Was Truesdell familiar with the lasting friendship between Duhem and Hadamard?

In the mid-1960s several young American scholars contacted Hélène. Joseph O'Malley, who had among his first publications an article in the *Revue des questions scientifiques* on the connection which Duhem saw between cosmology and physics,[19] was just starting as a member of the Department of Philosophy of Marquette University. It was there that he had defended his doctoral dissertation, "Material Being and Scientific Knowledge according to Pierre Duhem."[20] He now wanted to join forces with his mentor, Professor F. J. Collingwood,[21] "to make Duhem's thought more immediately accessible to students and teachers here, and to contribute to the interest in his doctrines which Professor Wiener's translation of *La théorie physique* has provoked to a certain extent."

O'Malley introduced this statement of his in his letter of July 16, 1965, to Hélène by reporting Collingwood's conviction that "most of the important philosophers of science in the English speaking world have been greatly influenced by the thought of Pierre Duhem. Yet it remains unfortunately true that your father has not received the recognition in this field which he truly deserves." While this was a most accurate account, it would, if published, have certainly fallen upon deaf ears on the part of those philosophers who greatly benefited from reading Duhem and left their readers in the dark about the measure of their indebtedness to him.[22]

The third and the last paragraphs in O'Malley's letter must have particularly pleased Hélène, whom O'Malley also asked to comment on the contents of his article attached to his letter. In those paragraphs O'Malley set forth an all-important principle to be followed by anyone who tries to do justice to the thought of another:

> The work of preparing the dissertation involved attention to the persons who were personally acquainted with your father. Among these writings your book, *Un savant français: Pierre Duhem*, was most valuable in helping me to appreciate the man, Pierre Duhem, as a person. And such an appreciation (am I correct in thinking that he himself would agree?) is very important to a comprehension of the scientific and philosophic thought with which he has graced the world of learning.
>
> I hope that you will accept a copy of my article[23] as a very small token of my admiration for your father. If you would also be interested in seeing the dissertation, I would be very happy to send it to you. I fear that you would find it inadequate as an expression of the thought of Pierre Duhem; and I would be pleased to have any criticisms you would wish to make. It would help me to approach a correct appreciation and expression of his thought, which is *the most important thing* (emphasis added).

A little over a month later Hélène sent her reply in which she gave the following assurance to O'Malley: "Your article, which I was happy to read, renders my father's ideas well, ideas which I heard him set forth all his life." She expressed her hope that O'Malley and his wife, a former piano-student of Jacques Fevrier in Paris, would be able to come to visit her in Cabrespine where she would be most happy to talk about her father.

She stated her readiness to send O'Malley a copy of her father's "Notice" as well as a copy of her own biography of him. Finally she noted that she was expecting Mr. and Mrs. Donald Miller to arrive in Cabrespine the next day, August 24.

Hélène's reply could but further encourage O'Malley in his projects about Duhem. He thanked her for her generous offer and sent her a copy of his dissertation in return. Most importantly, his letter of September 1, to Hélène included lines that once more diagnosed the true situation about Duhem:

> So much of his doctrine has become an integral part of contemporary thought; yet, so often his thought is misrepresented even by those who have themselves adopted many points of his doctrine. One can surely say that his writings in the philosophy of science present the model after which most current thought is patterned.

Whereas this view could find a modest echo among philosophers of science in the United States, it could count on no favorable hearing in France, and not even in some Catholic circles. That from there something worse than sheer insensitivity could come forth was in full evidence in a brief note which O'Malley received from the Père F. Russo. The latter, who graduated from the Ecole Polytechnique, before becoming a Jesuit, had by then become known for his writings on the relation of science and religion.[24] O'Malley wrote to the Père Russo on December 26, 1964, on the advice of the Père Courtoy, editor of the *Revue des questions scientifiques*. O'Malley told the Père Russo about his good prospects of obtaining grants from the Belgian Amercian Educational Foundation for doing research during the academic year of 1965-66 on Duhem in France and that the Père Courtoy would help him with locating letters Duhem had written to scientists in Belgium. O'Malley hoped that the Père Russo would put him in contact with persons in France who would further his search. Most importantly, O'Malley outlined his research project:

It is my hope to conduct this research with a view to producing two books on Duhem. One would be an exposition of Duhem's conception of the nature and limits of scientific knowledge, specifically the knowledge of inanimate being proper to experimental and theoretical physics. This treatment of Duhem's thought would draw upon many other works, in addition to *La théorie physique*, and upon his personal corespondence wherever that treats of that subject. This work would include complete bibliographies of Duhem's writings, including translations of his works, and of other authors' writings on Duhem up to the end of 1965. The second book would include English translations of Duhem's letters dealing with the philosophy of science — letters to his daughter and his colleagues — and translations of some of his early articles that appeared in the *Revue des questions scientifiques* in 1892-1894, together with an introduction.

Added to this were the words of O'Malley that with regard to finding Duhem's letters in France the Père Courtoy "felt that you would be able to help greatly." To his consternation,[25] O'Malley received from the Père Russo a brief note, in an envelope postmarked December 26, 1964, where the crucial words, "la pensée de Duhem ne mérite pas une thèse," have the added disgrace of being underlined.

The negative attitude towards Duhem's thought in French secularist circles was exemplified by the answer which O'Malley received in September 1964 from Jean Ullmo, whose permission O'Malley had asked for to quote from an article of his on Duhem, published in 1933. What obviously baffled O'Malley in that article was not so much Ullmo's portrayal of Duhem as an enemy of all modern physics but as an unqualified positivist for whom physical theory offered no grasp on physical reality. Clearly, this was a rank misreading of Duhem's *Théorie physique* on Ullmo's part who in the same breath represented all great advances in physics as having been made in a realist conviction.

Even a most superficial reader of the *Théorie physique* could easily find there Duhem's emphatic answer to Ullmo's rhetorical puzzlement: "Only an incomprehensible miracle could guide our symbolism towards the real if that symbolism did not touch on it, and, if, on the contrary, the physicist did not claim to give with his hypotheses and formulas as exact a representation of reality as possible."[26] This call for realism was certainly curious on the part of Ullmo, an avowed admirer of Henri Poincaré who saw in physical theories a purely commodious method to co-ordinate sense data.

In thanking Ullmo, O'Malley asked him whether he had since changed these views of his on Duhem as "Duhem's doctrine is currently receiving appreciable attention in this country [USA]." O'Malley also was curious "as to the current status in France of Duhem's reputation as a philosopher of science." Ullmo's reply deserves to be quoted almost in full:

> My opinion about him [Duhem] has not changed and I reproduced it as it stood in my book, *La pensée scientifique moderne*, published by Flammarion in 1958. As to his actual place in France, his importance is recognized in the history of scientific thought and in the history of philosophy; the CNRS [Centre National de la Recherche Scientifique] has made a great effort to support the publication of his complete works. But I can tell you that the two great philosophers of science, Léon Brunschvicg and Gaston Bachelard, whom I have known well, shared my opinion about him. The philosophy of science ignores him today; works on philosophy in general never quote him; he has no influence at present; he is but a historic figure.

Ullmo had overlooked the fact that, as he voiced in that book his puzzlement quoted above, he changed at least his portrayal of Duhem by adding a footnote: "Duhem rightly speaks of an *act of faith* which alone assures us that these theories [of physics] are not a purely artificial system."[27] In order to do justice to Duhem, Ullmo now should have explained the sense in which Duhem spoke of that faith. But then Ullmo would have come up against a metaphysical realism underlying Duhem's epistemological dicta and he would have found this unpalatable.

The same was true of some of Ullmo's heroes, such as Brunschvicg and Bachelard. Duhem could, of course, have no appeal for Brunschvicg who favored a sort of idealist rationalism and whose thinking about science would have become suspect to Duhem for the simple reason that Brunschvicg lacked proper scientific training.[28] The dissolving by Bachelard, who at least had *licences* in mathematics, of basic epistemological questions into metaphors borrowed from genetics and sociology, represented the kind of disregard for logic that would have horrifed Duhem. Had Ullmo himself felt a fair respect for logic he would not have been taken by complete surprise in a conversation I had with him in Paris. Having by then written on the cavalier use of the word "chance" by most modern physicists[29] I was not surprised that Ullmo himself, a great admirer of the so-called "philosophy" of quantum mechanics or its Copenhagen interpretation, was taken aback as I kept asking him for a reply to the verb emphasized in my question: "What *is* chance?" To his credit, he admitted that my question made him think for the first time about the fallacy of attributing, however surreptitiously, a pseudo-ontological role to chance; a fallacy which, if I may add, is the basic support of that interpretation.[30]

At any rate, Brunschvicg, Bachelard, and Ullmo were agnostics and, in various measures, unsympathetic to Christianity in general and to Catholicism in particular. No wonder that non-Catholic philosophers sympathetic to Duhem were ready to hail him only as a supremely articulate "positivist," in total disregard of the purely methodological character of his endorsement of positivism and of his insistence on a realist epistemology.[31] One could have therefore expected that Catholic philosophers of science in France would have refused to share the opinion of those three (and others) on Duhem. As was noted above, almost exactly the opposite happened. At any rate, Hélène could have certainly put in a proper light O'Malley's setbacks had he informed her about them.

There is little to report about the contact which two other American scholars made with Hélène in the mid 1960s.[32] O'Malley himself gave up his plans on having learned from Donald G. Miller, a physical chemist at Livermore Laboratories, that he had been in contact with Hélène for several years in order to gather first-hand information about her father's work and scientific contacts. O'Malley, whose article in the *Revue des questions scientifiques* called him to Miller's attention, further found, on reading the typescript of Miller's article on Duhem soon to be published, that it was only fair to leave the field open to Miller. The latter opened the eyes of many to the existence in Duhem of a pre-eminent thinker when his article appeared in late 1966, the fiftieth anniversary of Duhem's death, under the title, "Ignored Intellect."

"Ignored Intellect"

The first letter which Donald G. Miller wrote to Hélène on September 20, 1957, reached her through the kind services of the Académie des Sciences. He asked her to send him various scientific reprints of her father's publications, so that he might complete a study of the importance of Duhem's contributions to thermodynamics. "In order to get as complete a picture as possible, any biographical material on your father and his career would be very helpful as well as the names of all his students, especially those who are still alive. Personal recollections of his friends and colleagues as well as your own would be most worthwhile. I realize that I am asking for a lot of material and effort on your part, but I do hope you will be able to help me in my study of your father's career."

Hélène's reply followed with great promptness, on the first of October. She apologized for being able to send to Miller only two monographs of her father on thermodynamics, and asked for their return at his convenience. She was, of course, more than happy to send him a copy of her biography of her father, which, she thought, would provide Miller with more than enough biographical information both about her father and his students. She also mentioned several of Duhem's friends still alive, most importantly, Hadamard. All of them were, in due course, contacted by Miller.

Miller's next letter (this and his subsequent letters were written in French) to Hélène followed three years later, on July 28, 1960, after he had obtained a Fulbright scholarship to spend a semester in Lille at the Institut Catholique in doing chemistry research in the laboratory of Gerard Lepoutre, a Catholic priest-professor there. It was from Lille that he advised her on December 13, 1960, that he and his would spend the Christmas vacation in Carcassonne and he hoped to be able to visit her at her convenience. Hélène replied on December 15th, assuring Miller that he and his wife could come any time. She asked only for an advance note of only one day, about which she specified that letters from Carcassonne to Cabrespine, separated by only 22 km, may take more than a day. Finally she expressed her hope that in Lille Miller had already met Kampé de Fériet, who had just re-edited a work of Duhem on hydrodynamics.[33]

To the note of thanks which Miller sent to Hélène following his and his wife's visit with her, she sent a fairly long letter on March 7, 1961. There she first expressed her thanks for the copy of R. Dugas' *Histoire de la mécanique*, but especially for all that he told her about "the esteem enjoyed by my father's work in the USA which touched me really at heart." Then she turned to the criticism which Dugas, in the preface of his book, made of Duhem for giving too much importance to Leonardo among the precursors of Galileo:

My father would have agreed with that criticism. Given the admiration in which my father's work is held in the United States, it may seem very strange to you that in his time, in France, he encountered the greatest difficulties to publish what he had written. However, Mr. Bouvy, librarian of the University of Bordeaux and editor of its *Bulletin Italien*, accepted with the greatest friendship whatever my father sent to that periodical. And only because the texts of those articles had been typeset by the *Bulletin*, did the publisher Hermann accept them, his expenses being thereby greatly reduced in bringing out in [three] volumes the *Etudes sur Léonard de Vinci*. But [for the purposes of Bouvy] it was necessary to center those articles around an Italian, in order that they may appear in that *Bulletin*. And my father felt that he had thereby put Leonardo on a pedestal where he did not belong.

Another point Hélène dealt with in that letter concerned Miller's question as to why Duhem, who felt so frustrated in provincial State Universities, did not leave Bordeaux and join an Institut Catholique, either in Paris or elsewhere.

He [my father] told me that he was asked to go to [the Institut Catholique in] Paris but he was offered a salary that would have made it difficult for him to make ends meet. But he also told me that this was not the reason for his not accepting that invitation. I think that to tell the truth, he loved the University of Bordeaux, and in spite of the ostracism of which he was the victim, he had a great influence there. I am sending you the text of a speech made by Mr. Calas, professor at the University of Bordeaux, and a delegate of that University, at the inauguration of a plaque that was placed on the house here. You see there the influence which Prof. Calas attributes to my father at the University. His memory remained in veneration in Bordeaux.

At any rate, my father's works were not better treated in Catholic circles than in State Universities. They even

pretended to ignore him [in those circles] and I could name
a Catholic savant who kept plagiarizing his work but who
never referred to him.

She closed her letter by expressing her great joy over the
possibility of seeing him again and notified him about her
having asked Hermann to send him complimentary copies of
volumes VIII, IX and X of the *Système du monde*.

The questions Miller posed to Hélène in his letter of
January 12, 1962, makes one wonder about the substantive
nature of his visit a year earlier. He asked Hélène whether her
father's correspondence still existed. "What happened to his
books? I was told in Paris that they were sold," he wrote to
her. He wanted to know the names of those who voted against
Duhem in 1913 when he was elected member of the Académie. He suspected that Le Chatelier was very hostile to Duhem
and that the same was also true of Perrin. He asked about the
nature of Duhem's stomach illness, when did Hélène leave Bordeaux for Paris, and what sort of a work was she doing there.

The long delay of Hélène's reply, more than a year, had
for its cause factors which she succinctly described in her letter
of April 24, 1962, as a five-month-long bout with influenza
and a fall in which she suffered a bad fracture "that caused me
much suffering and greatly impeded me in my tasks and I am
just beginning to recover." She was too optimistic. Two
months later, on June 30, to be specific, she had to tell Miller:
"Please kindly excuse me, but I had not a chance this year. I
once more went down with a very painful attack of rheumatism
which was all the more aggravating as I am alone in running
my little property and this is the very moment when the most
is to be done there. Finally, I am getting better and will shortly
turn to your manuscript and answer your questions." She
promised Miller to send him a copy of the book by Kampé de
Fériet.

On July 6 Miller acknowledged the receipt of the book adding that just before his departure from Lille he had met Kampé de Fériet "and that we have talked at length about the work of your illustrious father." Three weeks later Miller had received Hélène's long letter of July 16th in which she assured Miller about the great pleasure given her through reading his essay on her father. "Never perhaps has the work and person of my father been analyzed with so much care and sympathy: the daughter of Pierre Duhem is deeply touched." This was followed by some specifications. According to Hélène, her father never had

> stomach sickness in the strict sense of that word. But he had all his life, since his youth, frequent stomach cramps. He had, when he was 17 or 18 a great crisis of rheumatic fever which immobilized him for weeks, interrupted his studies, and forced him to repeat a year in school. Perhaps these rheumatisms left him with a heart lesion which was ignored, although after that he could not engage in rigorous exercise and was, at his request, dispensed from classes of gymnastics. But my father never saw a physician on that score because he was very sceptical about medicine and often voiced Molière's barbs.[34]

She advised Miller to add to the list of her father's enemies, besides Le Chatelier and Perrin, the name of Lippmann "who rejected his thesis and became his most determined enemy." As to the Catholic professor, who plagiarized him without referring to him, "I will not mention his name which I know only through the confidence of my father, and just as my father forgave him and never complained, I shall not speak of him."

As to her life in Thiais, she was succinct. Some of the details she gave were not entirely factual and objective, but her reporting about her years there reflected a soul purified through much suffering, a soul that for some time had wished that she had done certain things differently. However, Miller could not suspect this on reading the lines:

> Since I had no job in Bordeaux, I kept busy in Paris with [charitable] work where I went several months every year, obviously with my father's consent. We still had at that time close relatives in Paris. In 1915 and 1916 I was able to give small secretarial assistance to my father which satisfied him and of which I was very proud. This was my ambition and I think he would at the end have accepted it. Had he not died, I would have planned not to return to Paris that next winter but to try to work for him. This could appear very natural today but in my family, and when I was young, women who attended university were not tolerated and were called "blue-stocking."

Here Hélène telescoped two things. One was her indirect reference to not having had formal education, let alone university training, which would have qualified her to assist her father with competence. The other was the work itself, a sort of secretarial work. Her family might not have welcomed her doing such work outside her very home. But even her grandmother would have hardly objected to her becoming her father's secretary at home. Most importantly, in her comments there is not a touch of bitterness. If such a note was struck by her it related to the ill-treatment handed to her father. A case in point is the longest of the dozen or so notes she added to Miller's manuscript essay. The note is all the more noteworthy as it reveals her familiarity with some important developments in scholarly studies on medieval science in the 1940s:

> Certain criticisms of Anelise Mayer [sic][35] of my father's work appeared before the publication of the last posthumous volumes of the *Système du monde* and, notably, concerning the School of Oxford. The texts cited by my father seemed to do him justice and lessen the criticisms of Anelise Mayer that have the tone of systematic partisanship.

> To speak of my father's "partisanship" and "tendentious opinions" in his historical studies is itself revealing of a partisan mind, because all his assertions he sustained in the *Système du monde* were based on the complete quotation of texts.

She, no less than her father, could turn the weapon of logic to her best advantage. She had, no less than her father, a keen sense for the accuracy of facts and statements. She called Miller's attention to what Prof. Calas, as the representative of the University of Bordeaux, actually stated in Cabrespine about her father: "he never wanted to sacrifice truth either in respect to scientific or personal point of view. Certainly it is to men such as he that the French University system owes that perfect independence which it enjoys today."

On August 2, Miller thanked Hélène for the material and comments. "You know," he wrote, "that this manuscript is but a project. I shall redo it as soon as possible. When I finish it I shall send it to you for your criticisms." Six months later, on February 14, Miller wrote that he would have occasion to return to France in June. Still he had not finished the reworking of his article which he was circulating among historians of science for comments. On May 6, Hélène assured him that she would be very pleased to see him and Mme Miller again and talk about her father. "I would be pleased to show you a photo of him, unpublished, which I made of him and which I might suggest to you to put as a frontispiece of the study you are writing." She also suggested that he might contact Norbert Dufourcq and Dom Olphe-Galliard in Paris.

In his reply of May 15 Miller informed her that he had already visited in 1961 with the Benedictine Abbot who, in addition to giving him some valuable books, had provided him with the information that he had attended only an introductory course given by Duhem. By then Miller sent word to her that he and his wife would be in Carcassonne on June 19 or thereabouts. In recalling the visit in his letter of July 12, Miller spoke in superlatives about Hélène's hospitality and about her willingness to talk with him at length about her father and his work. One of Hélène's parting gifts to the Millers was a landscape of Duhem's which, so he informed her, he was on the point of having framed. In return Miller sent Hélène a copy of Clagett's *The Science of Mechanics in the Middle Ages* in which Clagett wrote that all research on medieval science is but an extension of the findings of Duhem. The letter also contained the information that on his way back Miller visited with Norbert Dufourcq and René Taton.[36] The latter called Miller's attention to Tannery's correspondence, while the former suggested to him to contact his sister, Mme (Henriette) Gallet.

On January 4, 1964, Norbert Dufourcq worte to Miller that he had found his manuscript article very interesting and asked him to send him "2 or 3 additional copies that would be sufficient to protect Mlle Duhem's rights with her lawyers." In his reply of January 7 Miller expressed his puzzlement about that stipulation and restated his resolve "to help Mlle Duhem." Miller's letter of March 19, 1964, informed Hélène that he had given a conference on Duhem to a group of historians of science at the University of California at Berkeley. Among the questions he was asked to answer was one by S. Drake, a well known Galileo scholar. Drake recalled that according to Favaro, the editor of Galileo's complete works, Duhem undertook his researches on medieval science at the suggestion of Leo XIII.[37] Another point on which Miller wanted clarification from Hélène concerned her father's anti-Thomism.

On April 14, 1965, Miller informed Hélène that he had received word from O'Malley concerning the latter's doctoral dissertation and that he tried to obtain the documents from the Sorbonne about the rejection of Duhem's doctoral dissertation. Miller was by then in possession of Duhem's dossier as a civil servant but found the material very difficult to decipher. He also hoped to be in France during the summer to read a paper at an international conference on physical chemistry. "If it does not inconvenience you, we could extend our itinerary through France. This would give us another opportunity to speak once more of the career and works of your father." Miller also broached an item that was uppermost in his mind: "You have told me," he wrote in the same letter of April 14, 1965, "and rightly so, during my visit of 1963, that you do not want to let the documents, such as the booklet of your father's publications and photos, leave the area [of Cabrespine], lest they be lost. If you permit, perhaps I could make photocopies in Carcassonne and return the originals the same day."

Hélène's reply of April 24 contained a warm invitation to the Millers: "I count on your taking your meal here with me. It will be a very simple and modest affair, but this way we shall all the time talk of all that relates to my father." She apologized for not having yet replied to the inquiry about Favaro. Constant work and recurring rheumatism were impeding her. About the same time Miller learned from Norbert Dufourcq that he would not be back in Paris before mid-September.

On June 1, Miller informed Hélène about the exact time of his arrival in Carcassonne. He expressed his hope that during much of the 26th of August he could be in Cabrespine and do the copying of the "documents." A week later he wrote that instead of the 26th he and his wife would arrive on the 24th. On June 22 Hélène replied at length. While she was looking forward to the visit "with great pleasure," she felt that she had to clarify one point in advance: "If the documents you want to copy are the notes taken by my father — extracts from manuscripts that had been lent to him for very short periods of time, and to which I made an allusion in the 'Life' I wrote, these notes are not 'unpublished.' They were entered into the volumes of the *Système du monde* as documentation of all the historical discoveries made by my father."

No less important, though in a different sense, are Hélène's replies to the question raised by Drake and her clarification of her father's anti-Thomism:

Unwilling to trust my memory entirely, I did some research that convinced me that my reminiscences were correct. It is absolutely false that Pope Leo XIII (who did not even know my father's name) should have charged him with the task of studying the physics of the Scholastics. It is the chance — or Providence, if you like - that gave him that task. My father was always interested in the history of science, looking for the manner of the birth and development of physical theories, but he did not think that modern science owed anything to science in the Middle Ages. Studying Roberval and Cardan, he investigated what the latter owed to Leonardo. It was while reading Leonardo that my father got the insight, just as he said in the beginning of the second volume of the *Etudes sur Léonard de Vinci,* that many of Leonardo's fragments of thoughts were notes taken from books he had read. This lead my father to look for authors whom Leonardo might have known and he was thus lead to Albert of Saxony, and through him, to the Parisian masters. This was for him an extraordinary surprise of which I keep a most vivid recollection.

It would be an error to oppose my father to Saint Thomas. First, he never studied Saint Thomas from the point of view of religious philosophy. What he saw was that the scientific discoveries of the 14th century could not have been made if one kept to the notions of Aristotle and that the decree of Etienne Tempier, condemning certain peripatetic propositions, allowed modern science to be born. But my father notes that it was Saint Thomas who first enounced the idea of *mass.*

Miller departed from Cabrespine with a batch of photos of Duhem, some of them framed, so that he might make a copy of them in California. His letter of September 24 informed Hélène that the photos, shown at the History of Science Club in Berkeley had been mailed back and voiced his confidence that the glass cover of some of the photos remained unbroken. During that visit he must have repeatedly broached the idea of bringing Duhem's correspondence to the USA to be properly photographed there: "I have obtained information on the best way of mailing your father's correspondence. There is a postal classification which is called Air Parcel Post in English which can be used to send packages less than 20 kilos. It is possible to send such packages with registered mail. All that is needed is to do the package carefully (or packages if there are several) and to let me know the price of postage by registered airmail. I can buy here the coupons that can be changed into stamps in France and send them to you. This way you will not need to pay the postage." Added to this letter was a copy of Miller's letter to H. Cirker, President of Dover Publications, whom he urged to publish an English translation of Duhem's *Evolution de la mécanique*.

Miller's letter of January 24, 1966 makes it clear that Hélène was most reluctant to confide that correspondence to the postal service, let alone to a transatlantic journey. "On reflecting on this problem," he wrote to her, "it seems that you may perhaps have reason to be diffident of the mail." He continued: "Still I find that historians of science are most interested in that correspondence. My colleagues at Berkeley and the director of the History of Recent Physics Project suggested to me the following: Request a grant to go to France, go to Cabrespine, copy the correspondence in Paris, take the originals back to Cabrespine, and then return to the States." Were Hélène agreeable to this project, he would apply for the grant.

In his letter of April 5, 1966, Miller told Hélène about his good chances of receiving a grant, provided he would obtain her permission to do so, and he recalled his earlier letter, "to take the originals to Paris to be photocopied (or do the same in Cabrespine), return to Cabrespine in order to give them back to you, and then return to the States." On June 6, Miller informed Hélène that he had received from the University of California (San Diego) a travel grant which included the sum

of one thousand new francs as payment to Hélène for the rights
of making a copy of that correspondence. He had to have,
however, by June 27, Hélène's written consent. "I hope that
you will allow me to make one more visit and copy the correspondence. All the learned world shall be grateful to you for
having made it available to scholars and for having made, in this
way, better known the glory of your father's works."

Hélène's letter of June 15 began with a reference to the
bad weather and the consequent flare up of her rheumatism, in
addition to her daily chores. All this prevented her from making
the investigations requested from her. But on the most important point she hastened to give full satisfaction to Miller: "Of
course, I am giving you my agreement to copy the correspondence of my father" and she underlined this phrase. She also
expressed her hope that Mme Miller would also come.

Upon receiving Hélène's permission to copy the correspondence of her father, Miller quickly made arrangements for
his visit in early September. He hoped to see Norbert Dufourcq
as well. On August 18 he wrote to him that he was still
looking "for the enemies of Duhem," and thought that they
could be best tracked down from Duhem's letters. He felt that,
since Norbert Dufourcq's father and Duhem were close friends,
perhaps there were references to those enemies in Duhem's
letters to Albert Dufourcq: "If those letters still exist, would you
allow me to make a xerox or microfilm copy of them? I want
to deposit them in the library of the University [of California]
and in that sense the letters would become published [public],
because they would be available to scholars eager to study
them. If you have letters that you would allow me to copy but
at the same time you would not want them to become available
to everybody, I would keep them unpublished."

Ten days earlier, Miller wrote to Hélène that he expected
to arrive in Carcassonne in mid-morning, September 2, and, if
her health allowed, do with her the "cataloguing of the letters
by person during the next two or three days (that is Saturday,

Sunday, and Monday), if necessary. If not I can do it myself. Then I would go to Montpellier to make copies of the letters (as well as the booklet of publications) with the method known as xerox. I do not know how much time this would take. Perhaps two to four days. I would certainly return on Saturday, the 10th of September."

Hélène sent her reply on August 19th. "I will be in Cabrespine on September 3 and I will help you with the classification of all the correspondence of my father. I will now begin to gather all that may be of interest to you. Of course, you will have dinner [lunch] with me; you will excuse the simplicity of the menu, but thereby you would lose less time than by returning to Carcassonne for lunch. On re-reading your letter of June 6, I see that you have obtained for me a stipend for the rights of copying the correspondence. I thank you very much."

Miller came and was given full access to the correspondence. He first tried to do the copying in Carcassonne, then in Montpellier. Xeroxing at that time in the provinces of France was as yet far from the easy affair which it had by then become in the United States. Miller felt that it was best to take with him to California Duhem's scientific correspondence, comprising about a thousand letters, all of them written to him. In all evidence he had acted with Hélène's presumed permission. In her subsequent letters to Miller she expressed the minimum of complaint about the increasingly longer time which it took for Miller to do the copying.

Miller's letter of October 4, was mostly taken up with news about his article on Duhem, which was to be published in the December 1966 issue of *Physics Today*, a monthly review "with forty thousand subscribers." He expressed his pleasure over this good fortune of securing a proper appreciation "of your father on the fiftieth anniversary of his death." In conclusion he stated that he "had just begun the work of the correspondence. This will be slow because of the large number of documents, but it will be done." As shown by Hélène's letter of October 21, she was very pleased with the news about the forthcoming article in *Physics Today*, and hoped that her request for two or three reprints would not be taken for impoliteness. She seemed to have been overawed by the one-hundred dollars which Miller and his brother, also a chemist, obtained for her from the University of California. And she certainly showed the kindest feelings for Mme Miller: "Would you please thank Mme Miller for her kind remembrance of me and tell her how pleased I would be to see her if you come again to France." She promised to write later in great detail. For the moment her time was taken up by the visit of Henriette. Attached to her letter was a copy of an article, of which more shortly, on Duhem which had been published in September in *Midi Libre,* a Montpellier daily.

On December 19 she thanked Miller for the receipt of the check which he and his brother obtained for her from the University of California in San Diego. She hoped that the weather was not as inclement in California as in Cabrespine and she asked Miller to thank his wife for the pen she sent to her. "This letter is written with that pen and I am overjoyed with it." She did not inquire about the correspondence.

On January 6, 1967, Miller sent her a copy of the December issue of *Physics Today*, with his article, "Ignored Intellect," in it, lavishly illustrated with photos lent by Hélène.[38] As to the copying, Miller wrote: "I am in the process of copying the letters, but it goes slowly. It is very clear that it would have been impossible to copy all the correspondence even in one month. I shall begin to send the letters back in the measure in which I complete a sufficiently large batch." Miller's further news during 1967 was that he had been invited to contribute an article on Duhem to the *Dictionary of Scientific Biography*. "There is no doubt that his work and contributions are now beginning to receive the attention they deserve." As to the xeroxing of the correspondence, Miller wrote in the same letter of May 24, 1967, that "it was still being done," but "the work goes very slowly because I am very busy." Miller's letter of August 9 contained much the same about the slow progress of copying, preceded by the news that the *Revue des questions scientifiques* decided to publish his article in *Physics Today* in French translation

Three full years later, on June 15, 1970, Miller wrote: "I try to finish copying the correspondence. Unfortunately this goes very slowly because I am overwhelmed with work. But I assure you, the correspondence is carefully kept." Miller also mentioned that he had just received an inquiry from Harry W. Paul, a historian at the University of Florida, who was at that time gathering material in Paris for an article, to be published in the *Catholic Historical Review* on Catholic scientists in France during the anticlerical times of the Third Republic. "Your father takes a central place," Miller continued, adding that Paul considered it very important that all personal and other items relating to Duhem be carefully preserved. Miller also asked Hélène to preserve carefully Duhem's unpublished manuscript on capillarity, which he did not have time to study carefully: "I still have the impression that it deserves publication." The same day Miller also wrote to Norbert Dufourcq. He asked him to to do everything to conserve all items relating to Duhem, "Even the correspondence of Mlle Duhem is of importance because Pierre Duhem is a very important figure in the history of science." In conclusion, Miller wrote: "I still have his correspondence to be copied. Unfortunately, I am burdened with work, mostly because I am now assistant mayor of our town of 40,000 inhabitants. It is therefore very difficult to complete the work [of copying]."

Norbert Dufourcq's reply of August 1, 1970, was brief: "I remember you well. I can tell you that Mlle Duhem, though tired, is in good health and that my older sister, Mme Gallet, is taking care of her and sees her once a year. I will transmit to her your letter, in any case. I do not think that on the death of

Mlle Duhem, the items relating to the *savant* would be destroyed." The tone of this letter clearly indicated a growing unease among the Dufourcqs about Miller's taking so much time in xeroxing the correspondence, a sentiment shared by Hélène, although she was very polite about it in her last letter to Miller, dated August 22, of the same year:

I am embarrased about replying with so much delay to your kind letter and thank you for having sent me a copy of the draft of your article [for the *Dictionary of Scientific Biography*] about my father. I have had friends visiting with me and this delayed my writing letters.

I have read your article with the greatest interest and joy. It is for me a great happiness to see how many are interested in the life and work of my father. I have therefore read your article with the greatest interest and I have no criticism to register except for a small detail: when you say that my father's mother (Alexandrine Duhem, *née* Fabre) descended from a family that originated in Cabrespine, but she descended from there on her father's side. On her mother's side she descended from a Parisian family which included, during Louis XIV, a municipal official in Paris and a notary, also in Paris, who became appointed secretary to the King.

I understand that all your duties make it a big task for you to copy the letters received by my father. When you have completed the work, I would be happy to have the letters back.

I hope that Mme Miller is in good health. I have kept a very pleasant memory of her kindness. Please convey to her my best regards.

I presume that I can keep the draft of your article. Otherwise, you have only to write and I shall return it immediately.

Believe, I pray, dear Monsieur Miller, in my gratitude for what you are doing on behalf of my father, and with my best regards, H. Pierre-Duhem

Her signature on this letter seems to be her last signature extant. Its lines were just as firm as her signatures dating back to 1935 when she began to identify herself as Hélène Pierre-Duhem. Her resolve to promote her father's memory against incredible odds had not diminished a whit in almost four decades.

Miller next wrote to Hélène more than a year later, on October 12, 1971. He began with family news and with a reference to his duties as municipal counsellor. "Here is good news. Volume IV of the *Dictionary of Scientific Biography* has just appeared. I cannot obtain any reprint, but here attached you find a xerox copy of my article on your father. As I have earlier mentioned, the length of that article indicates that the editors understand the great importance of your father's work. I am satisfied with the article, although Mr. Gillispie, editor-in-chief, imposed on it some disagreable changes."

Those changes may very well have borne on what Miller tried to say on Duhem's achievements as a historian and philosopher of science. Still to be published were subsequent volumes that carried much longer articles on Sarton and Koyré, neither of whom did any science, but whose work in the history of science was largely aimed at offsetting and discrediting the impact of Duhem's vast researches and conclusions. Nothing of this was to be suspected either by Hélène or by Norbert Dufourcq, who a year later, December 12, 1972, thanked Miller for a copy of his article which, in Norbert Dufourcq's words, "sets everything straight." In May, next year, Dufourcq assured Miller that Hélène was still alive, though very weakened, but that he "could attempt to go and see her." In early August 1973, Miller and his wife once more visited Hélène in Cabrespine.

On August 28, 1973, Miller wrote to Hélène a letter of four very short paragraphs. In the second he stated that he and his wife had returned to their home on August 14. The first consisted of two sentences: "My wife and I were very pleased to have seen you three weeks ago. We keep a pleasant memory of your hospitality and of the opportunity of talking once more about your father." Hélène had been dead for almost a year when Miller wrote his next letter to her on February 21, 1975, expressing his hope that his two daughters, who would be in France in the summer, might visit her in Cabrespine.

Guarding a memory

Apart from the Miller's visits, Hélène's last dozen or so years on earth had but a few interruptions worth recalling. They all related to her religiously guarding her father's memory in spite of her advancing years. She was seventy-five when 1966 brought the fiftieth anniversary of her father's death. She preferred to celebrate it, as she told Miller in her letter of October 21, 1966, "in intimacy and in a touching manner." This was an indication of her not feeling as energetic as she had only a few years earlier. She let Dr. Girou write a commemorative article, "Cinquantenaire d'un grand savant: Pierre Duhem," in the Midi Libre of Montpellier. It contained an error which, if taken seriously, must have brought tears to Hélène's eyes. As he turned to the Système du monde, Dr. Girou, an old friend of Hélène, described it as a "colossal work of which six volumes have appeared and his daughter, Hélène, who dedicated herself to her father's memory, plans to assume the publication of this enormous work which then would prolong the radiance of that universal mind." As an eye-ear-throat specialist, but a very old one, Dr. Girou failed to diagnose in himself that foremost sign of most octogenarians, which is forgetfulness. No such excuse can be offered for those historians of science who at that time were but half as old as that venerable doctor in Carcassonne. They almost to a man ignored Duhem, while busily celebrating the fiftieth anniversary of the death of Ernst Mach who, unlike Duhem, was really a positivist and in the deconstructionist sense of that word and who, as a historian of mechanics, was no match for Duhem.

Short was indeed the list of French philosophers and historians of science who expressed interest in the call of Bounhiol and Boudot, two professors at the University of Bordeaux, to participate in a special session in honor of Duhem, in the framework of the meeting of the Association Française pour l'Avancement des Sciences in Bordeaux in July 1967. The list was contained in the letter which Boudot wrote to Hélène on May 14, 1967, on behalf of Bounhiol, secretary of the meeting.[39] Boudot took the view that to her alone belonged the honor "of either opening or closing the session" and asked her whether she could give the title of her speech. Apparently, Hélène sent a reply to Boudot's letter of April 21, 1967, and held out the hope that she might attend the meeting. In that letter Boudot wrote: "When I was given the task of organizing the section on the philosophy and history of science and of proposing a theme for our papers, my decision was prompt: it was imperative that we speak of Pierre Duhem, physicist, philosopher, and historian of science. This suggestion was met with full approval on the part of all concerned." Boudot assured her that the session would last only two days (July 11-12) and would involve only a small number of participants, "a rather inadequate homage to the one who remains one of the glories of the University of Bordeaux."

While a trip from Cabrespine to Bordeaux would have taxed too much the strength of Hélène, already seventy-five, she could still take very energetic action when she found Hermann et Cie failing to live up to their contractual and informal obligations. The former related to their being inexplicably remiss in sending her royalties, the latter to their not bringing out in a reprint edition Duhem's *Théorie physique* and his *Traité d'énergetique*. Berès was indeed more than surprised when in late December 1966 he received on both matters official summons which Hélène initiated on December 12, 1966, in the offices of M. Jarassé, *huissier de justice*, in Paris. It was stated in the summons, among other things, that Mlle

Duhem had failed to receive, since 1960, royalties for the sales of the *Système du monde.*

As it turned out, the sales of almost two-thousand volumes amounted to royalties of about ten thousand new francs. Hermann et Cie had indeed been very negligent in communicating with Hélène. She did not even know that meanwhile Hermann moved from Place de la Sorbonne to Blvd St Germain! But the supreme irony came when Berès resorted to the old tactic of offense as being the best defense. On January 4, 1967, he wrote to her: "Allow me to recall the fact that it was we who took the initiative to complete, after fifty years of somnolence, the publication of the *Système du monde.*" Further insult was added to injury when on February 23, 1967, Berès referred to the "great expenses" of his firm to make the publication of the *Système du monde* possible. Obviously, at Hermann et Cie no change of mind, let alone a change of heart, had taken place. Nor was it realized there that in Hélène they were confronted with one who signed her name as Hélène Pierre-Duhem, to indicate her total commitment to being the guardian of her father's memory.

In September 1971, Hélène saw to it that the fifty-fifth anniversary of her father's death would be properly remembered in her own part of the world. The *Midi Libre* of Montpellier devoted almost a full page to an interview with her under the headline: "Une gloire de la science française dort son dernier sommeil à Cabrespine où le village entier garde son souvenir." Of the three photos illustrating the report, one showed Duhem, another a drawing of his of the Château of Cabrespine. The third showed Hélène herself, sitting in an easy chair, with a fur around her shoulder, showing to the Mayor of Cabrespine one of her father's albums of drawings. Her face was expressive of age as well as of clarity of mind and determination. Appropriately, the report came to a close with the words: "Fifty-five years after the death of the great savant, his daughter watches over the purity of his memory and the people of Cabrespine proudly keep pointing out 'the house of the savant' to tourists who happen to come by."

During the last dozen or so years of her life, Hélène received regular visits from Marie-Madeleine during the summers. In 1973 her health began to give way rather rapidly. In October Henriette arrived to take stock of the situation and noticed her spells of incoherence. She was in particular concerned about Hélène's inability to keep a close eye on what she had inherited from her father. Unable to keep complete balance as she moved about, she burned her legs one day. Marie-Madeleine, whom she had made in 1969 the heiress of all her possessions, and especially of the Duhemiana, now began to spend every alternate week with her. In early March Hélène was taken to the hospital in Carcassonne. On March 25th, the feast of the Annunciation, she told Marie-Madeleine that the Virgin Mary had just told her that she would soon come for her. About the same time she kept muttering, in great anxiety, the words: "les papiers, Marie-Mad, les papiers . . . les papiers . . ." She meant the scientific correspondence of her father. She was much more concerned about them than her polite written words to Miller would have indicated. She had been dead for more than five years when that correspondence was finally returned to the soil of her beloved France and to the rightful owner there, Mlle Marie-Madeleine Gallet.

On April 10, 1974, she suffered a cardiac seizure, but quickly rallied. Marie-Madeleine now began to look for a convalescent home for her. On April 15, the hospital assured her that Hélène was doing fine. Marie-Madeleine spent much of the 23d of April with Hélène and looked forward to another visit as she took the evening train back to Paris, arriving at home at 7 in the morning the next day. Four hours later her telephone rang. It was the hospital of Carcassonne: "Mlle Duhem died this morning." Three days later she was laid to rest next to her father.

Among those who attended the ceremony, there was only one, Marie-Madeleine, who came from a distance. Her presence symbolized Hélène's deep ties to the Dufourcqs. Without them she could not have become a heroic guardian, however reluctant at first, of her father's memory and inestimable intellectual bequest.

Appendix

How was Pierre Duhem's *Système du monde*
published?

Fragments of a correspondence
collected, with a foreword,
by Hélène Duhem

We have told elsewhere[1] how an essay planned on the
"origins of statics"[2] was to become the two volumes that carry
that very title and how the book planned on the "origins of
dynamics" became — in proportion to the discoveries that
marked the investigations of Pierre Duhem on that virgin
territory — the huge work known as *Le Système du monde,
Histoire des doctrines cosmologiques de Platon à Copernic*, which,
though unfinished, will comprise nine large volumes.

By the summer of 1912, the manuscript of the work had
already reached alarming proportions, with no completion yet
in sight, and the question of its publication posed itself in a
disquieting manner. Pierre Duhem asked himself with anxiety
if that work which required such labor of him and was favored
by so many unforeseen findings, would ever see print. Indeed,
the size of the work could easily discourage any publisher.

The fragments of correspondence which we now publish
will shed a better light than would any commentary on the
fears experienced on that account by Pierre Duhem and on the

unusual supports he encountered in that difficult moment. Thanks to them the *Système du monde* could finally be published. First of all, there were Messrs. Hermann, father and son, whose good will was fully on hand to facilitate that publication; there was Mr. Gaston Darboux, perpetual secretary of the Académie des Sciences, and Mr. Bayet, director of Higher Education. They, on being asked, put all their powerful influence behind a good cause and obtained from the Ministry of Public Instruction a subvention that allowed the publisher to undertake the task. But, above all, there was the Père Bulliot.

It is a fact that Pierre Duhem never wanted to ask for anything for himself. He had knocked at the door of Messrs. Hermann. Had they declined to publish his work, perhaps he would have approached other publishers, just as unwilling to face the same difficulties, and the *Système du monde* would have run the risk of never being published. But the Père Bulliot kept watching, and without any doubt also Divine Providence that sent him to Messrs. Hermann at the moment when, rather perplexed, they did not know what reply to give to the author.

The Père Bulliot had immediately realized the crucial importance of that work. He also had confidence in the future and rightly guessed that posterity would prove him right. With indefatigable tenacity he undertook procedures that would have displeased the author. He had in fact to assure the author that he had undertaken those procedures only in his own name, because to solicit anything would have dismayed Pierre Duhem. It seems indeed that the Père Bulliot had some difficulty in obtaining from him the two official letters which Messrs. Darboux and Bayet expected so that they might definitively grant what they had already promised.

The Père Bulliot died before Pierre Duhem.[3] Later, when after the author's decease the economic difficulties disrupted the publication of the *Système du monde,* the Père Bulliot, unfortunately, was no longer there to solicit again from the respective powers the material help necessary for the publisher to complete the publication of the work. The years went by, the moves we have made brought no result; . . . people seemed to forget that the manuscripts of four important volumes, entirely finished at the death of their author, were buried in the vault of the Institut to which we had confided them for safekeeping. Abroad it was supposed that the premature death of Pierre Duhem prevented him from going farther than volume V, published shortly after his death, and I am inclined to believe that the revelation made by us[4] about the existence of these manuscripts and of their being forgotten occasioned a small scandal among some scholars. Happy scandal at any rate! Many admirers of the historical researches of Pierre Duhem rallied. Mme Paul Tannery and Mr. Georges Sarton published in *Isis* an appeal on behalf of the publication of the rest of the *Système du monde*.[5] At the same time, the Académie Internationale d'Histoire des Sciences held a special session at which many French and foreign savants participated and called for the publication of the unpublished manuscripts of the *Système du monde* and urged that the material subvention so far lacking be finally provided.

There came, however, no subvention. Should one be astonished? . . . But in the absence of financial assistance, the publisher felt greatly encouraged to resume the printing of the unpublished material. He listened to the wish voiced by Mr. Abel Rey, a wish endorsed by the members of the Académie Internationale d'Histoire des Science, as well as to the appeal of Mme Paul Tannery and Mr. Georges Sarton. Without any other help than this precious moral support, the Director of the Librairie Hermann sent to press volume VI of the *Système du monde* that will soon appear together with the second edition of the first five volumes. We owe to him real gratitude.[6]

Cabrespine, December 24, 1937   Hélène Pierre-Duhem

★ ★ ★

A. Hermann to Pierre Duhem, Paris, June 2, 1912

Dear Monsieur, I rather regret the letter I wrote you yesterday. I would be sorry to see your work published by another publisher. To this you could rightly reply: 'If you want to publish my work give me more favorable conditions.' At any rate, I would be grateful if you gave further details about your work, then we could perhaps consider both the possibility of my involvement in the publication of your work and the possibility of giving you the author's rights. Please, kindly accept, dear Sir, the expression of my affectionate and devoted sentiments.

A. Hermann to Pierre Duhem, Paris, July 31, 1912

Dear Monsieur, I have just returned from a trip. Following the receipt of your kind communications, I am, as before, too perplexed about taking a decision concerning the publication of your great work. My incompetence in science and its history forces me to put myself entirely in the perspective of sales. I am afraid that they will not cover the cost of printing which I estimate to be about 40,000 francs. It seems to me that such a publication can be undertaken only with a subvention that would safeguard the publisher against all risk. I know that several persons, among them the Père Bulliot, are keenly interested in the publication of your work. If you authorize me to undertake some steps, I could perhaps obtain the necessary subvention.

Of course, if in view of the subvention, the enterprise would bring profit, I am ready to share it with you.
Please, kindly accept . . .

The Père Bulliot to Pierre Duhem, Clamart, August 7, 1912

Dear Monsieur Duhem, My guardian angel sent me a few days ago to Messrs. Hermann at the very moment when they deliberated with no small perplexity about your great work.

Though very keen on publishing it, they are worried about the immediate financial returns.

On the on hand, these gentlemen estimate the cost of publication to be 35,000 francs at the minimum, or perhaps even 40,000, and, so they told me, they do not want to commit themselves to more than 25,000 francs.

On the other hand, Divine Providence did not lead you, a man of science, whose researches touched on many topics, to complete this scholarly masterwork, without a purpose that cannot be deprived of its aims.

Your work, through its impartial presentation of history alone, is the justification of the Encyclicals *Aeterni Patris*[7] and *Pascendi*.[8] It comes at the moment when our philosophy is in full development. Therefore its speedy publication cannot be a matter of discussion, only the best means of achieving it. And since such a work will not soon be undertaken again and its source materials become more and more unavailable, one should assure its long endurance through the choice of good quality paper. Therefore the practical means, which imposes itself, is a subvention from one of the Academies interested in the topic or all three Academies if they wish to, or perhaps a generous donor, such as Prince Roland Bonaparte, so I am told. Mr. Picard, with whom I spoke without mentioning you, assured me that the Academies have funds of which they do not know what to do and that this should not pose a difficulty.

All this may be somewhat optimistic, but it only proves that there is an attempt to be made which has to succeed. In these conditions would you authorize me to take some steps, or ask someone more influential to take them? What would you say to Mr. Jordan's contacting the Académie des Sciences to which Prince Bonaparte gives generous support each year? I would gladly see Mr. Boutroux who is interested in our philosophy. Would you see someone at the Académie des Inscriptions? It seems to me, convinced as I am of its enormous importance, I would make a good case on behalf of that work.

I confess, on the other hand, that I would resent this kind of work being published with the help of people other than Catholic. It is we who must share the cost with the publisher. Also I pray above all to Divine Providence to furnish us with the necessary means. Were I to obtain them, the whole thing would be quickly done . . . .

The Père Bulliot to Pierre Duhem, Clamart, August 12, 1912
Dear Monsieur Duhem, Of course, I act only in the name of Mr. Hermann alone. I asked him to send me, to that effect, a letter which he did. But at this moment nobody is at home. Thus nothing would be gained by trying to find this one or that one of the people in question. Once they are back home I will hurry to see them. . . . Thank you for having given so much attention to my article.

The Père Bulliot to Pierre Duhem, Autun, Sept. 20, 1912
Dear Monsieur Duhem, How supremely ungrateful I must seem in your eyes! It is now weeks that I am suffering on account of it, for, believe me, I am unable to forget it. I have not yet been able to sit down at my desk, although I am getting close to doing so. I shall resume Friday or Saturday at the latest the letter I began writing to you in Clamart. As it will not require a reply from you, you will be very kind in sending me just a word of introduction to Mr. Delbos. Mr. Hermann will go to Mr. Darboux. I shall press on with these steps. I have been on forced labor[9]. . . .

Victor Delbos to Pierre Duhem, Paris, Dec. 5, 1912
My very dear friend, Your letter reawakened in me not so much a friendship that never dies, but a remorse that troubles me from time to time. How many times I wanted to write to

you, to thank you for what you send me for my instruction and pleasure! And also to ask you as to whether and when you want me to resume my reading of Leonardo!

Alas! my laborious life is stupidly dissipated within a multitude of necessary tasks, and very much taken up by concerns of professional importance.

Meanwhile, what a crushing labor you are carrying on, compared with which mine seems very light. I keep asking myself how you can find sufficient strength.

I have seen the Père Bulliot, and I told him what, in my opinion, needs doing most. One should knock at the door of the Académie des Sciences (our Académie [des Sciences politiques et morales] has no available resources), and, through the Académie des Sciences at the door of the Institut [de France] which also has funds available. The person who can best secure that subvention is <u>Darboux</u>, both because of the authority he has at the Académie des Sciences, and by his participation at the Central commission of the Institute. — Needlesss to say that if the Central commission is to be convinced, I shall talk as convincingly as possible with my confrères who represent us there. If, on the other hand, there are a few steps that I can take in order to facilitate the publication of the immense work (in every sense of that word, and especially in its best sense), you know that I am quite ready.

You also know that I shall be very happy to see you and talk with you when you come to Paris.

I add my compliments to Mademoiselle Duhem to my expressions of friendship towards you.

Very affectionately, my dear friend.

I have to write my Malebranche: when I come to his "science," I shall undoubtedly have recourse to your insights.

The Père Bulliot to Pierre Duhem, Clamart, Dec. 10, 1912

Dear Monsieur Duhem, Finally, I can write to you with a clear head!

First, although this may be infinitely too late, allow me to thank you from the depth of my heart for having received me in Cabrespine and for the delightful day that you let me spend there. Together with my stay in Autun with my sister and my brother-in-law, this is my best memory of my vacation. I have enjoyed it, I am still very much enjoying it. . . .

But let us return to the great question, the one which has so great a hold on my heart. I know that Mr. Hermann is, in a way, wholly oblivious to your instructions. Happily, his son remembers them better and is in the process of drawing up, according to them, a proposal for Mr. Darboux. I think that the step has been taken. I shall go tonight or tomorrow to ask about the result.

Since Mr. Delbos has written to you, you know as much as I do about his thinking. His opinion, which is also that of Mr. Boutroux, is that Mr. Darboux is the means par excellence to succeed at the Institut. Now, he is too intelligent a person for me to insult him by doubting his good will.

For the moment, dear Monsieur Duhem, I take my meals here with the secretary of the *Revue de philosophie.* You know that a secretary is a perennial beggar. Each time we pronounce your name, I am certain to hear this refrain: "Will not Mr. Duhem renew his past generosities toward the *Revue de philosophie?* Would he not honor us with a chapter from his book?" I cannot help transmitting you this request, because, in order to reply, you have but the problem of choosing from a wealth of possibilities. Could you not, for instance, give us the chapter on infinity or some other chapter? . . .

Please accept, dear Monsieur Duhem, the expression of our respect and very devoted grateful sentiments. (I speak for the group).

The Père Bulliot to Pierre Duhem, Dec. 17, 1912

Dear Monsieur Duhem, Let me tell you about my joy over the news about the step you yourself made with Mr. Darboux. Be so kind as to let me know the result. Have you presented him with your Table of Contents?

Then, if there is still no success, I shall do everything I can.

The Père Bulliot to Pierre Duhem [Dec. 31, 1912?]

It is to you that I send my first greetings for the New Year, but on the condition that you answer only mentally. You know all that I wish for you: the happy achievement and sumptuous printing of a work with which you are all too familiar, then health and peace for you and for Mademoiselle Hélène, her presence, as frequent as possible, in Bordeaux and in Cabrespine; finally, to conclude, the discovery of some new and unknown manuscript of Buridan. . . .

No news from Mr. Darboux at Hermann. I shall try to see Mr. Boutroux tomorrow and to urge him to intervene with Mr. Darboux. I wish to know what can be expected from him.

The Père Bulliot to Pierre Duhem, Friday, January 3, 1913

Dear Monsieur Duhem, Thank you for your kind letter. I am glad to know that you are today in Arcachon where, I regret, I cannot have a part [of your company]. But I shared it in Cabrespine. I wanted to go this Tuesday to the Foundation Thiers. A sudden bout of flu prevented me from doing so.

Wednesday, I could not see Mr. Boutroux who gave me an appointment for yesterday. Beforehand I dropped in at Hermann.

Mr. Darboux is in the South, rather sick, so Mr. Boutroux told me. I saw that he was worried on that account, not for the moment, because he will return around January 10, but his health leaves something to desire.

Mr. Boutroux had forgotten that it was through Mr. Delbos that he had heard of your work. But he did not promise me an intervention. However, he told me that the published work would certainly obtain a prize from the Ministry [of Public Instruction] and also a subscription. (On that last point I could not very well understand why it was not possible to have one before the printing.) After the reply of Mr. Darboux could not you attempt, or let someone else attempt, something from this side [of the Ministry], if necessary?

Mr. Boutroux is convinced as I am that the work, of interest to the world of learning, cannot help but sell well in the long run. May God help you to pursue forcefully the much desired goal.

Gaston Darboux, Perpetual Secretary of the Académie des Science, to Pierre Duhem, Paris, January 23, 1913

My dear Duhem, I am rather late in replying to you. But since you have written to me concerning your work, I went to Marseilles where my granddaughter and myself were retained by sickness. And since my return, eight days ago, I have been overwhelmed with matters to attend to.

Concerning your work, I see but one solution. Let the publisher determine the number of copies that ought to be subscribed to, to cover the costs. After that you can turn to the Direction de l'Enseignement Supérieur which, in analogous cirumstances you can recall, agreed to a considerable subscription to allow for Méray to publish his *Leçons*.[10] After a few words exchanged on this subject, I have the impression that Bayet would receive your request very favorably.

As to the Académie, perhaps it can request from the Institut a subvention drawn from the Debrousse Funds. Because, personally speaking, the Académie is in the red. Still, it would be imperative that you be able to furnish me with an estimate of the cost of publication, of the span of time it would require. I keep your note of 46 pages to which you may refer. But hurry up!

Yours very devotedly, G. Darboux.

Letter of the Director of the Enseignement Supérieur to Pierre Duhem, February 6, 1913.

Dear Monsieur, I have read with the greatest interest the letter and the documents you have kindly sent me. I know how deeply committed you have been for several years to the history of science and also know of the remarkable discoveries you have made in that domain of ideas.

I ask for a few days so that I may study the means of giving you satisfaction. Could you tell me over how many years the publication would spread and what would the price of each volume would be?

Letter of the Père Bulliot to Pierre Duhem, Chartres, 4 rue de la Bourdinière, March 2, 1913.

Dear Monsieur Duhem, I hasten, as you can imagine, to know the reply of Mr. Bayet. Mr. Darboux seemed to Mr. Hermann to have a very sincere interest in your work. I cannot say that much about Mr. Boutroux, with whom the interest seemed to be more a matter of principle than a personal one. If Mr. Bayet would not give a satisfactory answer, one should look quickly in a different direction and, just as your friend Mr. Delbos thinks, make known your historical studies as widely as possible. When will the third volume of Leonardo da Vinci appear?

The Director of L'Enseignement Supérieur to Mr Pierre
    Duhem, March 15, 1913

Dear Monsieur, I agree that you have the right to deplore
the administrative delays and I apologize. However, I can assure
you that no forgetfulness is involved in any way and that I have
a very keen desire to give you satisfaction and facilitate the
publication of a work that will do great honor to French
science. I hope to send shortly, and before Easter, an official
reply.

The Minister of Instruction publique et des Beaux-Arts to
    Pierre Duhem, Paris, March 22, 1913

I have already been familiar with the learned works to
which you devoted your energies when the Director of
Enseignement Supérieur spoke to me about your project to
publish in about ten volumes a "Histoire des doctrines cosmologiques de Platon à Copernic." This is a great work that
cannot fail to bring honor to French science. My administration
will therefore gladly give its assistance. As soon as the conditions of publication are definitively laid down, your publisher
should feel free to submit me a contract.

Please, Monsieur le Professeur, accept the assurance of my
most special regards,

On behalf of the Minister of Instruction publique et des
Beaux-Arts, the Minister of Enseignement Supérieur, Conseiller
d'Etat, Bayet

Victor Delbos to Pierre Duhem, Figeac, April 6, 1913

I have been wanting to write you for a long, my dear
friend, but as always I had a very heavy first semester. . . .

I would have liked very much to have supported the aims
of the Père Bulliot more effectively. But what to do? I am
convinced that nothing can be expected from our Académie

[des Sciences politiques et morales]. It has no means to dispose of. It is the Académie des Sciences which is by far the richer. But according to what the Père Bulliot has told me, Mr. Boutroux is hardly moving at all.

And yet, my dear friend, how sad it would be if you were not helped in your work, so beautiful, so fruitful, and disinterested! This immense work of reconstructing the scientific ideas of the past is one of the most useful things one can do; and with what assurance, with what erudition you are carrying on with it!

I am pained on feeling powerless to be of service to you. I beg you to let me know if you ever think that some steps on my part in any way can be effective.

Convey my regards to Mlle Duhem; to you my best friendly greetings and most affectionate handshake.

Gaston Darboux, perpetual secretary of the Académie des Sciences, Paris, April 9, 1913

My dear Duhem, The Ministry asked a report from me on your request for subvention and I sent a very favorable one. On the other hand I know that Mr. Bayet is very favorably disposed, but I don't know the outcome. The Institut will give you, I believe, a subvention of 2,000 francs.

If I write to you today, it is to tell you that in connection with the creation of non-resident members, several of my confrères put forward your name. I believe that if you draw up your report of candidacy, you have a strong chance of being elected. Let me know your thinking on the matter.

Pierre Duhem to Gaston Darboux, Bordeaux, April 10, 1913

Monsieur and dear Teacher, What gratitude should be mine! For the past two years I have been full of anxiety. I have undertaken a crushing project and I have very much feared that it might become useless owing to the impossibility of publishing it. If it is at long last on the point of being published, I owe it entirely to you, because, without you, I would not have thought of turning to Mr. Bayet, nor, probably, the chance of seeing my request approved by him. The subvention which you made me anticipate as coming from the Institute brings my hopes to fulfillment. I therefore cannot express to you my gratitude vividly enough.

The question you pose to me takes me by surprise and perplexes me very much. I thought that the nominations of non-resident members would be made by the Académie, as are those of the corresponding members, without any initiative taken on the part of the ones considered. I would have been extremely honored if the Académie had chosen me, and confident in the justice of your judgment if the Académie had not felt it necessary to designate me.

If the nomination for non-resident member supposes an act of candidacy, what should I do? I would be glad to write to the Académie that its choice appears to me a honorable one if the Académie is to take my letter for an act of deference. But that letter, isolated as it is from all other steps, would it not appear a bit derisive? Yet I do not see any other way of putting forth my candidacy.

Perhaps the Académie would wish that I add a list of my publications. But the mere thought of summing up the twenty volumes and three hundred articles or memoirs I have published fills me with great dismay. At any rate, even if I could overcome that dismay and set myself to putting together that resumé, it would mean a considerable work; it would take at least two or three months. I do not think I have the right, in order to gain a personal satisfaction, to take that time from the time I must devote to the work I have undertaken. — Shall I have enough time to finish it?

If I do not have the leisure to draw up a summary of my work, even less do I have the leisure to make visits aimed at promoting my candidacy. Even if I had the time, I would surely not prevail on myself to make those visits. All my life I have too often deplored the use of visits for promoting candidacies in order to conform to that procedure now. I admit, however, that I would find inopportune the creation of a new title of non-resident academician if it meant for the corresponding members not to reside . . . at their home but to rush to Paris to beg for votes there. It is the fear of this outcome that prevented me from signing the petition addressed to the Académie by its correspondents. I would not therefore like to support, however slightly, by my example an abuse that I dislike.

Under these conditions, should I address a letter of candidacy to the Académie? Should not I feel satisfied by the simple fact of the title of corresponding member, especially if the creation of a new title may diminish a bit the older prestige? I hesitate and I see only one reasonable means for overcoming this indecision: it is to abandon myself blindly to your decision and do as you would counsel me.

Whatever the advice you shall give, I shall thank you for it in advance, while at the same time I extend to you the homage of my deep respect.

A. Hermann to Pierre Duhem, April 11, 1913

Dear Monsieur, I had a rather long conversation yesterday with Mr. Laurent who summoned me to the Ministry and I now summarize it for you.

First of all the question of principle can be considered as settled and the ministerial subscription has been obtained for you. It remains now for us to work out the innumerable details of the contract, which will be long and meticulous as are all affairs that connect the State and the individuals.

1. The ministerial subscription will be only for 250 copies instead of 300 but at a price slightly higher per printed sheet so

as to keep the subscription the same. As a result the sale price will be slightly increased.

2. The Ministry obligates itself only for one volume per year, in order to keep the subvention within its normal budget.

3. It will be necessary to furnish as soon as possible one sample page printed on the selected paper with the font chosen. Please, kindly send me a page that I may typeset immediately. (I would like to propose to you a glossy paper, the same I use for the physics of Ollivier[11] and of Chwolson.[12])

I would now like to ask you for some information that will be useful for me to draw up the contract with the State:

1. The number of volumes (I have answered: about 10).

2. The length of each volume (I have answered: about 500 pages similar to the "Léonard de Vinci.")

3. Will there be many texts in small print and diagrams in the work?

4. What shall be the average amount of text in Greek per volume; I use on purpose the expression, average amount, to establish an average price for each volume.

5. Do you think that some volumes will considerably exceed the average of 500 pages and by how much?

6. Do you think you can guarantee the publication of one volume per year or about, because the Ministry reserves the right to annull the contract in case of an interruption of more than two years between the publication of one volume and the next (a most unlikely event).

7. Do you have the intention of reproducing in facsimile, in the form of tables separate from the text, original documents and, if so, in what number? (Perhaps this would be a good idea, but if you decide to do so I would need to know before signing the contract in order to foresee additional expenses and ask for a subvention).

Please, excuse me for annoying you with all these details, but it is necessary to provide with all possible details the Ministry which appears to be extremely well disposed toward your work. I think I must add that, judging from my conversation with Mr. Laurent, it is due above all to the influence of Mr. Darboux that the Director of Enseignement Supérieur decided to help us in such a powerful manner with the publication of your book.

It remains for me to express the pleasure I feel on seeing at last the moment approach for the publication of a work which cost you so much effort and to assure you of all my care about its publication. We shall use absolutely new fonts, and I am convinced that you will be satisfied by the physical execution of this work.

A. Hermann to Pierre Duhem, Paris, April 17, 1913

Dear Monsieur, I eagerly wait the typographic sample I requested from my printer in order to submit it to you. Meanwhile I am sending you, under a separate cover, two samples of paper of good quality. Tell me if the one marked with # 287 would be satisfactory. The one marked # 289 is more beautiful but also much more costly. The # 287 represents already three times the price of ordinary paper, but I think that it is a good idea to do the printing on a quality paper. It will show the font very well and the line drawings will look as good as on glossy paper.

Jules Hermann to Pierre Duhem, Paris, April 21, 1913.

Dear Monsieur, I am giving order for the composition of a new sample page in accordance with the specifications you have kindly given, and I shall send it to you shortly. I have also seen that the Institut has voted for you 2,500 francs but I think that this sum will be unnecessary for us; if, however, it will be necessary to justify its use and to apply it to the publication of your work, it seems to me that it may be used for an increase of your royalties, but I repeat that we do not have a need for it, because the Ministry supports the publication in a manner sufficient to cover all risk. . . .

For your work, by taking a very nice alfa paper (with fonts used for Tisserand's *Mécanique céleste* and Appel's *Mécanique*), one will obtain a very nice imprint (at a cost of about 1 franc per page).

By taking the other kind of paper, the imprint will be equally very good, but the cost of paper will be 2.50 francs per page which will force the raising of the sale price by as much, which is rather annoying.

I suggest the following solution: let one half of the edition be on alfa paper, which will give very beautiful volumes, and the other half on the other paper, to be sold to bibliophiles at a higher price.

Jules Hermann to Pierre Duhem, Paris, April 21, 1913.

Dear Monsieur, I have forgotten to tell you this: the Ministry subscribed to ten volumes of about 500 pages each — but if there are more volumes, I will have to produce gratuitously 250 copies of volumes XI and following!

It is therefore important to plan things to end with 10 volumes, which is perhaps not easy to do in advance. Perhaps in that case you would reserve the 2,500 francs for that purpose.

Jules Hermann to Pierre Duhem, Paris, May 31, 1913.

Dear Monsieur, I hasten to acknowledge the receipt of your letter and of your two drawings. I have sent to you two days ago the beginning of the galleys of your book. I hope that you have received them. I waited to draw up our contract until the Minister signed mine, but the Minister cannot sign my contract except on seeing a page printed on the paper chosen. The paper matters little to him, provided he sees it together with the font adopted (such is administration!). I hope to receive by mail samples of that paper within two days. In any case the typesetting will not be delayed because it has already begun.

The Director of Enseignement Supérieur to Pierre Duhem, January 31, 1914.

Dear Monsieur, Have I thanked you for sending volume I of your learned work? I am not certain and therefore I feel obliged to let you know how much I was touched by what you have kindly said of me in the Foreword. You have exaggerated what I was able to do, but I am glad to have been able to help, however slightly, to facilitate the publication of your work which, I know, will do great honor, in every respect, to French science.

With my devoted greetings, Bayet

The Secretary of the Institut to Pierre Duhem, February 3, 1914

Dear Monsieur, The Institut has accorded you 2,500 francs drawn on the Debrousse funds. The sum will be sent you in a few days and you can claim it in Bordeaux.

With the homage of my respectful greetings, R. Régnier

Camille Jullian to Pierre Duhem, Paris, December 17, 1914

My dear friend, I found the two volumes on my return. Thank you. This will bring me joy: the joy of the artist, the joy of the savant, the joy of the researcher. You make me believe that I am all that by understanding you. I ask for the opportunity to speak at the meeting of Friday. I think you will be pleased with what I will say.

Notes

Chapter One

[1] See bibliography of Duhem's works in *Uneasy Genius*, entry 1891-1.

[2] Quoted in full in *Uneasy Genius*, p. 98.

[3] Eugène Fromentin (1820-1876), a painter of considerable reputation, was also the author of an enormously successful interpretation of painting in the Low Countries, *Les maîtres d'autrefois. Belgique-Hollande* (1876), where he argued that the chief appeal of their painters was due to their faithfulness to the genius of the land. Duhem found in that book inspiration for his contention that physicists too should cultivate their subject in conformity with the genius of their nation. On Fromentin's influence of Duhem's own ideal of landscape painting, see my introduction in *The Physicist as Artist: The Landscapes of Pierre Duhem* (Edinburgh: Scottish Academic Press, 1988).

[4] One of them is reproduced, ibid., as illustration 96.

[5] Duhem made at that Congress an intervention that created quite a stir (see *Uneasy Genius*, pp. 112-15). That in subsequent years he repeatedly spoke about it at home is shown by the fact that Hélène recalled it as one of her childhood memories in her biography of her father, *Un savant français: Pierre Duhem* (Paris: Plon, 1936), pp. 157-58.

[6] The full text of that letter is given, ibid., pp. 55-66.

[7] P. B. Lacôme, "Théories physiques à propos d'une discussion entre savants," *Revue Thomiste* 1 (1893), pp. 676-92 and 2 (1894), pp. 92-105.

[8] On Dufourcq's life and work, see *Mélanges Albert Dufourcq: Etudes d'histoire religieuse*, préface de Georges Goyau (Paris: Plon, 1933).

Chapter Two

[1] The best account is in A. Dansette, *Histoire religieuse de la France contemporaine* (Paris: Flammarion, 1948), of which an abbreviated translation in two volumes by J. Dingle appeared in 1961, under the title, *Religious History of Modern France* (New York: Herder & Herder).

[2] The photo on the cover of the brochure shows about twenty young women and girls, on the steps of the main entrance of the house, with Mlle de la Girennerie in the foreground. The photo on the back cover also shows her, surrounded by young women. There the photos are credited to *La vie heureuse* (see next note).

[3] "Les Ateliers Sainte-Agnès," *La vie heureuse* (April 1903), and references to the issue of Dec. 1, 1901, of *La Réforme Sociale* and to the April 1905 issue of *Le Bulletin de la Société Internationale pour l'Etude des Questions d'Assistance*.

[4] In *Le Gaulois*. Edmond Rostand (1868-1918) was best known for his dramas *Cyrano de Bergerac* and *L'Aiglon*.

[5] Antoine-Frédéric Ozanam (1813-1853) was one of the founders of the Société de Saint Vincent de Paul, a Catholic lay organization of charitable works, and author of remarkable studies on Dante. The cause of his beatification was introduced in 1923.

[6] Marie Duhem must have meant the first wife of Georges Goyau, *née* Lucie Félix-Faure, a well known writer, who had been married for ten years to Goyau.

[7] On Récamier, who accompanied Philippe, duc d'Orléans (1869-1926), on his explorations in Africa and in the Arctic, see "Eloge funèbre du Docteur Joseph Récamier, membre associé de l'Académie des Sciences, Belles-Lettres et Arts de Lyon, présenté à l'Académie dans sa séance du

7 mai 1935," par Mr le Docteur P. Gouillioud (Lyon: Société anonyme de l'imprimerie A. Rey, 1935), 12pp.

[8] Georges Goyau (1866-1939), who in his writings pleaded for a dynamic participation of the Church in modern social and cultural affairs, was best known for his nine-volume work, *Allemagne religieuse*, published between 1898 and 1913.

[9] Paris: Desclée de Brouwer, 1912.

[10] That the book was difficult to find and rather expensive indicates that the "Racinet" in question was either the lavishly illustrated *Le costume historique*, or the two-volume *L'ornement polychrome*, both published in the 1870s and 1880s. Did Hélène try to obtain a copy in order to please Mlle de la Girennerie?

[11] The Père Lucien Laberthonnière (1860-1932), an Oratorian, championed moral dogmatism as an antidote to a strictly intellectual understanding of the faith.

[12] Charles Maurras (1868-1952) was sentenced to life-imprisonment in 1945 for his collaboration with the Germans, but released for poor health in 1948.

[13] *Charles Dickens: A Critical Study* (New York: Dodd, Mead, 1906).

[14] Duhem painted Emile Désiré-François Eudes (1843-1888) in too favorable light. For his participation in various incendiary actions, especially in the Rue de Lille, Eudes was condemned to death, but given clemency shortly afterwards, a point overlooked by Duhem. Eudes remained to the end a Marxist activist and a supporter of L. Blanqui, the French Karl Marx.

[15] The minister in question served in the cabinet of Gaston Doumergue which resigned in June 1914.

Chapter Three

[1] The recipient of that letter is unknown. For quotations from it, see *Uneasy Genius*, p. 259

[2] From a conversation with Mr. B. Tissier, Mayor of Cabrespine.

[3] For Jordan's obituary on Duhem, see *Uneasy Genius*, p. 32, note 91.

[4] Monnet could only mean Camille Matignon (1867-1934), professor of chemistry at the Sorbonne. The change of heart attributed by Monnet to Matignon should seem all the more startling because, following Berthelot's death, Matignon wrote a highly laudatory commemorative article, "Marcelin Berthelot," in the leading French scientific bimonthly, *Revue générale des sciences pures et appliquées* (May 18, 1907), which came out in English in the *Smithsonian Institution Annual Report* (Washington, D. C., 1908), pp. 669-684.

[5] A. Fliche (1884-1951) was the leading French Church historian of the first half of this century. He started his academic career in Bordeaux in 1910 and held Duhem in the highest esteem.

[6] See note 3 above.

[7] During my visits to the University of Bordeaux in the early 1980s, I was able to obtain the information that its Library received about 200 books from Duhem's library, but that no list of them had apparently been ever drawn up.

[8] Commemorative articles published on Duhem between 1917 and 1920 are discussed in *Uneasy Genius*, pp. 230-240.

[9] See *Uneasy Genius*, p. 222, note 5.

[10] Glaring, indeed, is the slighting of Duhem in G. Beaujouan's contribution, "Medieval Science in the Christian West" (pp. 468-532) in *History of Science, Vol. 1, Ancient and Medieval Science from the Beginnings to 1450,* ed. R. Taton, tr. A. J. Pomerans (New York: Basic Books, 1963). The French original was published in 1957, or three full years after the

publication of volume VI of the *Système du monde* and of the reprinting of the three volumes of Duhem's Leonardo studies, a further aggravating circumstance.

[11] The reference is most likely to Charles Benoit (1901- ?), a biochemist.

[12] Léon Lyon-Caen (1877- ?) was a jurist.

Chapter Four

[1] The sketch of the cross, almost 2 meters high, was sent to her on March 14, 1933, and she paid in full the bill of fifteen hundred francs on May 29.

[2] Of the Latin and French text, as composed by Dufourcq and given here, the quality of the former came, of course, naturally from a professor of Church history, whose first phase of scholarly work related to the critical edition of various Acts of martyrs.

In Memoriam
D. D. Petri Duhem
olim in Universitati Burdigalensi
professor egregius,
Scientia claruit, fide vixit,
Non minus virtute quam cultura conspicuus,
Amicus pauperum, divitum exemplar,
Prodere voluit nullatenus praeesse,
Magis quam amicos veritatem dilexit,
Errores profligans, errantium compatiens
Neminem habuit adversarium, nisi veritatis
Onustus meritis, sui plane immemor
Gloriam adeptus est sed honores refugit
Dignus a Christo in coelis coronari.

Il a brillé par la science, il vécut la foi
Non moins remarquable par sa vertu que par sa culture
Ami des pauvres, modèle des riches
Il voulut servir point du tout commander

Plus encore que ses amis il a aimé la vérité,
Pourpendant les erreurs, patient pour les égarés
Il n'eut pas d'autres ennemies que cause de la vérité
Chargé de mérites, oublieux de lui-même
il a obtenu la gloire mais il a fui les honneurs
Digne d'être couronné au ciel par le Christ

[3] The royalty statement sent for 1932 also shows the sales for each of the previous half a dozen years.

[4] The children were Henriette (1902), Mathilde (1903), Norbert (1904), Marie (1910), Louise (1913), Pierre (1918), of whom the first three were the "machurés."

[5] Duhem's own signature is reproduced under his frontispiece photo in *Uneasy Genius*.

[6] Boche is a very pejorative French nickname for Germans.

[7] Philbert Maurice d'Ocagne (1862-1938), member of the Académie des sciences, was a mathematician.

[8] The sum was equivalent to the yearly earning of an agricultural laborer. See *Statistique générale de la France. Annuaire statistique. Cinquante-et-unième volume — 1935* (Paris: Imprimerie nationale, 1936), pp. 239-240.

Chapter Five

[1] See note 3 to Chapter Three.

[2] The letter, of December 20, 1889, is quoted in full in *Un savant français*, pp. 117-19.

[3] The reference is to the policy, which became known as *ralliement*, of Pope Leo XIII who in his encyclical *Immortale Dei* (1885) urged Catholics, and those in France in particular, to participate in democratic forms of government, however secularist in tone.

[4] Of the physicists mentioned by Hélène, Perrin showed the greatest dislike for Duhem's ideas on physics. De Broglie showed increasingly great understanding of Duhem's reasoning. As to Charles Fabry, he acknowledged that Duhem was the most articulate representative of the anti-atomist view. On Fabry, see *Uneasy Genius*, p. 302. Curiously, Hélène did not mention Paul Langevin who as early as 1904 attacked Duhem's ideas as "medievalization" of physics. See ibid., pp. 289-91.

[5] Among foreign scientists appreciative of Duhem's works were Gibbs, Ostwald, Van't Hoff, and young Max Planck, to mention only a few.

[6] Duhem himself told that story in the "Notice" he wrote prior to his election to the Académie des Sciences. It is entry 1913-1 in his full bibliography in *Uneasy Genius*.

[7] S. P. Langley, "The History of a Doctrine," *Science* 12 (1888), p. 74.

[8] The simplicity and neatness of Duhem's experimental apparatus to demonstrate the emission of alpha-rays greatly impressed G. H. Bryan, a leading British thermodynamicist, on the occasion of his visit in Bordeaux. See *Uneasy Genius*, p. 193.

[9] In writing in Query 31 to the *Opticks* that "God in the Beginning form'd Matter in solid, massy, hard, impenetrable, moveable Particles" Newton failed to realize that if such were the case, no momentum could be transferred from one atom to another, which simply meant the end of all physics, and certainly of Newtonian physics.

[10] Had Koyré provided a name index to his *Etudes galiléennes*, the occurrence there of Duhem's name over fifty times, a number far greater than the entries for any other modern author mentioned, he would have immediately revealed that he had in mind not so much Galileo as Duhem.

[11] Much of what appeared in the *Revue universelle* (vol. 65, 1936, pp.154-85), was taken up by the text of Chevrillon's long letter and by Duhem's letter to the Père Bulliot. The latter is reprinted in full as document 15 in my *Scientist and Catholic: Pierre Duhem* (Front Royal: Va.: Christendom Press, 1991) and its French version, *Pierre Duhem: Homme de foi et de science* (Paris: Beauchesne, 1991).

[12] The reference is to the ninth volume of Dufourcq's *L'Avenir du Christianisme*. Its first seven volumes appeared between 1908-1914 (new editions, 1924-25). The eighth volume came out in 1931. The last or tenth volume, dealing with the 18th century, was published posthumously in 1952. A two-volume abridgment of the first nine volumes was published in 1938 and 1949, respectively.

[13] A small octavo volume of 147pp and part of a series of monographs on prominent French Catholic thinkers of the first decades of this century.

[14] All of them are discussed in *Uneasy Genius*.

[15] Jordan's biographical essay on Duhem was written in wartime, a period of "union sacrée" in France. Consequently, Jordan had one more additional reason to call attention to the genuinely democratic aspects of Duhem's comportment and convictions.

[16] *The New York Times*, Dec. 21, 1983, p. A26, cols. 4-5.

[17] S. G. Brush, "Should the History of Science be Rated X?" *Science* 183 (1974), pp. 1164-72.

[18] See pp. 26, 53, 146.

[19] *Isis* 27 (1937) p. 161.

[20] The expression was part of the title of an invited lecture of mine, "Damned with Faint Praise: or the Fate of Pierre Duhem," given at Boston University on March 13, 1979, as part of the Nineteenth Annual Program, 1978-79, of the Boston Colloquium for the Philosophy of Science.

[21] B. Ginzburg, "Duhem and Jordanus Nemorarius," *Isis* 25 (1936), pp. 341-62.

[22] See note 20 above.

[23] "The Message of Leonardo: His Relation to the Birth of Modern Science," *Scribner's Magazine* 65 (1919), pp. 531-40. For further details see *Uneasy Genius*, pp. 417-18.

[24] See *Uneasy Genius*, pp. 418-419.

[25] He signed it first on October 22, 1936. Mme Tannery signed it on November 9, 1936.

[26] 26 (1937), pp. 302-03.

[27] See *Uneasy Genius*, pp. 181-82.

[28] Mme Tannery, *née* Marie Prisset (1862-1945), was also a well-known historian of science. Volume 4 of *Osiris* was dedicated to her and to her husband's memory.

[29] The reference is to entry 1913 - 1 in the full bibliography of Duhem in *Uneasy Genius*.

[30] *Archeion*, 1937, fasc. 1-2, p. 128.

[31] Ibid., p. 129.

[32] Ibid., p. 123.

[33] Ibid., p. 135.

[34] Ibid., p. 139.

[35] A. Rey, "Pierre Duhem. Historien des sciences," ibid., p. 131.

[36] Ibid., p. 134.

[37] Ibid., pp. 134-35.

[38] Ibid., p. 124. Hadamard would have hardly recalled all those years with such affection if he had sensed any "antisemitism" on Duhem's part.

[39] A. Dufourcq, "Les origines de la science moderne d'après les découvertes récentes," *Revues des deux mondes* 16 (1913), pp. 349-78.

[40] *Archeion*, pp. 124-35.

[41] Ibid., p. 140.

[42] Ibid., p. 141. The book in question is Aldo Mieli's *La scienza greca: i prearistotelici* (Firenze: Libreria della Voce, 1916).

[43] *Archeion*, pp. 141-42.

Chapter Six

1 The list of those present at the meeting was given in note 1 (pp. 121-122) in *Archeion* 1937, fasc. 2-3.

[2] Dufourcq sent Hélène a clipping from the August 15, 1935, issue of *Journal des Débats* which began with the information that since January 28, 1932, there existed at 13 Rue Du Four an Institut d'Histoire des Sciences which, although incorporated in the Faculty of Letters, had connection with all the five Faculties and that its director was Abel Rey, holder of the chair of the history and philosophy of science at the Sorbonne. The rest of the report was about the volume *Thalès* (Paris: Félix Alcan, 1935), or the first of a series of yearly publications planned by the Institut. Among the contributors to the first volume were de Broglie, Laignel-Lavastine and Hélène Metzger — all three names underlined by Dufourcq. Abel Rey, born in 1873, first taught philosophy at the University of Dijon before moving to the Sorbonne in 1919, where a special chair in the history and philosophy of science was created for him in October 1930.

[3] The series started in the late 1920s The range of the topics covered in any section can be gathered by a mere look at the back cover of any issue where the titles of many other issues are almost invariably listed.

[4] No copy of that draft was kept by Hélène. Its contents can, however, be reconstructed from Dufourcq's letter of March 13.

[5] Jean-Baptiste Guiraud (1866 - 1953), author of many books, was editor-in-chief of *La Croix* between 1929 and 1939.

[6] For landscapes of Duhem relating to the area of Ainhoa, see *The Physicist as Artist: The Landscapes of Pierre Duhem* (Edinburgh: Scottish Academic Press, 1988), p. 12.

[7] O. Manville was the editor of *L'Oeuvre scientifique de Pierre Duhem*, or *Cahier 2* of *Tome I* of *Série 7* of *Mémoires de la Société des sciences physiques et naturelles de Bordeaux* (1927), 554pp.

[8] The reference is to the August 15-31, 1936 issue of *Revue générale des sciences pures et appliquées* (p. 472).

[9] Jacques Cavallier, who was killed by a motorcyclist on March 21, 1937, had been professor of physics at the Sorbonne before he became director of French Higher Education in 1926.

[10] On Langevin's attacks on Duhem, see note 4 to Ch. 5.

[11] Hélène added that Borel also recalled his having published, with a nice commentary, in 1919 in *Revue du mois* her father's essay on Maxwell, originally written in 1916, and asked Dufourcq whether he wanted one of the three copies of that issue in her possession.

[12] Louis de Launay, *L'Eglise et la science* (Paris: Bernard Gasset, 1936).

[13] A mere look at the numerous books written by Gonzague Truc (1877-1972) should make it clear that his serious interest in defending the supernatural, mainly by portraying saints and prominent Catholic writers, such as Claudel and Pascal, kept him apart from Maurras' wing in the Action Française.

[14] This article of Guiraud in *La Croix* was unavailable to me.

Chapter Seven

[1] The book in question is Gilson's William James Lectures given at Harvard University in the fall of 1936 and published under the title, *The Unity of Philosophical Experience* (New York: Charles Scribner's Sons, 1937). There in the last chapter, in speaking about the breakdown of modern philosophy with an eye on Hume's role in generating a purely pragmatist approach Gilson wrote: "Even scientists were joining the chorus. P. Duhem, a Catholic, and a physicist of good repute, deemed it necessary to revive the nominalist interpretation of science and pit Ockham once more against St. Thomas Aquinas" (p. 293). Such was a strange reading of Duhem's emphatic endorsement of Aristotelian natural classification and realist epistemology in *La Théorie physique*.

[2] *Cosmologie héllénique* (I-IX); *L'Astronomie latine au moyen âge* (X-XVIII); and *La crue de l'Aristotélisme* (XIX-XXVII).

[3] See note 7 to Ch. 6.

[4] The photo is frontispiece in *Uneasy Genius*.

[5] The Abbé Blanc also remarked briefly on Duhem's support of the Action Française and of Maurras "whose doctrines were condemned by the Holy See." This was the kind of vague phrase that unintentionally could suggest that Duhem had endorsed ever so slightly the pagan philosophy of Maurras.

[6] I have not been able to locate a copy or clipping of that article by Hélène which must have appeared in *L'Express du Midi* toward the end of June.

[7] *Un savant français*, p. 105.

[8] Since 1983 in the Archives of the Académie des Sciences, Paris.

[9] My efforts to locate the Père Bulliot's correspondence at the headquarters of his order in Paris led to no result. There is a letter from Duhem to the Pére Bulliot in the Archives of the Institut Catholique of Paris, dated December 23, 1914. There Duhem expressed his firm hope that

the Père Bulliot would live to see the victorious end of the war. The Père Bulliot died on January 30, 1916, at the age of sixty-three, after having been reinstated as honorary dean at the Institut where he could not serve for several years for his having refused higher ecclesiastical orders to take in a stride the closing and confiscation of thousands of Catholic institutions by Combes' virulently anticlerical government. In the same letter Duhem expressed his satisfaction that Mgr. Baudrillart had accepted the directorship of Bulliot's project of publishing the works of medieval scholastic philosophers dealing with science, especially the works of Buridan and Oresme, a directorship which Duhem had already declined with great regret.

[10] Dufourcq was both right and wrong. Federigo Enriques (1871-1946) was the author of books in which science and its history and philosophy were interpreted in a markedly rationalistic spirit. Among his publications were *Problemi della scienza* (1906), translated as *Problems of Science* (Chicago: Open Court, 1914), with an introduction by Josiah Royce, and *Scienza e razionalismo* (1912). Curiously, Dufourcq seemed to remain unaware of the true bearing of Enriques' close ties with Hermann et Cie, and therefore with Freymann, although they could be guessed from the publication in 1934 of Enriques' booklet, *Signification de l'histoire de la pensée scientifique* (68pp) which appeared as Nr 161 in Hermann's series, *Actualités scientifiques et industrielles*, subsection, "Philosophie et Histoire de la pensée scientifique." There the next-to-last chapter was entitled, "L'histoire objective de Duhem," a blatant misconstruction not only of Duhem's thoughts about the aim and structure of physical theory, but also of his aim in writing the *Système du monde*. Enriques, who spoke rather condescendingly of the volumes of "respectable thickness" of the *Système du monde*, claimed that Duhem undertook its writing "with the firm intention to diminish the role of Galileo" (p. 57). While this was a wholly unfounded speculation on the part of Enriques, he could have authoritatively talked of what he had first-hand knowledge, namely, his own rationalism. He must have known that the latter was based not so much on solid arguments as on the setting up of Galileo and others as oracles who, by creating science, discredited once and for all metaphysical and religious reasoning. Freymann must have been fully familiar with that booklet of Enriques, who, if he had personal contacts with Freymann, could but dispose him very adversely against the resumption of the publication of the *Système du monde*, whatever superficial praise he might have heaped on its author.

[11] Joannés Wehrlé (1865-1938), a younger fellow student of Duhem at the Ecole Normale, subsequently became a priest. Among his works was a monograph on Victor Delbos.

[12] Victor Delbos (1862-1916), a classmate of Duhem at the Ecole Normale, was professor of philosophy at the Sorbonne and well known for his interpretation of Spinozism and German idealist philosophers.

[13] Maurice Blondel (1861-1956), also a fellow student of Duhem at the Ecole Normale, was professor of philosophy at the University of Aix-en-Provence, and a chief representative of intuitionism.

[14] By Albert Dufourcq and, after his death in 1952, by his first son, Norbert, who, as will be seen, took over from his father the task of assisting Hélène in the publication of the *Système du monde* and who by the time of her death in 1974 was in possession of most of her dossiers concerning the publication of that work.

[15] My efforts to identify that *France réelle* led to no result.

[16] Or to quote from a letter of November 18, 1985, from Hermann to Dr. Eric L. Ormsby, Director of Libraries at the Catholic University of America: "Sans nous engager, il nous semble qu'entre 1919 et 1939, c'est à peu près 600 titres qui ont été publiés par les éditions Hermann." Personal communication from Dr. Ormsby to the author.

[17] Among Johan Nordström's publications was *Moyen Age et Renaissance: Essai historique*, translated from Swedish into French by T. Hammar (Paris: Librairie Stock, 1933), or volume VI of *Norstedts Världhistoria* (Stockholm). There, in chapter vi, "La scolastique et les sciences de la nature" (pp. 100-108), Nordstrom gave a remarkable summary of Duhem's discoveries about medieval science.

Chapter Eight

[1] Norbert Dufourcq (1904-1990) directed the music section of Larousse. He was at the same time professor of organ at the Ecole de musique and president of the French association of organists.

[2] Elie Joseph Cartan (1869-1951) was a leader in the study of finite groups, topology, and transformational methods.

[3] Joseph Pérès (1890-1966), a member of the Académie des Sciences, was an authority in theoretical mechanics.

[4] As most dossiers, the one relating to the subvention to the publication of the *Système du monde* too was sent to the "pilon" (papermill) twenty years after its completion, or around 1980 at the latest.

[5] The publication by Sarton in question was his *The Appreciation of Ancient and Medieval Science during the Renaissance (1450-1600)* (Philadelphia: University of Pennsylvania Press, 1955).

[6] The historian, who was asked to comment on my paper on Duhem at Boston University (see note 20 to Ch. 5), admitted his complete bafflement on Sarton's silence of which he became aware only after reading my paper. It seems that it is the privilege of gurus in the establishment to be above any and all suspicion, indeed of criticism.

[7] Jules Duhem earned his scholarly reputation by his impressive doctoral thesis, published in 1943 and 1944, in two parts of which the first was the text, *Histoire des idées aéronautiques avant Montgolfier* (Paris: F. Sorlot), the other a collection of illustrations, *Musée aéronautique avant Montgolfier, recueil de figures* (Paris: F. Sorlot).

[8] Gaston Dupouy, born in 1900, wrote *Eléments d'optique électrique* (1952).

[9] I could not obtain biographical details about him.

[10] L. Leprince Ringuet (1901-   ), then in his fifties, rather misjudged the attitude of the physicists of his generation toward Duhem.

[11] On L. Roy and his work on electromagnetics, see *Uneasy Genius*, pp. 304-06.

[12] From *La Croix* the report was taken over in full by *La Croix de l'Aude*. I have used xerox copies of the clipping from its two issues, October 27 and November 3.

[13] For details, see *Uneasy Genius*, p. 190.

[14] Raymond Calas (1914-   ) did notable research in stereochemistry and became the laureate of the American Chemical Society in 1988.

[15] Letter quoted in full in English translation in *Uneasy Genius*, p. 190 and in French original in *Pierre Duhem: Homme de foi et de science*, pp. 116-17. Its first publication is, of course, in *Un savant français*, p. 179.

[16] P. P. Wiener served as editor of *Journal for the History of Ideas* and of the *Dictionary of the History of Ideas*.

[17] On Langevin's very hostile attitude toward Duhem and his work, see note 4 to Ch. 5.

[18] This is well attested by the half a dozen references to Duhem in M. Cohen's *Studies in the Philosophy of Science* (New York: Frederic Ungar, 1949). There is a world of a difference between the perspectives on history as demanded by Duhem's findings and Cohen's sympathies for Marx, Hegel, and Dewey.

[19] The volumes did not show extensive use or study, a fact which I could easily ascertain during my visits with Saurel's son, Mr. Paul Saurel (New York City), who was very generous in giving me access to everything in his possession concerning his father's contacts with Duhem.

Chapter Nine

[1] Jean Langevin gave 17 Rue Saint Romain, Paris VI as his address, and Littré 57-58 as his telephone number. De Nobele was and is still located at 35 Rue Bonaparte.

[2] Adrien Bruhl, classical scholar and one-time member of the Ecole Française d'Athènes et de Rome.

[3] Max Black (1909- ?), philosopher of mathematics and linguistics.

⁴ On Lemoine, see *The Physicist as Artist*, p. 1.

5. See *Uneasy Genius*, p. 433.

⁶ These two figures anticipate the coming of the new franc, equal to 100 old francs.

⁷ I could not obtain biographical details about him.

⁸ M. Lacoine's article, "Pierre Duhem et Anneliese Maier," was published a year later, 69 (1956), pp. 325-343.

⁹ Dom Olphe-Galliard was a student in Bordeaux in 1910-13.

¹⁰ The *Traité d'énergetique* was reprinted in 1986 by Blanchard in Paris.

¹¹ It was my good fortune to meet him in person in Paris in the Fall of 1986 while he was visiting with his mother, who still vividly and very fondly recalled her memories of Duhem.

¹² On Taton's slighting of Duhem, see note 10 to Ch. 3.

¹³ The words, "liberating influence," are of C. C. Gillispie. See my *The Road of Science and the Ways to God* (Chicago: University of Chicago Press, 1978), p. 418, note 7. I have heard others too to speak in a similar vein.

¹⁴ See "Duhem, Pierre," by R. J. Seeger in *The New Catholic Encyclopedia* (New York: McGraw Hill, 1967), vol. 4, p. 1095. Duhem's philosophical "attitude is best expressed in his *Physique de croyant* (1905), where he attempted to reconcile his scientific philosophy with his religious convictions." This statement will appear a howler to anyone who read that essay even with a minimum of care. There Duhem explicitly rejected the idea that the science of physics imposed on him any such burden.

¹⁵ At Boston University, during dinner, prior to my lecture, March 13, 1978. See note 20 to ch. 5 above.

[16] I failed to receive a reply from Seeger to my inquiry about his correspondence with Hélène.

[17] C. Truesdell, "A New Definition of a Fluid. II. The Maxwellian Fluid," *Journal de mathématiques pures et appliquées* 30 (1951), pp. 111-155. On Duhem, see p. 141.

[18] Truesdell dedicated to Duhem the first issue of *Archive for the History of Exact Science* (1960), where one reads on the page following the table of contents: "This journal seeks to uphold the tradition of P. Duhem and E. T. Whittaker, scientists and historians."

[19] "Physique et cosmologie: Leur relations dans la philosophie de la science de Pierre Duhem," *Revue des questions scientifiques* 77 (1965), pp. 49-65.

[20] J. J. O'Malley, *Material Being and Scientific Knowledge according to Pierre Duhem* (Marquette University; Ann Arbor, MI: University Microfilm, 1965).

[21] F. J. Collingwood, "Duhem's Interpretation of Aristotle on Mathematics in Science," in D. O. Dahlstrom (ed.), *Nature and Scientific Method* (Washington D. C.: The Catholic University of America Press, 1991), pp. 63-79.

[22] Kuhn was rightly charged with unintentional plagiarism. For details, see *Uneasy Genius*, p. 370.

[23] See note 19 above.

[24] F. Russo's article, which first appeared in French in *Cahiers d'Histoire Mondiale* (vol. III, no. 4), saw print in English as "Catholicism, Protestantism, and the Development of Science in the Sixteenth and Seventeenth Centuries," in *The Evolution of Science*, ed. G. S. Metraux and F. Crouzet (New York: UNESCO and New American Library, 1963), pp. 309-319.

[25] A consternation still felt by Professor O'Malley; personal communication, August 1991.

[26] J. Ullmo, "A propos de la physique de Duhem," *Revue de synthèse*, 6 (1933), pp. 221-224.

[27] There Ullmo decried the use of positivism as a cover-up for one's diffidence in realism, a sort of "humility often turned into proud and peremptory doctrine, as we see this in Duhem" (ibid., p. 223).

[28] Such a lack of competence was deplored by Duhem in a prominent public context in 1894. For details, see *Uneasy Genius*, pp. 112-15.

[29] See the first essay in my *Chance or Reality and Other Essays* (Lanham, Md.: University Press of America, 1986).

[30] As I argued in my "Determinism and Reality," in *The Great Ideas Today* (Chicago: Encyclopedia Britannica, 1990), pp. 276-302.

[31] Some of Duhem's most emphatic endorsements of ontology can be found in his early philosophical essays, which I collected and edited, with an introduction, under the title, *Prémices philosophiques* (Leiden: E. J. Brill, 1987).

[32] One of them, William McGucken, now professor at the University of Akron, was then doing graduate work at the University of Pennsylvania. In writing a term paper on Duhem it occurred to him that he might write his doctoral dissertation on him. "I had forgotten all about this until reminded of it by your letter," was his reply of June 13, 1991, to my inquiries whether he still had any communication from Hélène. Another was Harry W. Paul, of the University of Florida.

[33] Joseph Kampé de Fériet specialized in statistical analysis of turbulent flow and lectured in the subject at the University of Maryland in the 1950s.

[34] The reference is, of course, to Molière's famous play, *Le médecin malgré lui* (1666).

[35] It was a most considered view of Anneliese Maier (whose name is mispelled by Hélène) that Duhem was "fundamentally right." See *Uneasy Genius*, pp. 425-26.

[36] R. Taton was director of the Centre de recherches d'histoire des sciences, 12 Rue Colbert.

[37] In reviewing I. Roger Charbonnel's *La pensée italienne au XVI' siècle et le courant libertin* (Paris, 1919) in *Archivio di Storia della Scienza* (June 1921, pp. 137-38) Favaro began with remarks on the revival of Thomism as urged by Leo XIII. According to Favaro, Msgr. Noel, a disciple of the future Cardinal Mercier, was the channel for transmitting to Duhem the pope's wish that a thorough study be made of the scientific fertility of scholastic philosophy: "Thus did Duhem carry out the mandate received, through an intermediary, from Pope Leo XIII." An astonishing claim, indeed, on behalf of which Favaro should have offered something tangible, such as a letter from Msgr. Noel. At any rate, Leo XIII was already dead when Duhem, to his great surprise, stumbled on Jordanus Nemorarius as the first proponent of the idea of virtual velocity. Also, as frankness incarnate, Duhem would not have given the impression that he had exerted himself to the very limit of his strength over a dozen years for a reason other than what he had repeatedly specified. namely, that a careful tracing of the history of physics would prove right his idea of the aim and structure of physical theory. I owe my information on Favaro's claim to a letter to me from Dr. Donald G. Miller.

[38] In the article, Miller stated that he was "especially grateful to Hélène Pierre-Duhem for the invaluable information about her father's life and career so graciously given to me in several personal interviews." *Physics Today* 19 (December 1966), p. 53. The provenance of the photographs was not mentioned.

Appendix

[1] This is a note by Hélène who refers to her biography of her father.

[2] This work is now available in English as *The Origins of Statics* (Dordrecht: Kluwer Academic Publishers, 1991).

[3] See note 9 to ch. 7.

[4] References are to *Un savant français* and to the Duhem-issue of *Archeion*.

[5] The reference is to the appeal made in *Isis*, see note 26 to Ch. 5.

[6] Hélène certainly does her very best.

[7] *Aeterni Patris* was issued in 1979, almost at the very start of Leo XIII's pontificate.

[8] *Pascendi dominicae gregis* was issued by Pius X in 1907 to combat modernism.

[9] The reference is either to sickness or hard pastoral work or both.

[10] Hermann's reference to "Méray's *Leçons*" is puzzling. Charles Méray, a mathematician (1835-1911), published with Gauthier-Villars his books, among them a four-volume *Leçons nouvelles sur l'analyse infinitesimale* (Paris, 1894-99).

[11] Hermann published H. Ollivier's *Cours de physique générale* in 1913.

[12] Hermann completed in 1913 the publication in five volumes of the French translation of O. D. Chwolson's *Traité de physique*.

Index of Names

(continued from p. ii)

By the same author

The Physicist as Artist: The Landscapes of Pierre Duhem

The Absolute beneath the Relative and Other Essays

The Savior of Science
(Wethersfield Institute Lectures, 1987)

Miracles and Physics

God and the Cosmologists
(Farmington Institute Lectures, Oxford, 1988)

The Only Chaos and Other Essays

The Purpose of It All
(Farmington Institute Lectures, Oxford, 1989)

Catholic Essays

Cosmos in Transition: Studies in the History of Cosmology

Olbers Studies

Scientist and Catholic: Pierre Duhem

Is There a Universe?

Universe and Creed

Genesis 1 through the Ages

★ ★ ★

Translations with introduction and notes:

The Ash Wednesday Supper (Giordano Bruno)

*Cosmological Letters on the Arrangement
of the World Edifice* (J.-H. Lambert)

Universal Natural History and Theory of the Heavens (I. Kant)

Note on the Author

Stanley L. Jaki, a Hungarian-born Catholic priest of the Benedictine Order, is Distinguished University Professor at Seton Hall University, South Orange, New Jersey. With doctorates in theology and physics, he has for the past thirty years specialized in the history and philosophy of science. The author of thirty books and nearly a hundred articles, he served as Gifford Lecturer at the University of Edinburgh and as Fremantle Lecturer at Balliol College, Oxford. He has lectured at major universities in the United States, Europe, and Australia. He is an honorary member of the Pontifical Academy of Sciences, *membre correspondant* of the Académie Nationale des Sciences, Belles-Lettres et Arts de Bordeaux, and the recipient of the Lecomte du Nouy Prize for 1970 and of the Templeton Prize for 1987